ENGINEERING DESCRIPTIVE GEOMETRY

THE DIRECT METHOD

for

STUDENTS, DRAFTSMEN, ARCHITECTS, AND ENGINEERS

BY

CHARLES ELMER ROWE, B.S. (C.E.), E.M.

Professor of Drawing, The University of Texas

AND

JAMES DORR McFARLAND, M.S. IN E.E.

Professor of Drawing, The University of Texas
Registered Professional Engineer

SECOND EDITION—SIXTH PRINTING

D. VAN NOSTRAND COMPANY, INC.

PRINCETON, NEW JERSEY

TORONTO   LONDON

NEW YORK

D. VAN NOSTRAND COMPANY, INC.

120 Alexander St., Princeton, New Jersey
257 Fourth Avenue, New York 10, New York
25 Hollinger Rd., Toronto 16, Canada

*All correspondence should be addressed to the
principal office of the company at Princeton, N. J.*

Library of Congress Catalog Card No. 53–6527

First Published, June 1939

Seventeen Reprintings

Second Edition, March 1953

Reprinted, January 1954, January 1955,
July 1955, September 1956, June 1957

PREFACE TO THE SECOND EDITION

The authors, who have worked together on Descriptive Geometry for over a quarter of a century, are pleased to announce their coauthorship of this revised edition. The problem section of this revision contains virtually all new problems. Over fifty per cent of them are shown in layout form. This feature should have considerable appeal to both the student and the instructor.

The text of the first edition has been so well received that no extensive revision of this part of the book seemed desirable. However, some new illustrations have been added and the treatment of some subjects expanded.

Years of experience in teaching the "direct method" of Descriptive Geometry have convinced the authors that it has distinct advantages over the older or "Mongean Method." Students appear more interested in their work, learn a greater number of practical applications, and acquire a more usable understanding of the subject.

In this book problems are considered as space relationships and solved directly from the data as given. With the exception of Chapter XI, The Mongean Method, no use is made of ground lines, folding lines, traces of planes, or other devices characteristic of the original method of descriptive geometry. Thus, in the direct method, practically all of the student's time is available for learning to think in space. Since the drawing board constructions are thoroughly in accord with standard drafting room practice, the training obtained in descriptive geometry is directly available for the solution of the more difficult problems which arise in the experience of a draftsman or designer. It is a well recognized fact that the direct method of descriptive geometry is practical.

As a basis for the treatment of the subject, fourteen fundamental principles concerning simple conceptions of relationships in space are stated in the introductory chapter and discussed at appropriate places as the subject is developed. The systematic statement of these few fundamentals is helpful to the student as a working basis for the whole subject and to the instructor as a concise and effective method of rendering assistance.

Comprehensive instructions are given for determining the visibility of all edges or lines in any view of an object. This important subject has received little attention in most books, apparently on the assumption that students can determine the visibility of the edges by inspection without any particular instruction. In many cases, however, this is almost impossible without the use of a systematic method. Visualization of the object as seen in any view follows the determination of the visibility of its edges.

Since training in the visualization of lines, planes, objects, structures, and space relationships is an important objective in the study of descriptive geometry, simple but effective methods have been used to develop the powers of visualization which prevent the views of a drawing from seeming to be merely flat figures composed of lines. Only when a view is orientated and visualized does it appear as the actual object.

In this book particular emphasis is placed upon orientation, the mental process by which the student relates himself to any view of an object in such a manner that the view appears to him as the actual object would appear for that particular direction of sight. The methods used have been tested through years of experience with excellent results. Orientation as a factor in the process of completely visualizing any view of an object is extremely important in the case of auxiliary and oblique views.

The subjects of shades, shadows, and perspective are given more attention than is usual in most books on descriptive geometry. The extent of this treatment is such that the methods given provide a sufficient basis upon which to build a course in these subjects.

The solution of any problem involves visualization of the data and requirements, analysis of the space relationships, formulation of plan of solution in accordance with fundamental principles, and practical drawing board constructions. All problems are analyzed, the fundamental principles required for their solution are stated, and the drawing board constructions are explained.

Thus, the use of the direct method, training in the fundamental principles, drill in the analysis of problems, exercise in the determination of visibility, instruction in orientation, and practice in visualization, are factors in the development of the ability to think in space—the most important objective that can be attained by the study of descriptive geometry.

CHARLES ELMER ROWE
JAMES DORR McFARLAND

JANUARY, 1953.

CONTENTS

Numbers in Parentheses Refer to Pages

v

CONTENTS

CHAPTER X

CHAPTER XI

CHAPTER XII

CHAPTER XIII

CHAPTER XIV

ENGINEERING DESCRIPTIVE GEOMETRY PROBLEMS

The authors of this textbook have prepared workbooks designed for use with this or other textbooks using the direct method. All cover the same subject matter, but the problems in each are all different. Each workbook contains a sufficient number of problems for a three-semester hour course.

TO THE STUDENT WHO USES THIS TEXTBOOK

This textbook represents many years of learning and experience on the part of the authors. It does not treat of an ephemeral subject, but one which, since you are studying it in college, you must feel will have a use to you in your future life.

Unquestionably you will many times in later life wish to refer to specific details and facts about the subject which this book covers and which you may forget. How better could you find this information than in the textbook which you have studied from cover to cover?

Retain it for your reference library. You will use it many times in the future.

THE PUBLISHERS

ENGINEERING DESCRIPTIVE GEOMETRY

CHAPTER I

INTRODUCTION

1. Descriptive geometry is the science of drawing which treats of the exact representation of objects composed of geometrical forms and of the graphical solution of problems involving the space relations of these forms.

A structure or a machine is made up of parts composed of such solid forms as prisms, pyramids, cylinders, cones, etc. Each of the parts is bounded by surfaces which are plane, single curved, double curved, or warped. The surfaces intersect in edges which are straight or curved lines. The edges intersect as points at the corners. **Descriptive geometry** deals with the proper representation of all these elements or forms on the drawing and gives the methods of determining their true sizes, true shapes, and the true relations of one element to another. Engineering drawing and engineering descriptive geometry are not distinctly different subjects. Each includes much of the other. In fact, drawing may be considered to be elementary descriptive geometry. The constructions in engineering descriptive geometry are made by the methods of orthographic projection or drawing used in all drafting rooms.

The word " descriptive " in the name " descriptive geometry " means to represent or describe by drawings. Only very simple objects can be described by words, but a complicated object can be described completely and adequately by drawings which the designer uses to convey his ideas to the builder or manufacturer. Descriptive geometry makes use of the theorems of both plane and solid geometry. Many of the theoretical constructions of solid geometry are actually worked out on the drawing board.

The science of descriptive geometry was created by the genius of Gaspard Monge at the military school at Mézières, France, although some work along this line had been done by others. He worked out the theory in a remarkably complete manner and published his first book in 1795, after the subject had been " held as a military secret of great value " for

1

some thirty years. The subject was developed as an easy graphical means of working problems in the design of fortifications which previously had been solved by laborious mathematical computations. Descriptive geometry was recognized immediately as a fundamental subject for the training of engineers, and in a short time was included in the curriculum of all engineering schools.

Colonel Claude Crozet, who studied at the Ecole Polytechnique, where Monge was a professor, began to teach the subject at the United States Military Academy in 1816 and published the first book on descriptive geometry in the English language in 1821.

During the following one hundred years the numerous American writers on the subject followed closely the methods of Monge, and even at the present time most writers of textbooks do not depart greatly from the Mongean method. However, during the past decade or two there has been a marked tendency toward simplification by the adoption of the method of the drafting room and by the elimination of features which not only consumed much of the student's time but prevented descriptive geometry from being readily adaptable to practical engineering problems.

A technically trained draftsman knows that each view of a drawing is an orthographic projection, but he thinks of it as the object itself which he is seeing *directly*, with no thought of a plane of projection. The " direct method " of drawing is known as the observer's change-of-position method. When the draftsman draws a front view, he imagines he occupies a position directly in front of the object; when he draws a top view, he mentally changes his position so that he is looking downward upon the object; if the object is of such a form that an inclined direction of sight is necessary, he assumes he has moved to the required position.

The " direct method " of descriptive geometry is based on the same mental attitude, and as used in this book, includes all the solutions of descriptive geometry which are performed *directly* from the data as given, without the use of ground lines, folding lines, or the traces of planes. The essentials of the " direct method " are: first, the direct attitude of mind; second, visualization; third, analysis; and fourth, practical drawing board constructions which are in accord with the above conception.

THE FUNDAMENTAL PRINCIPLES OF DESCRIPTIVE GEOMETRY

2. In the study of descriptive geometry certain principles are fundamental. They are the space conceptions which seem to be the most important, since other space conceptions can be resolved into combinations of them. One of these principles or a combination of them is used in the solution of any problem. If they are thoroughly understood, and if the student can analyze the problem, the solution can be made in a systematic manner by constructions on the drawing board.

1. *The First Principle of Orthographic Drawing.*

The directions of sight for any two adjacent views are mutually perpendicular.

2. *The Second Principle of Orthographic Drawing.*

Corresponding points in adjacent views may be connected by parallel lines which represent the lines of sight for these views.

3. *The Third Principle of Orthographic Drawing.*

Measurements parallel to the lines of sight in all views adjacent to the same view are equal.

4. *A Normal View of a Line.* (*True Length.*)

A normal view of a line is one for which the direction of sight is perpendicular to the line.

5. *An End View of a Line.*

An end view of a line is one for which the direction of sight is parallel to the line.

6. *Parallel Lines.*

Parallel lines appear parallel in any orthographic view.

7. *Perpendicular Lines.*

Two perpendicular lines appear perpendicular in any view that is a normal view of either (or both) of the lines. They do not appear perpendicular unless the view is a normal view of at least one of them.

8. *The Principal Lines of a Plane.*

Through any point in an oblique plane the three principal lines of the plane may be drawn.

9. *An Edge View of a Plane.*

An edge view of a plane is one for which the direction of sight is parallel to some line of the plane.

10. *A Normal View of a Plane.* (*True Shape.*)

A normal view of a plane is one for which the direction of sight is perpendicular to the plane.

11. *Cutting Planes.*

A cutting plane will intersect any surface in a line.

12. *The Point Where a Line Pierces a Surface.*

The point where a line pierces a surface is located at its intersection with the line cut from the surface by a cutting plane containing the given line.

13. *The True Length of a Line by Revolution.*

The true length of a line may be found by revolving it to a position where it is perpendicular to an established direction of sight.

14. *The True Shape of a Plane by Revolution.*

The true shape of a plane may be found by revolving it to a position where it is perpendicular to an established direction of sight.

3. Notation.—The corners of an object and other points on a drawing made in the study of descriptive geometry are marked by letters or numbers. The letters on a drawing have subscripts which identify the view, or if the subscripts are omitted, the name of the view is given. In the case of solids the names of the views are preferable to subscripts. In other cases, if the view does not "hold together" well as a unit, subscripts are used. In many cases it is desirable to use both. Points used for constructions in the solution of a problem are numbered.

The subscripts indicate the name of the view. If B is a corner of an object, B_F is the front view, B_H is the top view, B_R is the right-side view, B_L is the left-side view, B_A is an auxiliary view, and B_O is an oblique view of the corner.

4. The Coordinates for a Point.—A point is located with reference to an origin by means of three coordinates. In Fig. 1 the point A is designated as $A(146)$ in which 1 inch is the coordinate of width, 4 inches is the coordinate of height, and 6 inches is the coordinate of depth with reference to the origin at zero. Only two coordinates are used for locating one view of a point. The distance to the right of the origin and the height above it locate the front view of point A, which is marked A_F. The distance to the right of the origin and the depth dimension locate the top view of A, which is marked A_H.

A line BC is designated by two of its points B and C, thus: $B(2\frac{1}{2}; 1; 7\frac{1}{2})$ $C(6\frac{1}{2}; 4; 6)$. Locate the points B and C as in Fig. 1. Join $B_H C_H$ for the top view of the line and $B_F C_F$ for the front view.

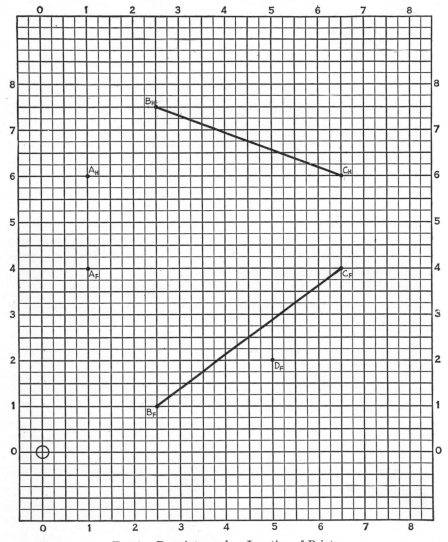

Fig. 1.—Descriptograph. Location of Points.

If any of the coordinates are unknown, "X" is used in the designation. $D(52X)$ is a point for which the coordinate for the top view is unknown.

The instructor may wish to mimeograph special problems, quizzes, or examinations. Where desirable, decimals may be used instead of common fractions.

5. The descriptograph is a heavy sheet of white drawing paper, size 11 by 15 inches, which has the coordinate lines of Fig. 1 printed on it in black. The problem sheets,* size $8\frac{1}{2}$ by 11 inches, are made of a good grade of bond paper through which these lines can be seen. They are plain paper with a title strip. The descriptograph is kept attached to the drawing board, and a sheet of problem paper is tacked down centrally over it so as not to cover the numbers. The points of the data for a problem are plotted with speed and accuracy.

The lines for the data of the problem should be drawn distinctly, but not so heavily as the lines in the required result. Construction lines and sight-lines should be drawn with a sharp pencil as light continuous lines.

6. Terminology for Lines on the Drawing Board.—The draftsman's use of the word " horizontal " for all lines drawn along the blade of the T-square used in its correct position, and the word " vertical " for all lines perpendicular to it is unfortunate and leads to confusion. For these lines on the drawing board, without any reference to their directions in space, the following distinctive terms may be used:

Lines drawn along the blade of the T-square are *T-square lines*.

Lines drawn perpendicular to the blade of the T-square are *ortho-T-square lines*.

---

* The descriptograph and problem sheets may be obtained from the University Co-Operative Society, Austin, Texas.

CHAPTER II

PRINCIPAL VIEWS

METHODS OF GRAPHICAL REPRESENTATION

7. All the various methods of representing objects by exact line drawings, used by draftsmen, engineers, and architects, may be classified under three types of theoretical space operations capable of producing views like those which the draftsman makes directly upon the drawing board. The rays of light from the object to the eye of the observer are assumed to produce upon a transparent picture plane a drawing which has the appearance of the object itself. By reference to Fig. 2, the following brief state-

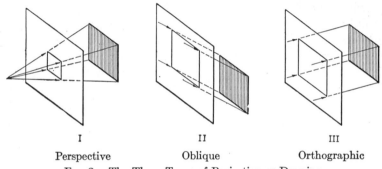

I   II   III

Perspective   Oblique   Orthographic

FIG. 2.—The Three Types of Projection or Drawing

ments explain the space conceptions upon which each type of drawing is based.

Perspective Projection or Drawing. The rays converge to a point after passing through the picture plane. A perspective is identical with a drawing which could be obtained by tracing the outlines of a building on a window pane while looking at it with one eye in a fixed position. The size of the drawing depends upon the relative location of the eye, the object, and the picture plane. Perspective drawing is the method used for making a realistic pictorial drawing.

Oblique Projection or Drawing.—The rays are parallel to each other and inclined to the picture plane. This method produces interesting results which are of considerable value, although an oblique drawing may

7

not be pleasing as a picture. A discussion of oblique drawing may be found in the books on engineering drawing.

Orthographic Projection or Drawing.—The rays are parallel to each other and perpendicular to the picture plane.

8. Orthographic Drawing.

A *line of sight* is an imaginary straight line from the eye to a point on the object. In orthographic drawing all the lines of sight for a view are parallel; therefore, the observer must be assumed to be at an infinite distance from the object, or the eye must be moved so as to look along each line of sight. An object can be seen in approximately the orthographic manner if its distance from the observer is very great compared to its size.

The direction of sight for a view is the direction of the parallel lines of sight for that view.

If the direction of sight is perpendicular to a face of the object, the orthographic view will show the true size and true shape of that face. This fact makes orthographic projection the only method generally suitable for drawings used in engineering and industry. Such a view, however, shows only two of the three rectangular dimensions of the object. In order to show the third dimension, it is necessary to draw another view taken in a direction at right angles to the direction for the first view. If the object is complicated, several views may be required to show all its details. Generally, orthographic drawing is used as multi-view drawing by which all the true relationships, true sizes, and true shapes of the many parts of a structure can be shown. It is the method of representation used in the study of descriptive geometry for the solutions of the problems of space.

The fundamental relations in space of three principal views with reference to each other and to the object itself are shown in Fig. 3. The simple rectangular object is placed in a natural position with its base horizontal. To obtain a front view, the draftsman or observer assumes a position directly in front of the most distinctive vertical face of the object and looks in a horizontal direction which is perpendicular to that face. To obtain a top view, he remains in front of the object and assumes that he bends over to look vertically down upon the object. To obtain a right-side view, the observer assumes that he moves to a position to the right of the object and looks directly at the right side of it in a horizontal direction which is perpendicular to the first two directions of sight. These views, made orthographically in three mutually perpendicular directions, are principal views of the object. By looking in directions exactly opposite to these, the draftsman may make three more principal views: the rear view, the bottom view, and the left-side view.

The three rectangular dimensions of this object are height, measured vertically; width, measured horizontally across the front; and depth, measured horizontally across the side. The term " depth " is used in the same sense that it is used in referring to the dimensions of a piece of furniture. A chest of drawers is said to have height, width, and depth.

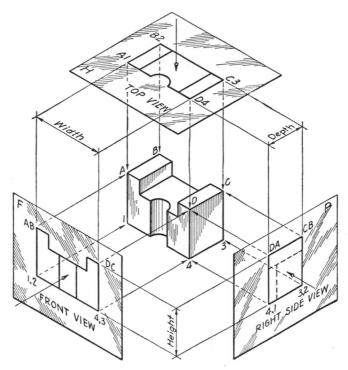

Fig. 3.—Sketch Showing Principal Views.

An inspection of the views of this object reveals the following facts regarding its dimensions: the front view has only height and width, the top view has only width and depth, the right-side view has only height and depth. Therefore, in order to show the three rectangular dimensions of an object by an orthographic drawing on a sheet of paper, it is necessary to make two views which are taken in directions which are mutually perpendicular, Principle 1.

The picture planes upon which the views are drawn in Fig. 3 are parallel to the respective faces of the object because the lines of sight are perpendicular to these faces. Each picture plane may be considered to be a sheet

of paper upon which the view is drawn. The front view is drawn on a
frontal picture plane F, the top view on a horizontal picture plane H,
and the side view on a profile picture plane P. The visible faces of the
object appear on the picture planes exactly as they are on the object.
All corners, edges, and outlines beyond the nearest face are also represented
in these views. In each view there are two lettered or numbered corners
for each line of sight. In every case the corner nearest the observer of a
view is given first. When looking at the top view alone, the observer
knows that the corners A, B, C, and D are above corners 1, 2, 3, and 4,
if this system has been used.

9. The Arrangement of Views.—In Fig. 3 the horizontal picture plane
H has indicated on it the horizontal lines of sight used for seeing the front

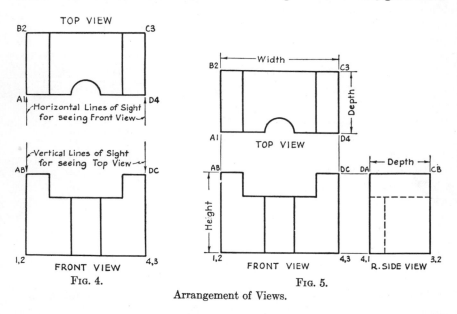

Arrangement of Views.

view, and the frontal picture plane F has on it the vertical lines of sight
used for seeing the top view. In order to show both the top view and the
front view on a single sheet of paper the views should be placed as shown in
Fig. 4, with the indicated lines of sight in alignment. This can also be
accomplished by revolving the plane H through an angle of 90° about its
line of intersection with the plane F so that its rear edge moves upward
and forward. The top view and the front view may be placed close
together as in Fig. 5. The fine lines joining corresponding points in these

adjacent views represent both sets of lines of sight shown in Fig. 4. They are called " sight-lines " in this book. In a similar way, the right-side view is placed adjacent to the front view and in alignment with it, using sight-lines between corresponding points. This arrangement of views has been adopted by the American Standards Association. It is generally known as the third angle or third quadrant projection or drawing; i.e., the object is considered to be in the third of the four parts into which space is divided by the intersecting picture planes H and F. Figure 177 and the explanation in Chapter XI give further information concerning the quadrants and planes of projection.

The arrangement of views shown in Fig. 5 is the most simple system. Consider the front view to be the object itself. The lines of sight for the top view point to the top of the object, and the top view is placed adjacent to the top face. The lines of sight for the right-side view point toward the right face of the object and the right-side view is placed adjacent to the right face. Consider the top view to be the object itself; then, the lines of sight for the front view point to the front of the object, and the front view is placed adjacent to the front face. Consider the right-side view to be the object; then, the lines of sight for the front view point to the front face of the object, and the front view is adjacent to the front face. In this system of arranging views every view is nearest its side of the object in an adjacent view.

10. Assignments. See Chapter XIV, Group 2A.

11. The first three fundamental principles of descriptive geometry, which are the three principles of orthographic projection or drawing, may be stated on the basis of the foregoing discussion.

THE FIRST FUNDAMENTAL PRINCIPLE OF DESCRIPTIVE GEOMETRY

12. The First Principle of Orthographic Drawing.

The directions of sight for any two adjacent views are mutually perpendicular.

Referring to Figs. 3 and 5, note that any view has only two dimensions. Consider the front view. It has height and width, but there is no information about the depth dimension in the front view because this dimension is perpendicular to the plane of the paper on which the front view is drawn. It should be evident that a second view, which is to show this dimension, must be made with its direction of sight perpendicular to that used for making the front view. Two views are available in these figures for showing the depth dimension because the direction of sight for either the top view or the side view is perpendicular to the depth dimension. It is also perpendicular to the direction of sight for the front view. Each of these views is adjacent to the front view. Views always should be arranged on the paper in accordance with this principle.

THE SECOND FUNDAMENTAL PRINCIPLE OF DESCRIPTIVE GEOMETRY

13. The Second Principle of Orthographic Drawing.—Corresponding points in adjacent views may be connected by parallel lines which represent the lines of sight for these views.

The views on a drawing should be arranged according to this principle, which simplifies the making of the drawing and assists in reading it. Imagine that a hole is drilled somewhere in the front face of the object in Fig. 5. Draw a sight-line to the top view and a sight-line to the right-side view to locate the hole in these views.

THE THIRD FUNDAMENTAL PRINCIPLE OF DESCRIPTIVE GEOMETRY

14. The Third Principle of Orthographic Drawing.

Measurements parallel to the lines of sight in all views adjacent to the same view are equal.

This principle is shown clearly in Figs. 3 and 5.

The depth dimension is the same for the top view and the right-side view.

These three principles are used in every case where an additional view is made in a drawing which has at least two views given. They are fundamental for both drawing and descriptive geometry.

15. Orthographic Dimensions.—The object shown in Fig. 6 is a rectangular block which is not placed in a natural position. The front view is taken in a selected horizontal direction, which also fixes the direction of sight for the side view. Although the rectangular dimensions of the object may be known, they do not appear in any of the views of this drawing. The directions of sight have established an orthographic system of height, width, and depth dimensions, which may be measured on the views.

In descriptive geometry, which deals so largely with inclined and oblique positions of lines, planes, and objects, the orthographic dimensions are of great importance. The rectangular dimensions are not the same as the orthographic dimensions unless the object is viewed in certain directions. Principle 3 refers to orthographic dimensions.

16. Horizontal Reference Plane.—The top view and the front view of an object are given in Fig. 7. The right-side view is to be drawn adjacent to the top view. This is an approved position for it, and in accord

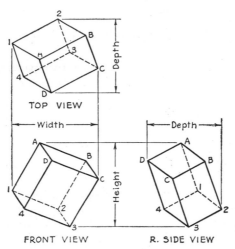

TOP VIEW

FRONT VIEW R. SIDE VIEW

FIG. 6.—Orthographic Dimensions.

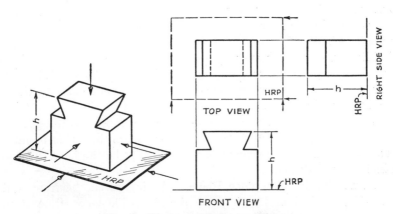

TOP VIEW

FRONT VIEW

FIG. 7.—Horizontal Reference Plane.

with Principle 1. Applying Principle 2, draw the parallel sight-lines from the top view toward the right. The location of the corners of the object on these sight-lines is determined by their relative heights shown in the front view, Principle 3. The heights are measured as in engineering from some level datum plane called the *Horizontal Reference Plane HRP* which may be assumed at any elevation; but usually the natural location for it is below the object. It appears as an edge view or line perpendicular to the sight-lines in any view which is adjacent to the top view. It should not be thought of as a reference line, because in space a plane is necessary as a datum for the various height dimensions of an object. The height dimension h is transferred from the front view to the right-side view by using dividers or by other means.

The height dimensions must be set off on the correct side of HRP in the new view. In the front view they are measured upward, which is toward the top view. They must be measured toward the top view in the right side view, otherwise the view will be reversed. The student should turn the drawing so as to read " Right Side View " horizontally and note the front of the object is at the left and the rear is at the right. This is called orientation of the right-side view.

If the draftsman prefers to locate HRP above the front view, the measurements are made away from the top view in all views which may be made adjacent to it. In the case of some symmetrical objects, the best location for HRP is through the center of the object. The horizontal reference plane is parallel to the picture plane for the top view. Therefore, it follows HRP will appear as an edge view in any view adjacent to the top view. HRP is never shown in the top view in an actual drawing. The method of this text uses picture planes only as a means of illustration, but finds a system of reference planes of great value in making the auxiliary and oblique views which are used extensively in the solutions of the problems of descriptive geometry. There are only two conditions to be observed; first, the reference plane must be perpendicular to the sight-lines; second, the measurements must be placed on the correct side of it. Otherwise, the draftsman is free to locate it most advantageously for either the given view or the required view, or both. This permits him to make a compact arrangement of views so that he can keep them within the limits of the drawing.

17. The Frontal Reference Plane.—Having given the front and top views of the object in Fig. 8, draw the right-side view adjacent to the front view. Use Principles 1, 2, and 3. Draw the sight-lines from the front view toward the right. It should be evident that the required depth dimensions may be measured from some *Frontal Reference Plane* FRP. In this drawing FRP is located behind the object, and appears as an edge view or a line in the top view and the right-side view. The depth dimension d is shown in both of these views. It should be noted that the drawing is between FRP and the front view in each case.

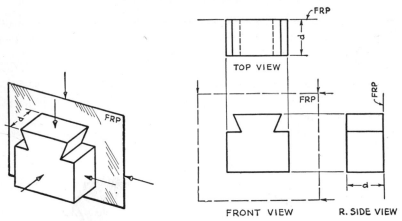

FIG. 8.—Frontal Reference Plane.

THE TYPICAL POSITIONS OF A PLANE

18. The seven typical positions which a plane may assume are indicated in Fig. 9. The arrows show the direction of sight for the top view,

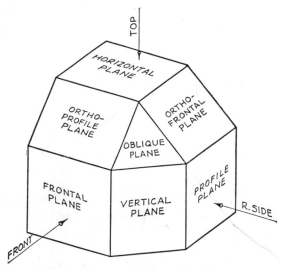

FIG. 9.—Typical Positions of a Plane.

the front view, and the right-side view. The positions of a plane are named and defined as follows:

A *horizontal plane* is a level plane. All points of a horizontal plane have the same elevation. Only one horizontal plane can be passed through a given point.

A *frontal plane* is perpendicular to the direction of sight for the front view. A frontal plane may be at the rear of an object or at any other location with reference to the object. Only one frontal plane can be passed through a given point.

A *profile plane* is perpendicular to the direction of sight for the side view. Only one profile plane can be passed through a given point.

A *vertical plane* is a plane which is perpendicular to a horizontal plane. An infinite number of vertical planes can be passed through a given point. Frontal and profile planes are special vertical planes.

An *orthofrontal plane* is a plane which is perpendicular to a frontal plane. An infinite number of orthofrontal planes can be passed through a given point. Horizontal and profile planes are special orthofrontal planes but are never referred to by this name.

An *orthoprofile plane* is a plane which is perpendicular to a profile plane. An infinite number of orthoprofile planes can be passed through a given point.

An *oblique plane* is one which occupies any position except those specified as the first six positions of planes. An oblique plane is inclined to the three principal planes.

Horizontal, frontal, and profile planes are known as the *principal planes*. They are of great importance in the study of descriptive geometry.

19. Assignments.—See Chapter XIV, Group 2B.

THE SEVEN TYPICAL DIRECTIONS OF A LINE

20. In Fig. 10 the cube is placed with its base horizontal. The directions of sight for three principal views are indicated as being perpendicular to the faces. The edges of the cube and the lines drawn on its faces show typical directions of a line, which are named and defined as follows:

A *horizontal line* is a level line. An infinite number of horizontal lines may be drawn in a horizontal plane through any point in the plane.

A *frontal line* is a line which is perpendicular to the direction of sight for the front view. An infinite number of frontal lines may be drawn in a frontal plane through any point in the plane. A frontal line may be on the rear face of an object.

A *profile line* is a line which is perpendicular to the direction of sight for the side view. An infinite number of profile lines may be drawn in a profile plane through any point in the plane.

A *vertical line* is a line which is perpendicular to a horizontal plane. It may be determined by the use of a plumb bob, and it is also called a plumb line. There are four vertical edges on the given cube.

A *horizontal-frontal line*, as the name indicates, is both horizontal and frontal. There are four horizontal-frontal edges on the given cube. This line is also called an orthoprofile line.

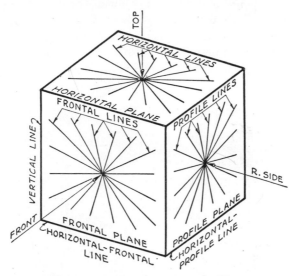

Fig. 10.—Typical Directions of a Line.

A *horizontal-profile line* is both horizontal and profile. There are four horizontal-profile edges on the given cube. This line is also called an orthofrontal line.

An oblique line is a line which is inclined to all the principal directions of sight. A line which passes through the given cube from any corner is an oblique line. There is no limitation upon its direction except that it cannot be in one of the first six directions.

Horizontal, frontal, and profile lines are called *principal lines*. They are of very great importance in the study of descriptive geometry by the direct method. Through any point in an oblique plane a horizontal, a frontal, and a profile line may be drawn. The oblique plane in Fig. 9 is bounded by a horizontal, a frontal, and a profile line.

21. Assignments.—See Chapter XIV, Group 2C.

THE VISUALIZATION OF A LINE

22. The pictorial sketch in Fig. 11 shows a drawing of a line AB in which the top view is $A_H B_H$, and the front view is $A_F B_F$. The front view shows the difference in elevation h of the two ends of the line. The most satisfactory way for a draftsman to learn to visualize the line in space is for him to lay his pencil along the top view of the line. Then, looking at the front view, he sees how much A is above B, and raises the pencil at A approximately this amount. By this means the pencil is placed in nearly the same position as the actual line in space.* The pencil and the line are said to slope downward, backward, and to the right. Figure 12 shows an

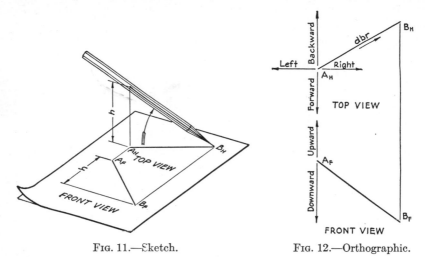

FIG. 11.—Sketch.   FIG. 12.—Orthographic.

Visualization of a Line.

actual drawing of the same line AB. The three principal directions in space are indicated at A. These directions are as follows:

First	Second	Third
Upward, u	Backward, b	Right, r
Downward, d	Forward, f	Left, l

The front view shows whether the line slopes upward or downward. The top view shows whether the line slopes backward or forward. Either

---

* For blackboard demonstration a ruler should be placed along the front view of the line, and the end corresponding to the front end of the line should be moved forward.

view shows whether it slopes to the right or the left. By using the first letters of each of these directions in the order given in the above table, the student may express the slope of the line as *dbr* in this case. This designation should be placed on the top view of the line with an arrow to indicate that the direction of slope has been taken from A toward B. The student should always visualize the lines on a drawing although he may not be required to express the results.

23. Assignments.—See Chapter XIV, Group 2D.

24. Problem 1. *To locate a point on a line.*

Analysis.—If a point is on a line it is on every view of the line that can be drawn. A sight-line from the point in one view will locate the point in an adjacent view at its intersection with the line; apply Principle 2. If the sight-line coincides with the view of a line, apply Principle 3.

Construction.—First Case.—Figure 13. *Given* three views of the

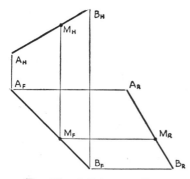

Fig. 13.—A Point on a Line.

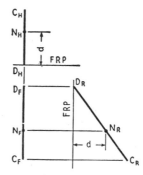

Fig. 14.—A Point on a Profile Line.

oblique line AB and the front view of the point M on the line AB. *Required* to locate the top and right-side views of M.

To find M_H draw a sight-line from M_F intersecting A_HB_H at M_H. To locate M_R draw a sight-line from M_F intersecting A_RB_R at M_R.

Second Case.—Figure 14.—If N_F is given for point N on the profile line CD, the sight-line to the top view does not intersect C_HD_H. Draw a side view of CD, which is intersected at N_R by the sight-line from N_F. By using Principle 3 the depth dimension d will locate N_H in the top view the correct distance from FRP and D_H.

To locate a point on a profile line, generally the best procedure is to use a side view.

25. Assignments.—See Chapter XIV, Group 2E.

26. Problem 2.   To draw a line which intersects a given line.

Analysis.—A line which intersects a given line passes through a point on the given line.

Construction.—Figure 15.—*Given* the top view and front view of the line EF and the top view of a line JK.

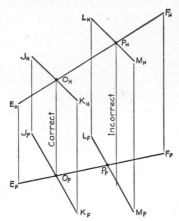

Required to draw JK so that it intersects EF.

In the top view $J_H K_H$ intersects $E_H F_H$ at the point O_H. Draw a sight-line from O_H to locate O_F on $E_F F_F$. Draw $J_F K_F$ through O_F. Then, JK is a line which intersects EF. Since conditions are not given which fix the direction of $J_F K_F$, an infinite number of solutions is possible. The line LM in this figure does not intersect the line EF. The apparent intersection P_H is not in alignment with the apparent intersection P_F. P_H and P_F are not views of the same point; therefore, the lines do not have a point in common and do not intersect.

Fig. 15.—Intersecting Lines.

27. Assignments.—See Chapter XIV, Group 2F.

THE DETERMINATION OF VISIBILITY

28. The determination of the visibility of the edges of an object is an important detail in making a drawing. The draftsman usually does not have the actual object placed before him so that he can see which edges are visible. The views which he draws to represent the object of his creative imagination, or the views which are required in the graphical solution of a problem, must be correct in this respect. Some rules for determining the visibility of the edges of an object as they appear in a drawing have been formulated. They are stated for a simple object such as a convex polyhedron. Complicated objects with notches or holes may present special problems in visibility, but in a general way the same rules apply.

RULES FOR VISIBILITY

(1) The entire outline of every view of an object is visible.

(2) The nearest corner or edge of an object is visible. Inspection of an adjacent view will determine which is nearest. If the bases of an object are perpendicular to its axis, the base at the nearer end of the axis is visible.

In Fig. 16 the front view shows that J is the nearest corner, and JA, JB, JC, and JD are the nearest edges to the observer of the top view, in which they are visible.

In the top view of the pyramid shown in Fig. 19, V, VA, and VB are found to be visible by inspection of the front view which shows that the

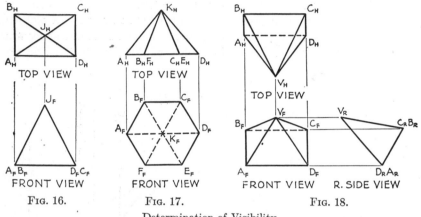

FIG. 16.   FIG. 17.   FIG. 18.

Determination of Visibility.

point V and the edges VA and VB are nearest to the observer of the top view.

(3) **The farthest corner or edge of a solid object is invisible if it falls within the outline of the view.**

In Fig. 17 the top view shows that K and the edges KA and KD are farthest from the observer of the front view in which they are invisible.

In the front view of the pyramid of Fig. 19, C, CA, and CB are found to be invisible by inspection of the top view, which shows that the point C and the edges CA and CB are farthest from the observer of the front view.

(4) **If a corner of a convex polyhedron falls within the outline of a view, the visibility of all edges terminating at this point is the same as the visibility of the corner.**

The visibility of the lines meeting at J in Fig. 16, at K in Fig. 17, and at C and at V in Fig. 19 follows this rule.

(5) **In any view of a convex polyhedron, if two edges appear to cross, one of them is visible, and the other is invisible.**

Meeting at a corner is not considered as crossing. If the visibility of one of these edges can be determined, this rule gives the visibility of all edges that appear to cross it.

In the front view of Fig. 18 if *BC* is known to be invisible, *VA* and *VD* are drawn as visible lines. In the top view if *VB* and *VC* are known to be visible, *AD* is drawn as an invisible line.

The application of rules 2, 3, 4, and 5 may be called the inspection method of determining visibility. In cases where none of these rules are suitable, the method of rule 6 will be successful.

(6) **At the apparent intersection of two edges in a view, a sight-line drawn to an adjacent view will locate a point on each edge and show which is nearer the observer, fixing the visibility of the edge in the first view.**

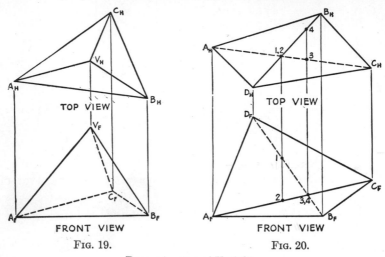

FIG. 19.   FIG. 20.

Determination of Visibility.

In Fig. 20 it is necessary to determine which of the edges, *AC* or *BD*, is visible in each view; and it cannot be done by simple inspection. To determine the visibility in the top view draw a sight-line from the apparent intersection at 1, 2. It locates 1 on *DB* and 2 on *AC* in the front view. Since point 1 is directly above point 2, it is visible in the top view, and the edge *BD* is visible.

To determine the visibility of these edges in the front view the sight-line from 3, 4 to the top view shows that 3 is in front of 4 and is visible in the front view. Then, edge *AC* is visible.

Rule 6 is of great importance and general usefulness. After considerable experience in the application of this rule it may be possible to imagine that the sight-line has been drawn to the adjacent view in many cases. The student, however, should always draw the sight-line and number the points as a matter of training as well as to show the instructor that the visibility was ascertained rather than assumed.

29. Problem 3. *To determine the visibility of two oblique rods which appear to cross in the principal views.*

Analysis.—From the apparent intersection of the center lines of the rods in any view a sight-line drawn to an adjacent view will locate a point on each line and show which is nearer the observer.

Construction.—Fig. 21.—*Given* the rods whose center lines are AB and CD. *Required* to determine the visibility of the rods.

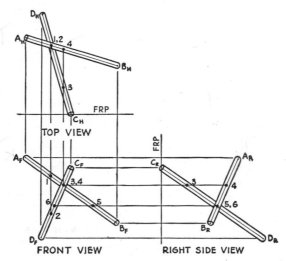

FIG. 21.—Determination of Visibility.

Draw a sight-line from the apparent intersection of the center lines at 1, 2 in the top view to the front view, locating point 1 on AB and 2 on CD. Point 1 is above point 2 and is nearer the observer of the top view. Then, AB is the visible rod in the top view. Draw a sight-line from 3, 4 in the front view to either the top view or the side view. In either case point 3 on CD is nearer the observer of the front view than is 4 on AB. Then, rod CD is visible in the front view. Draw a sight-line from 5, 6 in the right-side view to the front view. Point 5 on AB is to the right of point 6 on CD and is nearer the observer of the right-side view. Then, AB is the visible rod in the right-side view.

The visibility of the ends, which appear as ellipses, is found by rule 2.

30. Assignments.—See Chapter XIV, Group 2G.

CHAPTER III

AUXILIARY VIEWS

31. An auxiliary view is used for three purposes: first, to show the true form or size of some inclined face or detail of an object; second, to aid in showing an object which is in an inclined position; and third, to solve many of the problems of descriptive geometry.

In Chapter II it has been shown that the direction of sight for a principal view is perpendicular to the directions of sight for two other principal views. An auxiliary view is one for which the direction of sight is perpendicular to the direction of sight for only one principal view. From this definition it is evident that there are three classes of auxiliary views: first, auxiliary views for which the direction of sight is horizontal; second, auxiliary views for which the direction of sight is frontal; and third, auxiliary views for which the direction of sight is profile. An examination of Fig. 10 will show that there are an infinite number of horizontal directions, which are perpendicular to the direction of sight for the top view; that there are an infinite number of frontal directions, which are perpendicular to the direction of sight for the front view; and that there are an infinite number of profile directions, which are perpendicular to the direction of sight for the side view.

Only one of the principal orthographic dimensions of an object appears in an auxiliary view. The first class of auxiliary views shows the orthographic dimension of height; the second class shows the orthographic dimension of depth; and the third class shows the orthographic dimension of width.

THE FIRST CLASS OF AUXILIARY VIEWS

Auxiliary Elevations

Auxiliary Views Showing Height

32. Since man, following the law of gravitation, usually builds structures with vertical members resting upon a horizontal foundation, the simplest and most useful class of auxiliary views is that in which the

24

observer may be assumed to walk around the object so as to obtain a new position for the desired horizontal direction of sight. Fig. 22 shows a few of the possible auxiliary elevations of a simple object arranged in a band around it. These auxiliary elevations show the height dimension just as it appears in the four principal views which are also shown in the drawing. In fact, an auxiliary elevation is not very different from a front view or a side view; and it is not necessarily more complicated. If the front face of

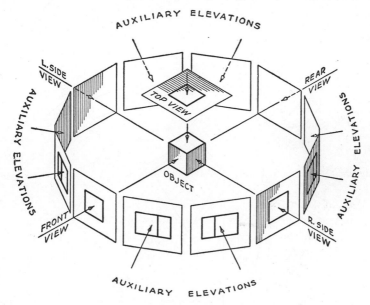

FIG. 22.—Horizontal Directions of Sight for Auxiliary Elevations.

the object is not in a frontal position, an auxiliary elevation may be drawn which is simpler than any of the principal elevations. The first three principles of descriptive geometry are used in making an auxiliary elevation.

The front view and top view of another object are shown in Fig. 23. Four auxiliary elevations have been drawn adjacent to the top view. Each of them has the same height h as the front view, and it is measured toward the top view from the horizontal reference plane HRP. In all auxiliary elevations the top of the object is toward the top view. In every case HRP appears as a line which is drawn at right angles to the sight-lines for the view.

The five arrows pointing toward the top view indicate horizontal directions of sight for the front view and four auxiliary elevations. Each auxiliary elevation shows the true shape of one face because the direction of sight is perpendicular to that face.

The direction of sight for auxiliary view Number 2 may be expressed concisely in these terms: "Draw an auxiliary elevation taken 30° in front of the left," meaning, "Draw an auxiliary elevation for which the direction of sight is 30° in front of that for a left-side view."

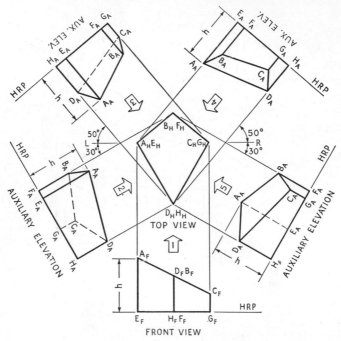

Fig. 23.—Auxiliary Elevations.

The drawing of the stand in Fig. 24 is an example of the use of an auxiliary elevation as an aid in drawing the front view of one of the legs which is shown in true form in the auxiliary view.

33. Orientation is the process by which the draftsman or the reader of a drawing relates himself to any view in such a manner that the view appears to him as the actual object would appear if he were standing on a horizontal floor. Although the process of orientation is always essentially mental, an actual change-of-position may be necessary in the case of an auxiliary view or an oblique view. A view appears "real" only when it is visualized as the actual object in its position in space.

The object in Fig. 23 has a horizontal base which appears as an edge view in the auxiliary elevations. To orientate each of these views, the draftsman moves to a position in which the base of the object appears horizontal and at the bottom of the view. In an auxiliary elevation, "upward" is toward the top view; and "downward" is away from it. The name of the view is lettered below it and parallel to the horizontal base.

The reader of the drawing should turn the paper around so as to read the name of each auxiliary view as a horizontal line of lettering. By this operation he will orientate the view so as to see it in the same manner as he would see the object.

Since an edge view of a horizontal reference plane *HRP* is used for making every auxiliary elevation, and an object may not have a horizontal base, this reference plane is generally used for orientating auxiliary elevations. In Fig. 23 *HRP* coincides with the base of the object.

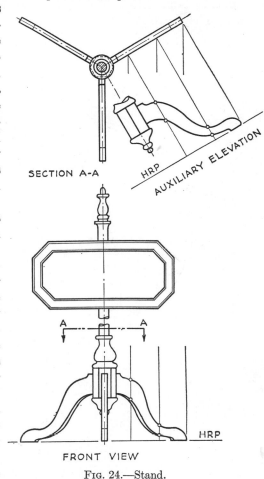

SECTION A-A

FRONT VIEW

Fig. 24.—Stand.

34. Assignments.—See Chapter XIV, Group 3A.

THE SECOND CLASS OF AUXILIARY VIEWS

Right-Auxiliary Views and Left-Auxiliary Views

Auxiliary Views Showing Depth

35. Right- and left-auxiliary views are somewhat like right- and left-side views. They have the same depth dimensions as the top view and the side

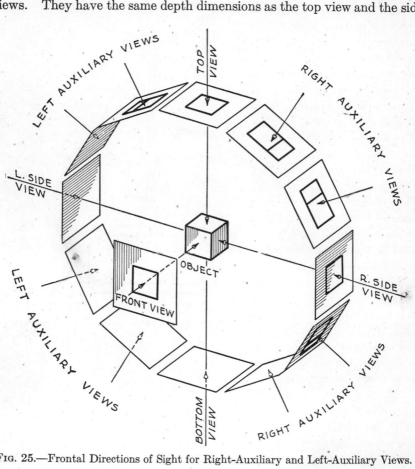

Fig. 25.—Frontal Directions of Sight for Right-Auxiliary and Left-Auxiliary Views.

view, but the direction of sight is inclined instead of being horizontal. Fig. 25 shows a few of the possible right- and left-auxiliary views of an object arranged in a band around it. For a right-auxiliary view the observer stands at the right side of the object and his direction of sight is either upward or downward toward the object. Similarly, for a left-auxiliary view the position of the observer is to the left of the object and his direction of sight is upward or downward toward the object.

The front and top views of an offset link are given in Fig. 26. Two right-auxiliary views and two left-auxiliary views are required. Sight-

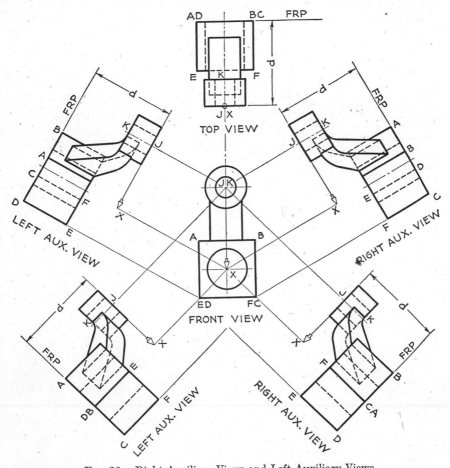

Fig. 26.—Right-Auxiliary Views and Left-Auxiliary Views.

lines are drawn from the front view in the desired directions according to Principle 2. A frontal reference plane *FRP* is located at the rear of the object and appears as an edge view in the top view. It is drawn as a line perpendicular to the sight-lines joining the given views. The same *FRP* is drawn at the desired location for each auxiliary view and perpendicular to the respective sight-lines. By means of dividers all depth dimensions, such as d, are set off along the sight-lines from FRP toward the front view, Principle 3. These measurements must not be set off on the opposite side of FRP, thereby reversing the view. An examination of the drawing shows that the cylindrical end is off-set toward the front view in every case.

36. Orientation.—An imaginary plumb bob X is shown hanging from point J in Fig. 26. The *plumb line* JX is used as an effective and reliable means of orientating auxiliary views. It is a vertical line which has a definitely marked lower end. If the observer relates himself to any view so that the plumb bob* appears to hang naturally, the view is orientated. He can do this either by moving to the proper position or by turning the paper. The name of each view is lettered below it and at right angles to the plumb line. This object has vertical edges such as AD and BC which can be used as plumb lines.

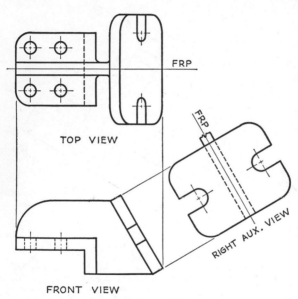

FIG. 27.—Motor Support.

The views of this object can be orientated also by means of FRP, which is a *vertical plane* that appears as a line parallel to the plumb line. Lastly, orientation can be accomplished by making the horizontal lines CF and DE appear horizontal, this method being possible because these are *normal views of horizontal lines.*

Figure 27 is an example of the practical use of a right-auxiliary view to show the true shape of the inclined face of the motor support. The

* In the auxiliary views the point of the plumb bob is located correctly, but the bob is represented by a symbol instead of a true drawing.

This symbol can be made by using a group of three holes in column 6 or 7 on the Braddock–Rowe Lettering Angle for its height and the slot for the slope of its sides.

auxiliary view also serves to furnish information for completing the top view.

37. An angle block with an inclined face which has a shallow cylindrical hole in it is shown in Fig. 28. The circles which represent this hole appear as ellipses in the top view and the right-side view. The most satisfactory way of drawing these ellipses is to draw a right-auxiliary view for which

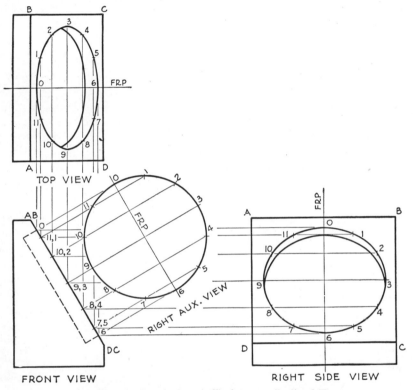

Fig. 28.—Angle Block. A Circle on an Inclined Face.

the direction of sight is perpendicular to the inclined face of the object. In this view the hole appears as a circle. Twelve symmetrically arranged points are selected on the circle; and sight-lines are drawn to locate them in the front view, where the circle appears as an edge view. Sight-lines from these points to the top view and to the right-side view are drawn. The frontal reference plane FRP is drawn through the center of the auxiliary view, top view, and side view. By use of dividers all the dimensions measured along the sight-lines on each side of FRP in the auxiliary view are transferred to the top view and side view. Due to the symmetrical arrangement of the twelve points, only three settings of the dividers are necessary. Note that the numbers 1, 2, 3, 4, and 5 are placed in all cases on the side of *FRP* which is away from the front view.

38. Assignments.—See Chapter XIV, Group 3B.

THIRD CLASS OF AUXILIARY VIEWS

Front-Auxiliary Views and Rear-Auxiliary Views

Auxiliary Views Showing Width

39. Front- and rear-auxiliary views are so named because they are somewhat like front and rear principal views. They differ from them in

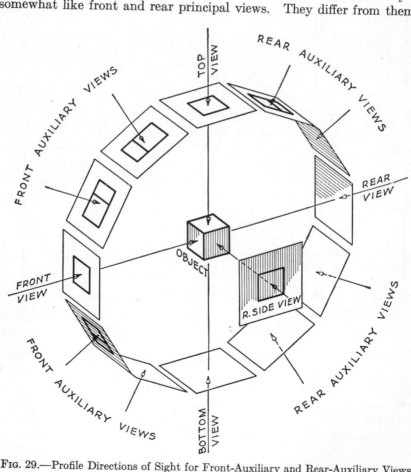

Fig. 29.—Profile Directions of Sight for Front-Auxiliary and Rear-Auxiliary Views.

that the direction of sight is inclined. For a front-auxiliary view the observer assumes a position in front of the object so that he can look either downward or upward toward it. For a rear-auxiliary view the observer's position is behind the object, and he looks downward or upward toward it. Figure 29 shows a few of the possible front- and rear-auxiliary views of a simple object arranged in a band around it. They show the width of the object just as it appears in the front view.

In Fig. 30 the front view and the right-side view of another object are given. Two front-auxiliary views and two rear-auxiliary views are required. Sight-lines are drawn from the right-side view in the directions which have been selected for seeing the desired auxiliary views, Principle 2. A profile reference plane PRP is drawn through the center of the front view. It appears in edge view as a line perpendicular to the sight-lines. A line representing the edge view of PRP is drawn at the desired location of

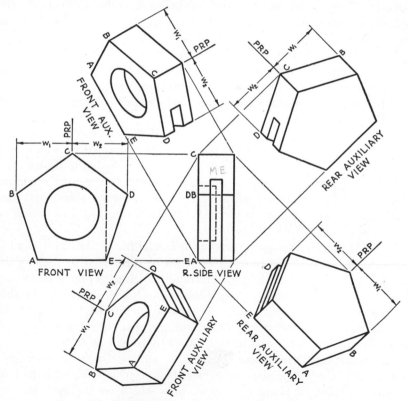

Fig. 30.—Front-Auxiliary Views and Rear-Auxiliary Views.

each auxiliary view and perpendicular to the respective sight-lines. The width dimensions w_1 and w_2 found in the front view are transferred to the proper side of *PRP* for each auxiliary view, Principle 3. The dimension w_1 is measured away from the right-side view in every case, and w_2 is measured toward it. These measurements must not be reversed. It should be noticed that the slot in the object is turned toward the right-side view in every view which is adjacent to it.

40. Orientation.—The auxiliary views in Fig. 30 can be orientated by means of the profile reference plane *PRP*, which is a vertical plane appearing as an edge view in each of them. If the observer assumes a position or turns the drawing so that *PRP* appears vertical, and the base of the object is downward, the view will be orientated. The name of the view is lettered below it and perpendicular to *PRP*.

41. Summary of the Methods of Orientation.—Four satisfactory methods of orientating the views of a drawing have been discussed. The methods of orientation are devised especially for auxiliary and oblique views. They do not apply to top and bottom views.

1. *By Means of Any View of a Vertical Line. Plumb Line Method.*— Any view of an object having a vertical line can be orientated by making that line appear vertical with its lower end downward.

If the object does not have a vertical line or edge, a hanging plumb bob can be drawn in each view.

2. *By Means of an Edge View of a Vertical Plane.*—Any view in which there is an edge view of a vertical plane can be orientated by making that plane appear vertical, and by determining which direction is downward.

Any view made by using a vertical reference plane can be orientated by means of that plane. Frontal and profile reference planes and some auxiliary reference planes are vertical. If the downward direction is not obvious, a plumb bob should be used.

3. *By Means of a Normal View of a Horizontal Line.*—Any view in which a horizontal line is shown in *true length* can be orientated by making that line appear horizontal, and by determining which direction is downward.

4. *By Means of an Edge View of a Horizontal Plane.*—Any view in which a horizontal plane appears edgewise can be orientated by making that plane appear horizontal, and by determining which direction is downward. All auxiliary elevations may be orientated by means of *HRP*.

42. Indicating Orientation.—A simple and satisfactory method of showing that the orientation for a view has been determined is to letter the name of the view below it on guide lines which are horizontal for that view. This method of indicating orientation may cause the name of the view to appear almost up-side-down on the paper.

42A. Orientated Names of Views as an Aid to Reading a Drawing.—If the reader of the drawing changes his position or holds the paper so that he reads the name of a view as a horizontal line of lettering, he gives his powers of visualization an opportunity to conceive of that view as the object itself which is being observed in the required direction of sight. The names of auxiliary and oblique views which have been placed in accordance with these methods of orientation are of great assistance in reading the drawing.

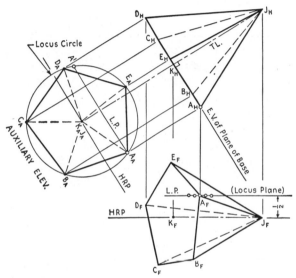

Fig. 31A.—Solution Using Locus Plane. First Case.

43. Locus Planes.—A locus plane may be used as a basic approach to the solution of some problems. Such a plane contains all the points which satisfy one requirement.

First Case.—In Fig. 31A point K is the center of a regular pentagon which is the base of a right pyramid whose vertex is at J. The pentagon may be inscribed in a $2\frac{1}{2}''$ diameter circle, and the corner A is to the right of K and $\frac{1}{2}''$ above it. Therefore, the locus plane for A is a horizontal plane shown above K_F. The edge view of the plane of the base is perpendicular to $K_H J_H$ which is shown in true length. The regular pentagon for the base may be drawn as an auxiliary elevation. In this view there are two loci for the corner A, the locus circle and the locus plane LP shown edgewise. These intersect in two points A_A and A'. The required corner is at A_A, to the right of K. With A_A located, the auxiliary elevation and top view may be completed as two simple views.

Second Case.—Fig. 31B. This problem differs from the previous one in that the locus plane is not parallel to the axis. The point M is the center of a square which is the base of a right pyramid whose vertex is at V. The square may be inscribed in a $2\frac{1}{2}''$ diameter circle and the corner A is

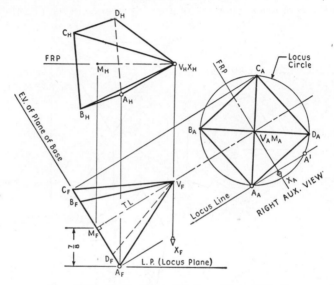

Fig. 31B.—Locus Plane Solution. Second Case.

in front of M and $\frac{7}{8}''$ below it. Therefore, the locus plane LP is horizontal and below M_F.

The edge view of the plane of the base is perpendicular to $V_F M_F$ which is in true length. This plane intersects the locus plane in a locus line shown as an end view at A_F. In the right auxiliary view the locus line intersects the locus circle in two points, A_A and A'. The required corner is at A_A which is in front of M_A.

Note that the front view and the auxiliary view are practically equivalent to a front view and a top view of the pyramid if the axis is thought of as being vertical. Two adjacent simple views such as these must be drawn.

44. Assignments.—See Chapter XIV, Groups 3C and 3D.

CHAPTER IV

OBLIQUE VIEWS

THE FOURTH FUNDAMENTAL PRINCIPLE OF DESCRIPTIVE GEOMETRY

45. A Normal View of a Line.

A normal view of a line is one for which the direction of sight is at right angles to the line.

This view shows the true length of a line. The sight-lines to an adjacent view are perpendicular to that view. One of the principal views may be a normal view. If the line is an oblique line, none of the principal views can be a normal view.

THE FIFTH FUNDAMENTAL PRINCIPLE OF DESCRIPTIVE GEOMETRY

46. An End View of a Line.

An end view of a line is one for which the direction of sight is parallel to the line.

An end view of a line is a point. This view is always adjacent to a normal view of the line. This principle is used in drawing the base of a right prism or pyramid that has an oblique axis. It is also used in the application of Principle 9.

Principles 4 and 5 are so closely related that they are illustrated by the same figures, and discussed together. The lines in Figs. 32 to 39 are shown in the pictorial drawing as an edge of the object, and in the corresponding orthographic drawing as the line which represents the edge.

Since the direction of sight for an end view is perpendicular to the direction of sight for a normal view, these views always are drawn adjacent to each other, Principle 1. This can be seen to be true for the vertical line AB, Figs. 32 and 33; the frontal line CD, Figs. 34 and 35; the horizontal line EF, Figs. 36 and 37; and the oblique line GK, Figs. 38 and 39. In Fig. 35, if an attempt is made to find an end view of CD adjacent to $C_H D_H$, the view $C_R D_R$ which is not an end view is obtained. This demonstrates that the end view must be adjacent to a normal view. Then, in Fig. 39 it is clear that an end view cannot be shown adjacent to either $G_F K_F$ or $G_H K_H$, and that a normal view such as $G_A K_A$ is required before the end view $K_O G_O$ can be obtained. The normal view is made by drawing sight-lines

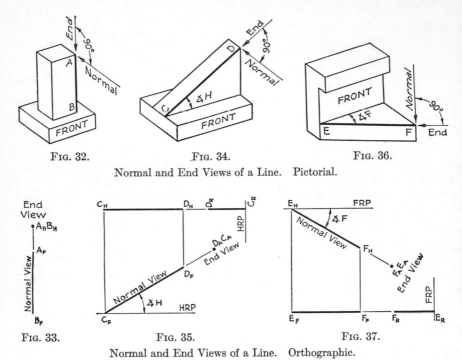

Fig. 32.   Fig. 34.   Fig. 36.

Normal and End Views of a Line.   Pictorial.

Fig. 33.   Fig. 35.   Fig. 37.

Normal and End Views of a Line.   Orthographic.

perpendicular to $G_H K_H$. In Fig. 40, the normal view is adjacent to the front view; and in Fig. 41, it is adjacent to the right-side view.

A study of Figs. 32 to 41 justifies the following statements:

1. If the sight-lines joining two views of a line are perpendicular to one of them, the other is a normal view.

2. If one of two adjacent views of a line is a point, the other is a normal view.

47. The Angle Between a Line and a Principal Plane.

A normal view of a line shows the angle the line makes with any plane which appears as an edge view in that view.

In Fig. 35, the angle that CD makes with a horizontal plane through C is shown as angle H. In Fig. 37, the angle that EF makes with a frontal plane through E is shown as angle F. In Fig. 39, GK makes angle H with

HRP, a horizontal plane. In Fig. 40, LM makes angle F with FRP, a frontal plane. In Fig. 41, RS makes angle P with PRP, a profile plane.

48. Assignments.—See Chapter XIV, Group 4A.

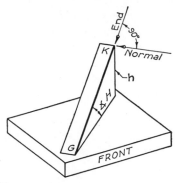

FIG. 38.—Normal and End Views of an Oblique Line. Pictorial.

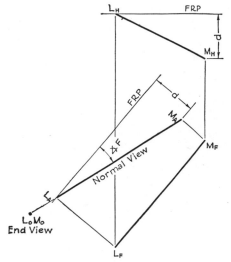

FIG. 40.—Normal and End Views of an Oblique Line.

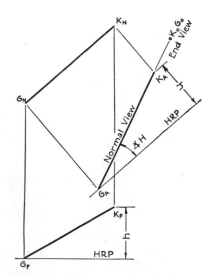

FIG. 39.—Normal and End Views of an Oblique Line. Orthographic.

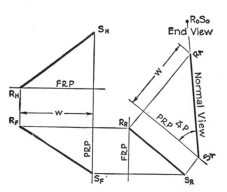

FIG. 41.—Normal and End Views of an Oblique Line.

THE SIXTH FUNDAMENTAL PRINCIPLE OF DESCRIPTIVE GEOMETRY

49. Parallel Lines.
Parallel lines appear parallel in any orthographic view.

Figure 42 shows a horizontal rectangle $ABCD$, for which the front and top views are given. In the top view the opposite sides are parallel. To check the truth of this principle a right-auxiliary view has been drawn in which A_AE_A is equal to C_AF_A, both being equal to b; and B_AE_A is equal to D_AF_A, both being equal to d, which has been obtained from the top view. Therefore, the right triangles $A_AB_AE_A$ and $D_AC_AF_A$ are equal, and the lines A_AB_A and C_AD_A are parallel. In the same way, it is seen that A_AD_A

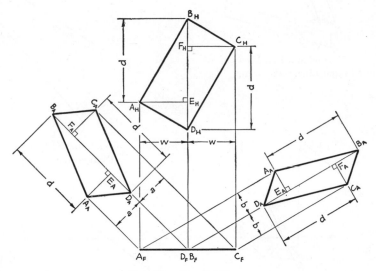

FIG. 42.—Parallel Lines.

is parallel to B_AC_A. The rectangle, which is shown in its true shape in the top view, appears as a parallelogram in the right-auxiliary view. A left-auxiliary view is drawn, which can be studied in the same way as further proof that this principle is correct.

As the direction of sight changes, two parallel lines may appear to approach each other until they coincide, or they may appear to shorten until they become points.

50. Assignments.—See Chapter XIV, Group 4B.

THE SEVENTH FUNDAMENTAL PRINCIPLE
OF DESCRIPTIVE GEOMETRY

51. Perpendicular Lines.

**Two perpendicular lines appear perpendicular in any view that is a
normal view of either** (or both) **of the lines.** They do not appear perpendicular unless the view is a normal view of at least one of them.

The pictorial drawing, Fig. 43, shows a vertical plane V and the lines
AB and CD perpendicular to it. Every line in the pentagon shown on V

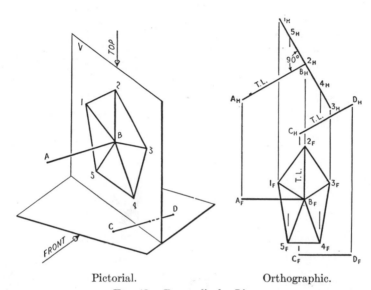

Pictorial.   Orthographic.

Fig. 43.—Perpendicular Lines.

is perpendicular to both AB and CD. Only five of the lines intersect
AB, and none of them intersect CD, but they are all perpendicular to AB
and CD.

In the orthographic drawing the lines AB and CD appear in true length
in the top view, and every line of the pentagon appears perpendicular to
them, except 2–B which is shown as a point. Evidently, 2–B is perpendicular to AB and CD, and it so appears in the front view where 2–B is
in true length. In the top view AB and 4–5 are both in true length and
they appear perpendicular.

If two lines appear perpendicular in a view in which neither of them
is shown in true length, the lines are not perpendicular in space.

52. An example of the application of Principle 7 * for drawing a line BC perpendicular to the oblique line AB is shown in Fig. 44. Only the front view of BC is given. In order to draw the perpendicular line BC, a normal view of one of the lines must be obtained.

The most obvious approach is to make a left auxiliary view, No. 1, for the true length of AB. Draw $B_A C_A \perp A_A B_A$. Use the depth dimension d to finish the top view.

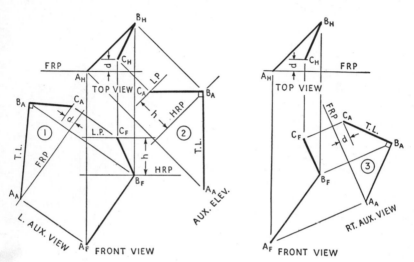

FIG. 44.—Perpendicular Oblique Lines.   FIG. 45.—Perpendicular Oblique Lines.

In some cases it may be more desirable (or necessary) to make the normal view adjacent to the view which shows only AB. This solution is shown in the auxiliary elevation, No. 2. Here $B_A C_A$ is drawn perpendicular

* Figure 42, which is intended to illustrate Principle 6, may be used for studying Principle 7. The top view is a normal view of all the lines shown, including those inside the rectangle. All the angles, right or acute, appear in true size in this view. In either auxiliary view, the right angles at the corners of the rectangle do not appear as right angles because the direction of sight is such that none of the edges are shown in true length. The right angles at E_A and F_A appear as right angles because the direction of sight is perpendicular to one of the lines, $B_A D_A$, which appears as a normal view. The acute angles at B_A and D_A formed by the diagonal $B_A D_A$ and the edges of the rectangle are not in true size, although one of the lines $B_A D_A$ is in true length. This shows that only a right angle appears in its true size in a view which is a normal view of only one of its lines.

to $A_A B_A$, and C_A is found in the locus plane LP, which is obtained from the front view. Sight-lines from the front view and the auxiliary elevation will intersect at C_H.

In other cases in which measuring is to be done along BC, it may be best to take the auxiliary view, No. 3, Fig. 45, normal to BC which is given in only one view. $A_A B_A$ will not be in true length, but since $B_A C_A$ is to be a normal view line, the right angle can be drawn, locating C_A on the sight-line from C_F. The depth dimension d is used for finding C_H.

53. Assignments.—See Chapter XIV, Group 4C.

OBLIQUE VIEWS

54. An oblique view is an orthographic view for which the direction of sight is oblique. Such a view can be drawn adjacent to only an auxiliary view, or another oblique view. Principle 1 states that the directions of sight for any two adjacent views are mutually perpendicular. The direction of sight for an auxiliary view is horizontal, frontal, or profile. An oblique direction of sight can be assumed perpendicular to any of these by Principle 7, but cannot be taken perpendicular to the direction of sight for a principal view. Therefore, the procedure for making an oblique view is to draw an auxiliary view, and then draw the oblique view adjacent to it. This is the only method of making the required right angle changes-of-direction-of-sight from a principal view to an oblique view.

Oblique views are used to show the true form of an oblique face of an object, to draw the principal views of an object placed obliquely, and to aid in solving many problems of descriptive geometry.

Figure 46 shows an object for which the front view and top view are given. An auxiliary elevation is shown; and there are four oblique views arranged around it, each adjacent to it. For these views the sight-lines are drawn from the auxiliary elevation, and the dimension x is obtained from the top view, which is adjacent to the auxiliary elevation. The dimension x is only one of the seven dimensions which are transferred from the top view to each oblique view. An auxiliary reference plane ARP is drawn in edge view through C, in the top view, and at a desirable location for each oblique view. All the necessary dimensions for making these oblique views are set off along sight-lines on the side of ARP which is away from the auxiliary elevation. As a check against the reversal of any view, note that C is the nearest point to the auxiliary elevation in the top view and in all oblique views, and that A is the farthest point in all these views.

Orientation.—The auxiliary elevation, Fig. 46, is orientated by means of the horizontal base of the object.   The oblique views are orientated by means of the **vertical** auxiliary reference plane ARP which appears as an edge view in each oblique view.

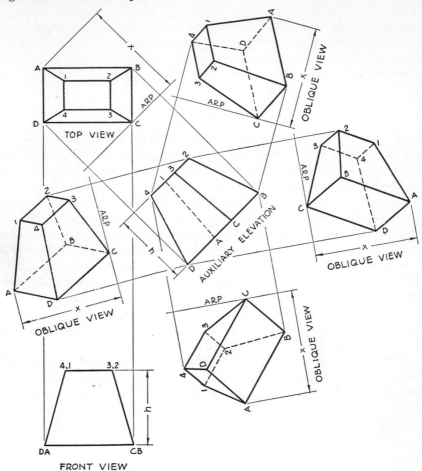

Fig. 46.—Oblique Views.

55. *Problem 4.   To draw a view as seen in a given oblique direction.*
Analysis.—The given direction of sight is an oblique line; therefore, a view which shows an end view of the line is an oblique view.   An intermediate auxiliary view which shows a normal view of the line of sight must be drawn.   Apply Principles 4 and 5.

Construction.—Fig. 47. *Given* the front view and top view of the right pentagonal pyramid and the arrow PQ as the direction of sight. *Required* to draw a view of the pyramid as seen in the direction PQ.

First, obtain a view of the arrow and the pyramid which shows a normal view of the arrow. An auxiliary elevation is used in this solution because

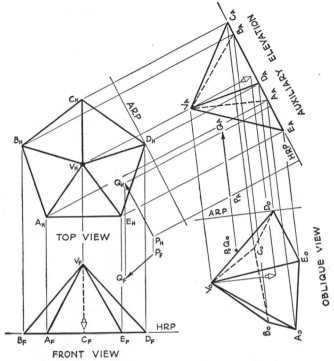

Fig. 47.—Oblique View in a Given Direction.

this view of the pyramid is easier to make than an auxiliary view adjacent to the front view. Next, draw an oblique view in the direction of the arrow, which will show the arrow as a point, and give the required view of the pyramid. Throughout this solution the arrow and the pyramid are treated as a unit. In the oblique view, note that the arrow shown as P_oQ_o if produced will not quite intersect the pyramid.

Orientation.—The auxiliary elevation and the oblique view are orientated by means of the edge view of the horizontal plane HRP and the edge view of the vertical plane ARP, respectively; or they may be orientated by the plumb line.

56. Assignments.—See Chapter XIV, Group 4D.

57. Principal Line Diagram.—The diagram of Fig. 48 is given for two purposes: first, to show how three principal lines which are perpendicular

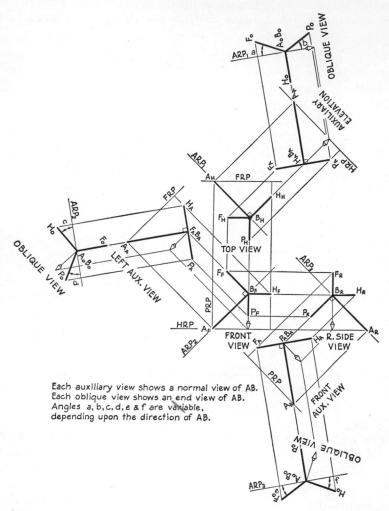

Each auxiliary view shows a normal view of AB.
Each oblique view shows an end view of AB.
Angles a, b, c, d, e & f are variable,
depending upon the direction of AB.

Fig. 48.—Diagram for Principal Lines Perpendicular to an Oblique Line.

to the oblique line AB appear in auxiliary views and oblique views which are respectively normal views and end views of AB; second, to show the orientation of each view.

This diagram gives the basis for planning all the possible auxiliary view solutions of the problem of drawing an object which has as its axis a given oblique line such as AB.

This diagram shows the top view and the front view of a horizontal line BH, a frontal line BF, and a profile line BP, each of which is drawn perpendicular to the line AB by Principle 7. First, three auxiliary views are made, one adjacent to each principal view. They all show a normal view of AB, having been drawn to comply with Principle 4. By Principle 7 the lines which were originally assumed perpendicular to AB in space appear at right angles to AB in the auxiliary views. Second, an oblique view, which is an end view of AB, Principle 5, is drawn adjacent to each auxiliary view. In these oblique views the three lines which are perpendicular to AB appear in true length and in every case one of them coincides with a sight-line.

Orientation.—A plumb bob is shown hanging from point B in each view. The plumb line method is most effective for orientating these views, although each of them can be orientated by another method. In the oblique views, the horizontal line BH is shown in true length and appears perpendicular to the plumb line, Principle 7.

58. Problem 5. To draw a right prism which has as its axis a given oblique line.

Analysis.—The simple views of a right prism are those in which the axis appears as a normal view or an end view. Therefore, if such views of the axis are obtained by Principles 4 and 5, two adjacent views of the prism may be constructed.

Construction.—Fig. 49. *Given* the front view and top view of the axis JK. *Required* to draw a right prism whose base is a regular pentagon having one of its sides horizontal and of a given length.

First Solution.—In this case a normal auxiliary elevation of the axis is drawn at $K_A J_A$ and the end view at $K_O J_O$. In the oblique view a horizontal line is perpendicular to ARP, which is the edge view of a vertical plane. Draw the edge ED perpendicular to ARP, and construct a regular pentagon which is an end view of the prism. Next, the auxiliary elevation of the prism is constructed. Note that these views are really like the top view and front view of an upright prism, but that they are not placed in this position on the paper. From these two views and by the application of the Principles 1, 2, and 3, the top view is drawn. Then, by using the top view and the auxiliary elevation, the front view is drawn by the same principles. The visibility of the corners and edges is determined by application of the rules for visibility.

Discussion.—The principal line diagram Fig. 48 shows that this problem may be solved by following any one of the three routes to the oblique view. An edge of the base may be made horizontal, frontal, or profile in any of the oblique views. The diagram also shows that if some line in the base of the object is to be horizontal, the easiest route is through an auxiliary

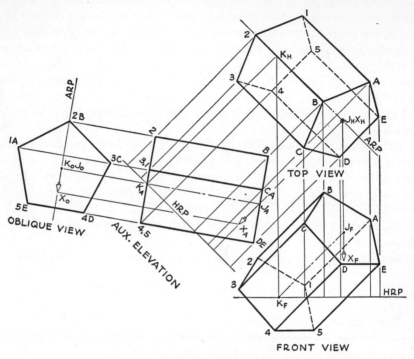

Fig. 49.—Object on a Given Center Line.

elevation; that if some line in the base of the object is to be frontal, the easiest route is from the front view through a right- or left-auxiliary view; and that if some line in the base is to be profile, the easiest route is from a side view through a front- or rear-auxiliary view.

Second Solution.—Fig. 50. In this case the normal view of the axis JK is made adjacent to the front view. Since one edge of the base is to be horizontal, a horizontal line JH is drawn in the top view and the front view perpendicular to JK. Then, this line is located in the left-auxiliary view and the oblique view. In the oblique view DE is drawn parallel to the horizontal line J_OH_O, and a regular pentagon is constructed. The construction of the other views is practically the same as that explained in the first solution. The first solution is preferable and should be used if space on the paper is available.

In either of these solutions the direction of the edge *DE* could be established by making *DE* perpendicular to the plumb line *JX*.

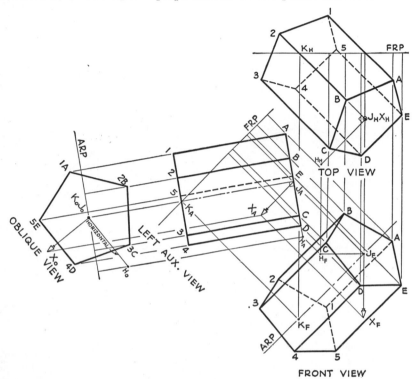

Fig. 50.—Object on a Given Center Line.

59. Problem 6. To draw a right cylinder having a given oblique line as its axis.

Analysis.—Two simple adjacent views may be drawn if a normal view and end view of the axis is obtained by Principles 4 and 5.

Construction.—Fig. 51. *Given* the axis *AB*. *Required* to draw a right cylinder of given diameter.

In this case the axis is located on the paper in such a manner that it is necessary to draw the normal view of the axis as a left-auxiliary view. With the end view of the axis $A_O B_O$ as a center, draw a circle of the given diameter as the end view of the cylinder. The adjacent auxiliary view is drawn as shown. These two views are like those which are ordinarily drawn for the top view and front view of a right cylinder resting on a hori-

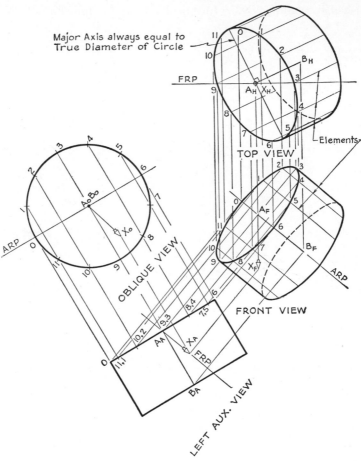

Fig. 51.—Cylinder on a Given Axis.

zontal surface, but they are not placed squarely on the paper because the axis of the cylinder is an oblique line. To draw the front and top views select equally spaced points on the circle. Locate two of the points on *ARP* and two on the sight-line through the center of the circle. After obtaining the ellipse for one end of the cylinder, that for the other end may be obtained by using elements parallel and equal to the length of the axis in that view. All the elements in the front view are equal to $A_F B_F$ in length. All the elements in the top view are equal to $A_H B_H$ in length. The views are orientated by means of the plumb line AX.

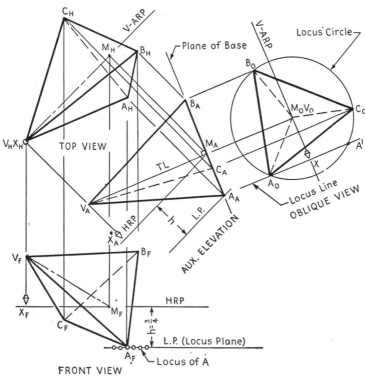

FIG. 51A.—Locus Plane Solution. Axis Oblique.

60. Locus Plane Solution.—In Fig. 51A, M is the center of an equilateral triangle which is the base of a right pyramid having its vertex at V. The corner A of the base is to the right of M and $\frac{3}{4}''$ below M. Therefore, the locus plane for A is horizontal and below M_F. After making an auxiliary elevation showing a normal view of VM and an edge view of the locus plane LP, the remaining construction is similar to that shown in Fig. 31B. In making this comparison the auxiliary elevation of Fig. 51A may be thought of as a front view after turning the paper so that the plumb line appears vertical in this view.

Assignments.—See Chapter XIV, Group 4E.

CHAPTER V

LINE AND PLANE PROBLEMS

61. There are many problems in engineering which deal with the relationships which exist in space between lines and planes. Descriptive geometry offers the most satisfactory method of solving such problems. The term "line" refers to a straight line unless otherwise specified.

PLANES

62. A plane may be specified and shown on a drawing by any of the following methods:

1. By two intersecting lines.
2. By two parallel lines.
3. By a geometrical figure such as a triangle, a circle, a square, or a parallelogram. Other figures may represent planes, but they should be checked to see that they are not warped or bent surfaces.
4. By strike and dip.
5. By three points not in a straight line.
6. By a point and a line.
7. By the traces of a plane (See Chapter XI. The Mongean Method.)

The information given for one of these methods may be transformed, in many cases, to that required for other methods.

If the plane is given by method 5, three points not in a straight line, the following transformations may be made:

Two intersecting lines may be drawn through the three points, Method 1.

A line may be drawn through two of the points and a parallel line through the third point, Method 2.

The points may be connected to form a triangle, Method 3.

Strike- and dip-lines may be found readily, Method 4.

A line may be drawn through two of the points, Method 6.

A ground line may be assumed, and the traces of the plane of the points may be found, Method 7.

63. In Fig. 52 four of these methods of representing a plane are given.

1. The plane is represented by the intersecting lines AB and CD.
2. The plane is represented by the parallel lines EF and GH.
3. The plane is represented by the triangle QRS.
4. The plane is represented by strike and dip.

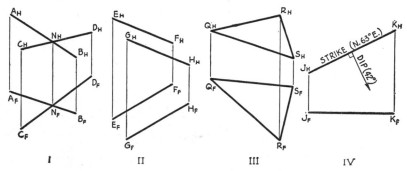

Fig. 52.—Four Methods of Representing a Plane.

64. The strike of an oblique plane is the direction of a horizontal line that lies in the plane. This term is adopted from geology and mining, in which it is defined as the direction of a line formed by the intersection of a stratum or vein with a horizontal plane. On a drawing this line is called the *strike-line*, or more briefly the *strike* of the plane. The direction of the strike-line usually is expressed as its *bearing*, a term well understood by surveyors and map makers. In Fig. 53-II the bearing of the line HR is N67°E with reference to the points of the compass shown in the top view. The "top" of a map is assumed to be north unless points of the compass are shown otherwise.

The dip of a plane is its downward inclination. More specifically, dip is the angle which a plane makes with a horizontal plane; and it is measured below the horizontal. The direction of the dip may be shown on a drawing by a line that is perpendicular to the strike, and extends downward in the plane. This line is called the *dip-line*. The angle of dip may be given in degrees on the dip-line. The angle which a plane makes with a horizontal plane is the same as the angle its dip-line makes with the horizontal plane.

The plane in Fig. 52-IV is completely specified by the strike-line JK, the dip-line, and the dip angle, 42°. The strike-line may be given by one point J and the bearing, N63°E. The dip may be stated as 42°SE. The southeast direction is understood to be perpendicular to the strike. This plane may be said to pass through the point J, strike N63°E, and dip 42°SE.

THE VISUALIZATION OF A PLANE

65. The roof of a house is shown in Fig. 53-I. AB, the ridge line of the roof, is the strike of either roof plane. The steepest line that can be drawn on the roof is the line CD, which is perpendicular to AB. To prove this, draw any other line CK on the roof. The length of CK is greater than the length of CD. The difference in elevation of C and D is the same as the difference in elevation of C and K; this can be seen in the front view. Since CD drops the same distance in a shorter length than CK, it is the steepest line that can be drawn on the roof. CD is the dip-line of the roof plane.

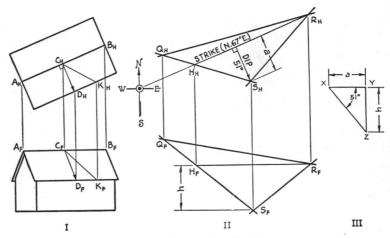

I   II   III

FIG. 53.—Visualization of a Plane.

The plane QRS in Fig. 53-II can be visualized by finding its strike and dip. To find the strike, draw the horizontal line R_FH_F. Locate H_H. Then H_HR_H is the strike of the plane. The points of the compass show that the bearing of the strike-line is N67°E. To indicate the dip, draw a line perpendicular to the strike in the top view, and terminating at the point S, the lowest point of the plane. An arrowhead should be drawn at the lower end of the line. QRS has the same strike and dip as the roof plane ABD. The dip angle can be estimated approximately by comparing the distance a in the top view with the height h in the front view. The triangle xyz in Fig. 53-III shows a right triangle constructed from this information, in which xy is horizontal and xz represents the dip-line. The dip angle is 51°, and might have been visualized as a little more than 45° without drawing the triangle.

As an aid in visualizing a plane, the following method is helpful. The upper long edge of a rectangular card is held horizontally above and parallel to the strike-line; then, the inclination of the card is made approximately equal to the dip of the plane. After several planes have been visualized with the assistance of the card, the mental process should function satisfactorily without it. If the dip angle is not required, the result of visualizing a plane may be expressed as the direction of the dip-line. For example, the plane in Fig. 53-II slopes downward, forward, and to the right; and *dfr* should be lettered on the dip-line.

66. Assignments.—See Chapter XIV, Group 5A.

67. Problem 7.   *To locate a line in a plane.*

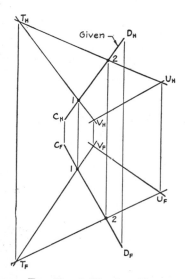

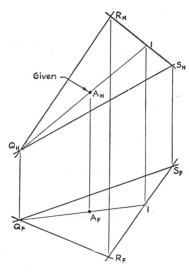

Fig. 54.—A Line in a Plane.   Fig. 55.—A Point in a Plane.

Analysis.—If a line intersects two lines of a plane at points that do not coincide, it lies in the plane.

Construction.—Fig. 54.   *Given* the plane *T U V* and the top view of the line *C D*.   *Required* to draw the front view of *C D*.

Line *CD* intersects *TV* at 1 and *T U* at 2 in the top view. Draw sight-lines to locate these points in the front view. Draw $C_F D_F$ through these points for the front view of a line intersecting *TV* and *T U*, and lying in the plane *T U V*.

68. Problem 8.   *To locate a point in a plane.*

Analysis.—If a point lies in a plane it lies on some line of the plane.

Construction.—Fig. 55.   *Given* the plane QRS and the top view of the point A.   *Required* to locate the front view of A.

In the top view draw the line $Q1$ through the point A_H.   Locate the line $Q1$ in the front view of the plane.   Then locate A_F on it.

THE EIGHTH FUNDAMENTAL PRINCIPLE OF DESCRIPTIVE GEOMETRY

69. The Principal Lines of a Plane.

Through any point of an oblique plane three principal lines of the plane may be drawn.

The principal lines of an oblique plane are horizontal lines, frontal lines, and profile lines.

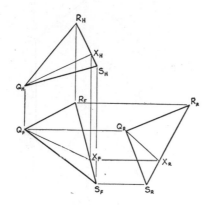

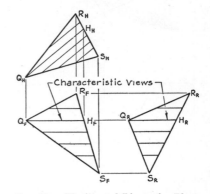

Fig. 56.—Oblique Line of a Plane.   Fig. 57.—Horizontal Lines of a Plane.

Figure 56 shows an oblique line QX, which lies in the oblique plane QRS.

Figure 57 shows a horizontal line QH, which lies in the oblique plane QRS.   Three views of this line are shown.   Usually a horizontal line of an oblique plane is located by first drawing the front view as a T-square line.   It appears to be horizontal in this view.   In the figure several horizontal lines have been drawn.

Figure 58 shows three views of a frontal line FS of the plane QRS.   Usually a frontal line is drawn first in the top view, where it appears to be frontal.   If the top view's not given, the line may be drawn in a side view.

Figure 59 shows three views of a profile line RP of the plane QRS.   Usually a profile line is drawn first in the front view as an ortho-T-square line.

In the direct method of descriptive geometry the principal lines of a plane are of outstanding importance in the solution of problems involving oblique planes.

70. Assignments.—See Chapter XIV, Groups 5B and 5C.

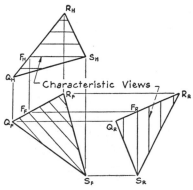

Fig. 58.—Frontal Lines of a Plane.

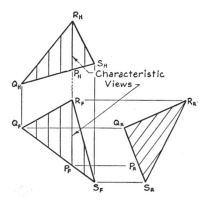

Fig. 59.—Profile Lines of a Plane.

THE NINTH FUNDAMENTAL PRINCIPLE OF DESCRIPTIVE GEOMETRY

71. An Edge View of a Plane.

An edge view of a plane is one for which the direction of sight is parallel to some line of the plane.

Although it is possible to look in the direction of any line of an oblique plane by Principles 4 and 5, an edge view is usually found by looking in the direction of one of the principal lines to obtain an auxiliary view which is an edge view.

First Example of finding an edge view of the plane ABC, Fig. 60.

An edge view of this plane is obtained by using a horizontal line of the plane. The horizontal line is found by Principle 8.

Construction.—Draw the horizontal line CH of the plane. Draw an auxiliary elevation for which the direction of sight is along CH. CH appears as a point, and the plane appears as an edge view $A_AB_AC_A$. The three points of the triangle should be located in this view to check the accuracy of the work. If the work is inaccurate, a slender triangle may be obtained instead of a line. The auxiliary elevation shows the angle which the plane makes with a horizontal plane represented by HRP. This is the dip angle of the plane.

Visualization.—The direction of the horizontal line and the edge view, which shows the dip of the plane, supply all information necessary for the visualization of the plane. The plane dips downward, backward, and to the right, at an angle of about 45°.

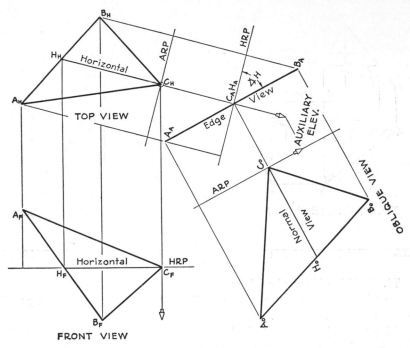

Fig. 60.—Edge View and Normal View of a Plane.

Second Example of finding an edge view of the plane TUV, Fig. 61. An edge view of this plane is obtained by using a frontal line of the plane.

Construction.—Draw a frontal line FT of the plane. Then draw a right-auxiliary view for which the direction of sight is along FT. In this view the frontal line appears as a point, and the plane appears in edge view. This view shows the angle F which the oblique plane makes with a frontal plane represented by FRP.

THE TENTH FUNDAMENTAL PRINCIPLE OF DESCRIPTIVE GEOMETRY

72. A Normal View of a Plane. True Shape.

A normal view of a plane is one for which the direction of sight is perpendicular to the plane.

To find a normal view of a plane by the auxiliary view method, first find an edge view of the plane by Principle 9. Then look in a direction perpendicular to the plane and draw a normal view.

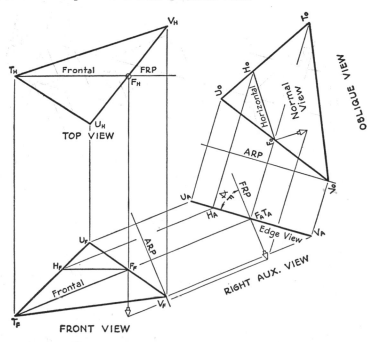

Fig. 61.—Edge View and Normal View of a Plane.

Construction.—Fig. 60. By Principle 9 the edge view of the plane was found in the auxiliary elevation. Draw sight-lines perpendicular to the edge view and obtain the normal view of the plane as the oblique view $A_oB_oC_o$.

In this view the triangle is shown in true shape, which means that all edges are of true length and all angles are of true size. In this view any desired construction in plane geometry may be performed: *i.e.*, a circle may be inscribed or circumscribed, and angles may be measured or bisected.

Figure 61 shows the solution for finding the normal view of the plane TUV adjacent to the edge view shown in the right-auxiliary view.

73. Problem 9.   *To show in a view of a truncated prism the true shape of the cut surface or section.*

Analysis.—Draw an edge view and a normal view of the oblique cut surface by Principles 9 and 10.   Show the prism in these views.

Construction.—Fig. 62.   *Given* the truncated prism.   *Required* to draw an oblique view which is a normal view of surface 1–2–3–4–5–6.

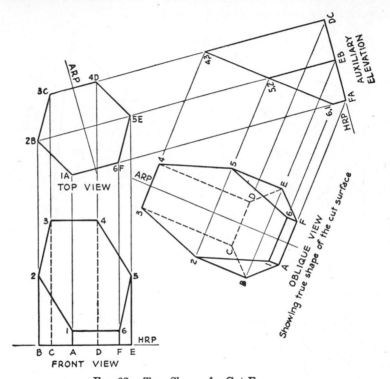

Fɪɢ. 62.—True Shape of a Cut Face.

An inspection of the oblique surface shows that it has two horizontal edges 4–3 and 6–1 which are shown in true length in the top view.   Draw the auxiliary elevation which shows an end view of these edges, and an edge view of 1–2–3–4–5–6.   With the direction of sight perpendicular to the edge view, draw the oblique view which shows the true shape of the cut surface or section.

74. Problem 10.   *To draw a circle in an oblique plane with its center at a given point.*

Analysis.—Find an edge view and a normal view of the plane. Draw the circle in the normal view, then locate it in the principal views.

Construction.—Fig. 63. *Given* the point O in the oblique plane $QRST$. *Required* to draw a circle of given diameter lying in the plane and with its center at O.

The ellipses which represent the circle in the front and top views may be drawn either as true ellipses or approximate ellipses. This construction is

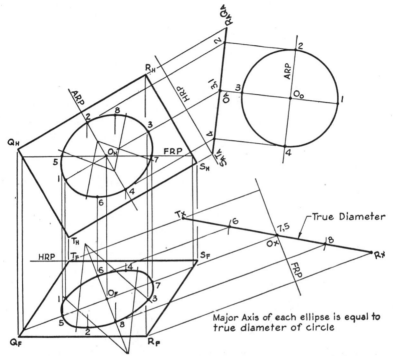

Fig. 63.—Circle in an Oblique Plane. Approximate Ellipse Method.

for the method of approximate ellipses. Obtain an edge view of the plane in the auxiliary elevation and the point O in the oblique view. It is not necessary to show a normal view of the plane in this view. Draw the circle with O_o as center. Select points 1, 2, 3, and 4 as shown; and locate them in the edge view and the top view.

In the top view 1–3 is equal in length to the diameter of the circle, and 2–4 is at right angles to it and foreshortened to the correct length for the minor axis of the ellipse. Construct the ellipse by the usual construction for an approximate ellipse.

Since the solution is by means of approximate ellipses, the construction for the top view is of no value for drawing the ellipse required in the front view. The construction for the front view is similar to the construction for the top view, but the true view of the circle is not required. On the edge view of the plane with O_X as a center and a radius equal to the radius of the circle, strike arcs locating the points 6 and 8. 6–8 is an edge view of the circle. Locate 6–8 in the front view and locate 5 and 7 on the frontal line through O, making 5–7 equal to the diameter of the circle. Construct the approximate ellipse with the axes 5–7 and 6–8.

Points for each ellipse have been shown in both views to show that the axes for one ellipse are not the axes for the other.

To show the circle as a true ellipse use only the first auxiliary view and the normal view, select twelve or sixteen points instead of four, and locate them in the top and front views.

75. Assignments.—See Chapter XIV, Groups 5D and 5E.

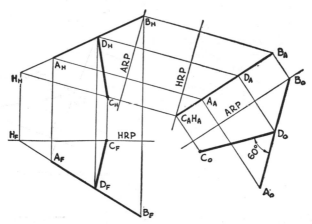

FIG. 64.—Line Making a Given Angle with a Line.

76. Problem 11.   To find the angle between two intersecting lines.

Analysis.—Since the lines lie in a plane, the angle between them can be found by obtaining a normal view of the plane, Principles 8, 9, and 10.

Construction.—Fig. 64.   *Given* the lines AB and CD.   *Required* to find the angle ADC.

Through C draw the horizontal line CH; find the edge view of the plane of AB and CD in the auxiliary elevation; draw a normal view of the plane showing the true size of the angle at $A_oD_oC_o = 60°$.

77. Problem 12. *From a given point draw a line that intersects a given line and makes a given angle with it.*

.Analysis.—The given point and the given line determine a plane. In the normal view of this plane the required line can be drawn, Principles 8, 9, and 10.

Construction.—Fig. 64. *Given* the point C and the line AB. *Required* to draw a line CD that intersects AB and makes 60° with it.

Through C draw the horizontal line CH of the plane ABC. Find the edge view of the plane at $C_AA_AB_A$ and the normal view of the plane showing C_O and A_OB_O. From C_O draw C_OD_O intersecting A_OB_O and making 60° with it. Locate the point D in the top and front views and draw the line CD in these views.

78. Assignments.—See Chapter XIV, Group 5F.

THE ELEVENTH FUNDAMENTAL PRINCIPLE
OF DESCRIPTIVE GEOMETRY

79. Cutting Planes.
A cutting plane will intersect any surface in a line.
The line may be straight or curved.

First Example of the application of Principle 11.

Find the intersection of the ortho-frontal cutting plane $O–F$ and the right pyramid, Fig. 65.

Since the cutting plane is given in edge view, inspection of the front view locates the points 1, 2, 3, 4, 5, and 6, at which the plane intersects the edges of the pyramid. In the front view the line of intersection coincides with the edge view of the cutting plane. Locate these six points in the top view on their respective sight-lines. Join them in succession to find the line of intersection of the cutting plane with each face of the pyramid. The complete polygon 1–2–3–4–5–6 is the required intersection.

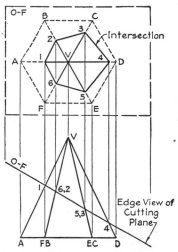

Fig. 65.—Intersection of a Plane and Pyramid.

Only the edge view of the cutting plane is shown in most cases.

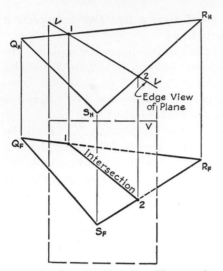

FIG. 66.—Intersection of a Plane and a Cutting Plane.

Second Example of the application of Principle 11. Find the line of intersection of a vertical cutting plane $V-V$ and an oblique plane QRS, Fig. 66.

Analysis.—The line of intersection of the planes is a straight line joining any two points in which the cutting plane intersects lines of the given plane.

Construction.—In the top view $V-V$ cuts QR at 1 and RS at 2. 1–2 is the line of intersection, and it coincides with $V-V$ in the top view. Locate points 1 and 2 in the front view and join them with a straight line. The front view of the cutting plane is indicated, and the visibility of the plane QRS has been determined. Usually only the edge view of the cutting plane is drawn.

THE TWELFTH FUNDAMENTAL PRINCIPLE
OF DESCRIPTIVE GEOMETRY

80. The Point Where a Line Pierces a Surface.

The point where a line pierces a surface is located at its intersection with the line cut from the surface by a cutting plane containing the given line.

First Example.—Figure 67 shows by sketch and orthographic views a plane QRS, which is pierced at the point O by the line AB. To find this point a vertical cutting plane $V-V$ is passed through the line AB; *i.e.*, it contains the line AB. The cutting plane cuts the plane QRS in the line 1–2. Line 1–2 intersects AB at the point O. O is the point where AB pierces QRS because it is on the line 1–2, which lies in QRS.

Construction.—Assume a cutting plane $V-V$, the edge view of which coincides with AB in the top view. $V-V$ cuts QR at 1 and RS at 2. Locate these points in the front view and draw the line 1–2. It intersects AB at O. Locate O in the top view. O is the required point at which AB pierces QRS. Note that there is very little construction in the solution of this problem. The front view of the line 1–2 is the only line drawn. The notation, however, should be complete. The student should appreciate the fact that the line AB, the cutting plane $V-V$, the line 1–2, and the point O coincide as one straight line in the top view.

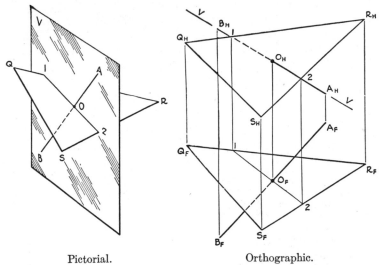

Pictorial.   Orthographic.

FIG. 67.—Point Where a Line Pierces a Plane.

An orthofrontal cutting plane may be used if preferable. The construction would be carried out in like manner.

Note.—The point at which a line pierces any surface can be found by this method if the line of intersection of the cutting plane and the surface can be drawn.

Second Example.—To find where the brace AC for the radio mast pierces the roof plane, Fig. 68, assume the vertical cutting plane $V-V$ that contains the line AC representing the brace. It intersects the roof plane in DE, found first as $D_H E_H$. The lines AC and DE are both in plane $V-V$ and intersect at F, the required point that is on both the brace and the roof.

To find where the mast rests on the roof, use the same construction and note that AB, the center line of the mast, is in the cutting plane $V-V$. In the front view the center line intersects $D_F E_F$ at B_F, the foot of the mast.

81. Assignments.—See Chapter XIV, Group 5G.

82. *Problem 13. To draw a perpendicular from a point to an oblique plane.*

First Method.—The method of Principal Lines.

Analysis.—If a line is perpendicular to two intersecting lines of a plane, it is perpendicular to the plane. For the two intersecting lines use two of the principal lines of the plane. Applying Principle 7, draw a line which is perpendicular to both of them.

Construction.—Fig. 69. *Given* the point J and the plane QRS. *Required* to draw a perpendicular from J to QRS.

First, draw the horizontal line QH of the plane and draw the top view of the required line at right angles to it. Second, draw the frontal line RF of the plane and draw the front view of the required line at right angles to it. Let K be any convenient point on the line so drawn. K should not be placed

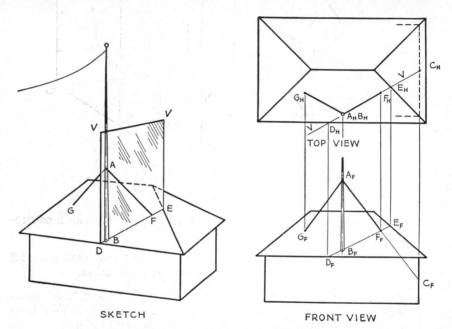

FIG. 68.—Point at which a Brace Joins a Roof.

at the apparent intersection of JK with either the horizontal or the frontal line. To do so would indicate that the student thinks JK intersects one of these lines. JK is perpendicular to both the horizontal and the frontal line but does not intersect either of them. By this method the foot of the perpendicular is not found.

Second Method.—Auxiliary view method.

Analysis.—An auxiliary view may show the point and an edge view of the plane. The perpendicular can be drawn in this view. The foot cf the perpendicular and the true length of the line will be shown.

Construction.—Fig. 70. *Given* point J and the plane QRS. *Required* to draw a perpendicular from J to QRS, and to find its true length.

Draw the horizontal line QH of the plane, and obtain in the auxiliary elevation an edge view of the plane. Locate J in this view. Draw JK perpendicular to SQR. It intersects the plane at O, and $J_A O_A$ is the true length of the perpendicular. To show JK in the top view draw it at right angles to QH, Principle 7. The front view is obtained by Principles 2 and 3.

83. Assignments.—See Chapter XIV, Group 5H.

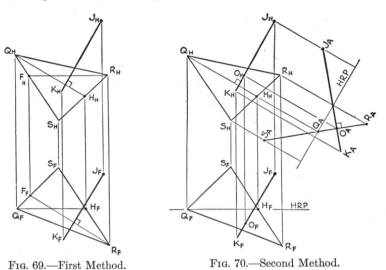

FIG. 69.—First Method.   FIG. 70.—Second Method.

Line Perpendicular to a Plane.

84. *Problem 14. To draw a solid whose base rests on an oblique plane.*

Analysis.—Obtain an edge view and a normal view of the plane. In each of these views the solid may be represented by a simple drawing.

Construction.—Fig. 71. *Given* the plane $QRST$. *Required* to construct on this plane with the center of its base at the point X a right prism of given altitude having a regular hexagonal base of given size and two edges of the base horizontal.

Draw the edge view of the plane as an auxiliary elevation. Locate the point X in the oblique view. With X as a center draw a regular hexagon having two of its sides perpendicular to ARP. This is the end view of the prism. In the auxiliary elevation draw a view of the prism showing its true height. The edges are perpendicular to the edge view of the plane and are drawn upward, which is toward the top view. The top view and front view are drawn by Principles 2 and 3.

85. Assignments.—See Chapter XIV, Group 5I.

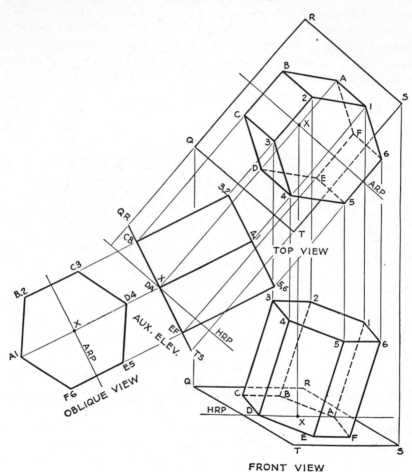

Fig. 71.—Object on an Oblique Plane.

86. Problem 15. *Through a given point to draw a plane perpendicular to an oblique line.*

First Method.—The method of Principal Lines.

Analysis.—Through the point draw two principal lines perpendicular to the given line. These intersecting lines determine the required plane.

Construction.—Fig. 72. *Given* the point R and the line CD. *Required* to pass a plane through R, perpendicular to CD.

Draw a horizontal line RH perpendicular to CD. Draw a frontal line RF perpendicular to CD, Principle 7. The points F and H may be selected anywhere on these lines but should not be placed at the apparent intersection with CD. F and H may be joined, if this is desirable.

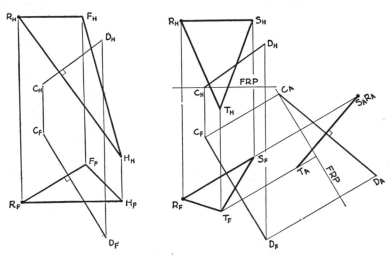

FIG. 72.—First Method.　　　FIG. 73.—Second Method.

Plane Perpendicular to a Line.

Second Method.—Auxiliary view method.

Analysis.—In an auxiliary view, which is a normal view of the line, the plane may be drawn in edge view perpendicular to the line.

Construction.—Fig. 73. *Given* the point R and the line CD. *Required* to pass the plane through R perpendicular to CD.

Draw a right-auxiliary view which is a normal view of CD and locate R in this view. Draw $R_A T_A$ perpendicular to $C_A D_A$. This is the edge view of the required plane. S is a third point in the plane. Draw sight-lines from S_A and T_A to the front view. S_F and T_F may be selected at any convenient points on these sight-lines. The top view of RST may be found by the application of Principles 2 and 3.

87. Assignments.—See Chapter XIV, Group 5J.

88. Problem 16. *Through a given line to pass a plane perpendicular to a given plane.*

Analysis.—The required plane is determined by the given line and a perpendicular drawn from any point in it to the given plane.

Construction.—Fig. 74. *Given* the line *JK* and the plane *RST*. *Required* to determine the plane *KJL* that is perpendicular to *RST*.

Draw the horizontal line *RH* and the frontal line *SF* in the plane *RST*. Draw the line *JL* perpendicular to both of these principal lines, as in Problem 13, first method. *KJL* is the required plane, and *LM* is its strike-line.

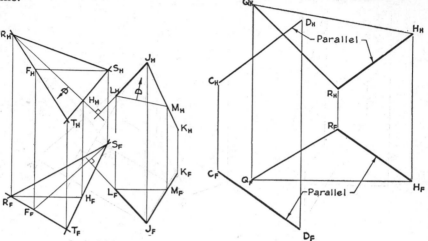

Fig. 74.—Plane Through a Line and   Fig. 75.—Plane Through a Line and Parallel
     Perpendicular to a Plane.   to a Given Line.

89. Problem 17.   *Through a given point to pass a plane perpendicular to two given planes.*

Analysis.—The required plane is determined by two lines drawn from the point, one of them being perpendicular to each plane.

Construction.—No figure.   Draw the perpendiculars to each plane by the first method of Problem 13.

90. Assignments.—See Chapter XIV, Group 5K.

91. Problem 18.   *To pass a plane through one line parallel to a second line.*

Analysis.—If a plane is parallel to a line, it contains a line which is parallel to that line.   Therefore, through any point on the first line draw a line parallel to the second line.   This line and the given line form a plane which is parallel to the second line.

Construction.—Fig. 75.   *Given* the lines *QR* and *CD*.   *Required* to pass a plane through *QR* parallel to *CD*.

Through R draw RH parallel to CD by Principle 6. QRH is the required plane. QH is drawn as a horizontal line to aid in the visualization of the plane.

92. Assignments.—See Chapter XIV, Groups 5L and 5M.

93. Problem 19. *Through a given point to draw a plane parallel to a given plane.*

Analysis.—Through the given point draw two lines, each parallel to one of two intersecting lines of the plane. If one of the required lines is partly determined by having one view given, draw in the given plane a line parallel to it. Then draw parallel to that line the adjacent view of the first line.

Construction.—No figure. Make the construction according to Principle 6.

94. Assignments.—See Chapter XIV, Group 5N.

THE THIRTEENTH FUNDAMENTAL PRINCIPLE
OF DESCRIPTIVE GEOMETRY

95. The True Length of a Line by Revolution.

The true length of a line may be found by revolving it to a position where it is perpendicular to an established direction of sight.

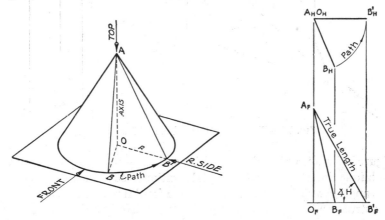

Fig. 76.—True Length of a Line by Revolution.

In Fig. 76 the oblique line AB is shown pictorially and by two orthographic views. Through A assume a vertical axis for revolution. Revolve the point B about this axis. The path of revolution of the point B is a horizontal circle. The revolution of the line AB about this axis generates a right circular cone. All the elements of a right circular cone are equal in

length and make the same angle with its base. If AB is revolved to the
frontal position AB', it can be seen in true length in the front view, where
it appears as the outline element of the cone. AB could be revolved so as
to occupy the position of the outline element on the left side of the
cone.

Construction.—AO is the axis of revolution. It appears as a point in the
top view. With $A_H B_H$ as a radius draw an arc for the path of revolution
and locate B at B'_H, so that $A_H B'_H$ is frontal. The front view of the path of
revolution is the edge view of a horizontal circle. B_F moves to B'_F on a line
perpendicular to the axis. $A_F B'_F$ is the true length of the line. The revolved
position of AB shows the angle H which the line makes with a horizontal
plane.

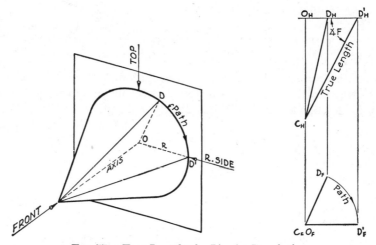

Fig. 77.—True Length of a Line by Revolution.

Figure. 77 shows pictorially and by orthographic views the revolution
of an oblique line CD into a horizontal position so as to show its true length,
and the angle F which the line makes with a frontal plane. The explanation
and construction is similar to that for Fig. 76, the only difference being that
the axis is orthofrontal insead of vertical. The right circular cone generated by the revolution of the line has a frontal base.

Principle 13 is a useful method of finding the true length of a line. There
is great latitude in the choice of construction in applying this principle. The
axis may be taken at either end of the line, and there are two possible
directions of revolution in each case.

96. Assignments.—See Chapter XIV, Groups 5O and 5P.

97. Problem 20. *Given one view of a point on a profile line that is the edge of a pyramid, to find the adjacent view of the point.*

Construction.—Fig. 78. *Given* the front view of each of the points A, B, and C on the edge VD. *Required* to locate each point in the top view.

First Method.—By means of a side view.

Draw a side view of the edge VD. Locate A on this view at A_R; and

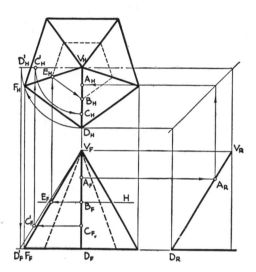

Fig. 78.—Location of Points on a Profile Line.

from this view take the point to the top view by means of a 45° line or a reference plane.

Second Method.—By means of a section parallel to the base of the pyramid.

Pass a horizontal plane H through the pyramid cutting the surface in a section shown in the top view by the dotted lines that are parallel to the lines of the base. E on VF is also a point in plane H, and the sight-line from E_F to locate E_H intersects V_HF_H at a satisfactory angle for accuracy. The line E_HB_H of the section locates B_H. If this method is thoroughly understood it is not necessary to draw the dotted lines of the section made by the plane H. Only one line, EB, is necessary.

Third Method.—By revolution.

Revolve the edge VD about a vertical axis through V to the position VD'; C_F moves to C'_F. Draw a sight-line to locate C'_H. The intersection is an accurate one because the sight-line is perpendicular to $V_HD'_H$.

Counter-revolve the line to its original position, and C'_H moves on the arc of the circle to C_H.

If the top view instead of the front view of any of the points had been given, the same method would be used; but the constructions would be in the reverse order.

98. Problem 21. *Given one view of a point on the surface of a cone, to locate the point in the adjacent view.*

Analysis.—If the cone has a circular base, the adjacent view of the point is located on a circle on the surface of the cone. It is also located on an element of a cone. Either the circle or the element can be used to locate the adjacent view of the point.

Construction.—Fig. 79. *Given* the right circular cone with vertex V and the front view of each of the points B and C on the front of its surface. *Required* to find the top view of each point.

First Method.—By means of the side view of an element.

This method is not shown, but by comparison with Fig. 78 it is clear that the element VB can be drawn in a side view just as the edge VD was drawn in the side view.

Second Method.—By means of a section parallel to the base of the cone.

Cut the cone by the horizontal plane H. The intersection is the circle through $E_H B_H$, the radius of which is $B_F E_F$. The required view of the point is B_H on this circle.

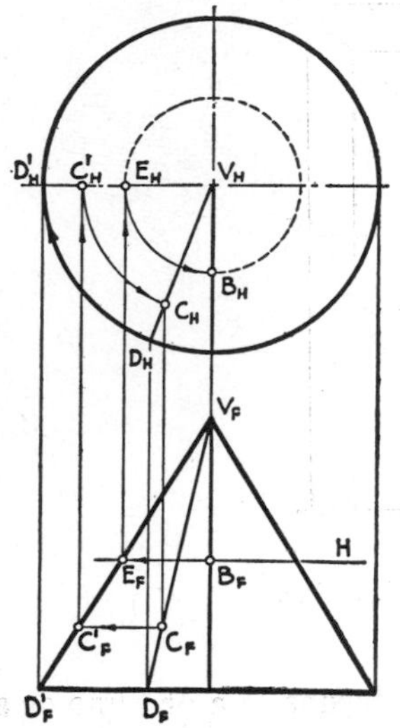

Fig. 79.—Location of Points on the Surface of a Cone.

Third Method.—By revolution.

Draw $V_F D_F$ through C_F. Draw $V_H D_H$. Revolve the element VD about a vertical axis at V to the position VD'; C_F moves to C'_F. Locate C'_H, counter-revolve the element to its original position, and locate C_H by the arc from C'_H.

In the case of a right circular cone, the constructions for the second and third methods are identical, the difference in the methods being merely in the mind of the draftsman.

Note.—These methods are to be used in all cases where a point is so near the front or the rear of the cone that a sight-line to the adjacent view would intersect the element at an angle too small for accuracy. If the top view of a point is given instead of the front view, the method is the same, but the drawing board construction is in the reverse order.

THE FOURTEENTH FUNDAMENTAL PRINCIPLE
OF DESCRIPTIVE GEOMETRY

99. The True Shape of a Plane by Revolution.

The true shape of a plane may be found by revolving it to a position where it is perpendicular to an established direction of sight.

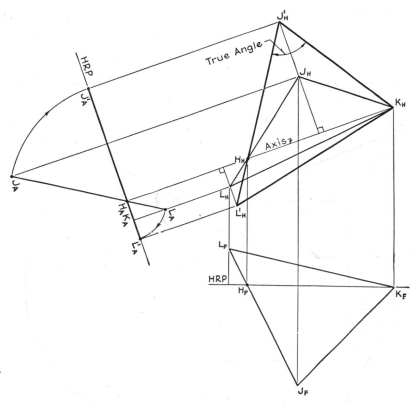

FIG. 80.—True Shape of a Plane by Revolution.

First Example of the revolution of a plane.

In Fig. 80 the oblique plane *JKL* is to be revolved into a horizontal position. For the revolution select a horizontal axis.

Construction.—Draw the horizontal line *HK*. Find in the auxiliary elevation an edge view of the plane and an end view of *HK*. Let *HK* be the axis for revolution. In the auxiliary elevation with *HK* as a center draw arcs for the revolution of *J* to *J'* and *L* to *L'*. *J'* and *L'* are in the horizontal reference plane which contains the axis. Therefore, the plane has been revolved into a horizontal position. The path of J and the path of L are circles which appear in edge view in the top view. The planes of these circles are perpendicular to the axis. Therefore, in the top view, J and L move outward from the axis on perpendiculars to the axis, and are located on the sight-lines drawn from the auxiliary elevation. $J'_H K_H L'_H$ is the revolved position of the triangle in the top view. It is not necessary to show the revolved position of the triangle in the front view. This construction saves space, but the superimposing of the true view on the top view is confusing in many cases.

Second Example of the revolution of a plane.

In Fig. 81 the oblique plane QRS is to be revolved into a frontal position. Select a frontal axis.

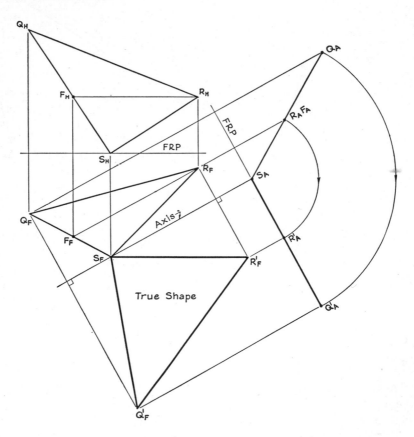

FIG. 81.—True Shape of a Plane by Revolution.

Construction.—Draw the frontal line FR and obtain an edge view of the plane in the right-auxiliary view. FRP passes through S. A frontal line of the plane QRS is drawn through S parallel to RF. It appears in end view in the auxiliary view. Use this line as an axis and revolve the plane into FRP as shown. Locate the points Q' and R' in the front view on the lines from Q_F and R_F drawn perpendicular to the axis. These lines represent the front view of the paths of revolution. $Q'_F R'_F S_F$ is the revolved position of the triangle and shows its true shape. Note that the axis has been so selected and the revolution has been such as to bring the true shape of the triangle into a clear space.

100. Problem 22. *To inscribe a circle in an oblique triangle by the revolution method.*

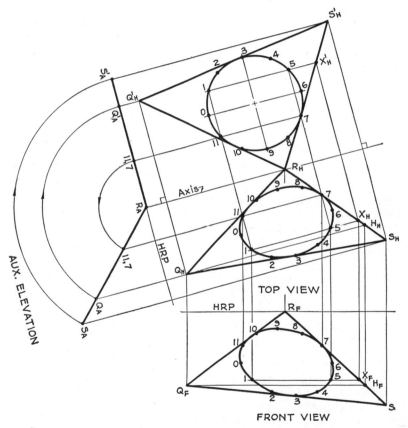

Fig. 82.—Circle in an Oblique Plane.   True Ellipse Construction:

Analysis.—Revolve the triangle into either a horizontal or a frontal position. Inscribe a circle in the triangle in its revolved position. Counter-revolve the triangle and the circle so as to locate the circle in the principal views.

Construction.—Fig. 82. *Given* the triangle QRS. *Required* to show the inscribed circle in the front view and the top view.

Find an edge view of the triangle in the auxiliary elevation. Select a horizontal axis through the point R, and revolve the triangle into a clear space, Principle 14. Inscribe the circle. Select twelve symmetrically spaced points on the circle. Locate them in the top view by counter-revolution. Each point lies on a perpendicular line drawn across the axis, which represents the top view of the path of counter-revolution. The distance of each point from the axis in the top view is found in either of two ways: first, by drawing an arc in the auxiliary elevation as shown for points 11 and 7; second, by drawing a line such as $1\text{--}5\text{--}X'_H$ parallel to the axis to intersect $R_H S'_H$ at X'_H, and drawing through X_H the line $1\text{--}5\text{--}X_H$ which also is parallel to the axis. The twelve points are located in the front view by either of two methods: first, by application of Principle 3 as in the case of points 11 and 7; second, by drawing horizontal lines such as $1\text{--}5\text{--}X_F$. In this solution the circle is represented by true ellipses.

101. Assignments.—See Chapter XIV, Group 5Q.

102. *Problem 23. To draw the shortest line from a point to an oblique line and to find its true length.*

Analysis.—The shortest line from a point to a line is the one which is perpendicular to it. To draw this line obtain a normal view of the given line. Draw the perpendicular line by Principle 7. Find the true length of the perpendicular.

Construction.—Fig. 83. *Given* the point C and the line RS. *Required* to draw the shortest line from C to RS and to measure its true length.

The auxiliary elevation shows the normal view of RS. C is shown in this view. Draw CK perpendicular to RS. Locate K in the top view and front view by drawing sight-lines. In this case the true length of CK is found by drawing an oblique view which is a normal view of CK and an end view of SR.

The true length of the shortest line is also called the shortest distance from the point to the line.

103. Assignments.—See Chapter XIV, Group 5R.

104. *Problem 24. To draw the shortest line between two oblique lines and to find its true length.*

Analysis.—The shortest line that can be drawn between two oblique lines is the common perpendicular. In a view which is an end view of one of the lines, the common perpendicular is drawn at right angles to the other line. This view is a normal view of the required common perpendicular. This solution uses Principles 4, 5, and 7.

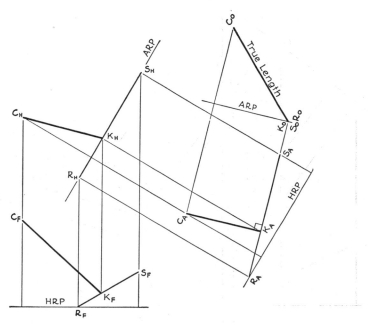

FIG. 83.—Shortest Line from a Point to an Oblique Line.

Construction.—Fig. 84. *Given* the oblique lines AB and CD. *Required* to draw the common perpendicular and measure its true length.

Draw the auxiliary elevation which shows a normal view of AB. Draw the oblique view which shows an end view of AB. In this view any line which is perpendicular to AB appears as a normal view. Therefore, by Principle 7, draw LS perpendicular to CD. Measure the length of LS. To draw LS in the auxiliary elevation locate S_A. Draw $S_A L_A$ perpendicular to $A_A B_A$. The drawing of LS in the oblique view and the auxiliary elevation requires a thorough understanding of Principle 7. Locate LS in the front view and the top view by Principle 2. In this case S_F is located with greater accuracy by Principle 3 because the sight-line intersects $C_F D_F$ at a small angle.

The true length of the shortest line is also called the shortest distance. Another method, using the edge view and normal view of a plane, is suggested by Problem 88, Chapter IX.

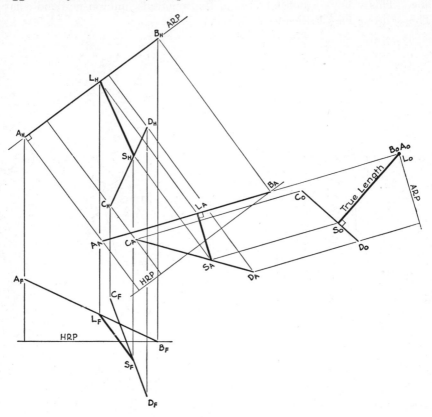

Fig. 84.—Shortest Line Between Oblique Lines.

105. Assignments.—See Chapter XIV, Group 5S.

106. Problem 25. *To measure the angle between a line and a plane.*

The angle between a line and a plane is the angle between the line and its projection onto the plane. This angle can be measured in the projecting plane of the line.

107. First Method.—The complementary angle method.

Analysis.—The line and a perpendicular from any point on it to the given plane determine the projecting plane mentioned above. The angle between the line and the perpendicular is the complement of the angle between the line and the given plane. Without finding the projection of the line on the plane, the true size of the complementary angle between the line and the perpendicular can be found in a normal view of the projecting plane.

Construction.—Fig. 85. *Given* the line AB and the plane PQR. *Required* to find the angle between AB and PQR.

From the point B draw the perpendicular BC to PQR by the first method of Problem 13. Draw the horizontal line AC. ABC is the projecting plane. Find the edge view of this plane in the auxiliary elevation

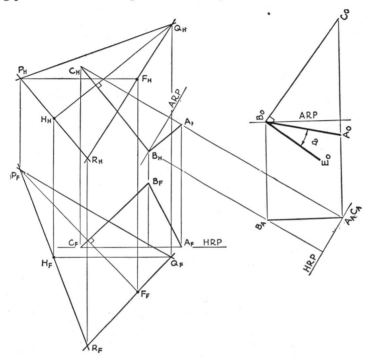

FIG. 85.—Angle Between a Line and a Plane. Complementary Angle Method.

and the normal view in the oblique view. The angle $A_0B_0C_0$ is the complementary angle. Draw B_0E_0 perpendicular to B_0C_0; and measure the angle $A_0B_0E_0$, which equals the required angle a.

108. Second Method.—The direct method.

Analysis.—The true size of the angle the line makes with the plane can be seen in a view that is the edge view of the plane and a normal view of the line. Such a view usually requires an auxiliary view that shows an edge view of the plane; an oblique view for which the direction of sight is normal to the plane; and a second oblique view, showing a normal view of the line.

Construction.—Fig. 86. *Given* line AB and the plane RST. *Required* to measure the angle between AB and the plane RST.

Draw the auxiliary elevation showing an edge view of the plane. AB does not appear in true length in this view. Second, draw an oblique view for which the direction of sight is perpendicular to the edge view of the

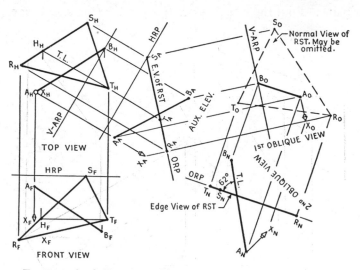

Fig. 86.—Angle Between a Line and a Plane. Direct Method.

plane RST. Only the line AB shown as $A_O B_O$ is required in this view. Third, draw a second oblique view for which the direction of sight is perpendicular to $A_O B_O$. This view shows a normal view of the line at $A_N B_N$; and the plane can be represented as an edge view because the first oblique view was made by looking normal to the plane. In any view adjacent to a normal view of a plane, the plane appears as an edge view. The reference plane ORP was taken to coincide with RST in the auxiliary view. Therefore, in the second oblique view ORP represents the edge view of RST without locating any of the points R, S, or T of the plane. The draftsman who uses this method without finding R, S, and T in all the views must clearly understand why they may be omitted.

109. Third Method.—Revolution Method.

Analysis.—If a line is revolved about an axis which is perpendicular to a plane, the angle the line makes with the plane remains constant.

The views needed for making such a solution are those showing an edge view and a normal view of the plane.

Construction.—Fig. 87. *Given* the line AB and the plane RST. Draw an auxiliary elevation showing AB and an edge view of RST. Select the axis for revolution, AC, perpendicular to RST. In the oblique view, taken normal to RST, show AB and the end view of the axis CA.

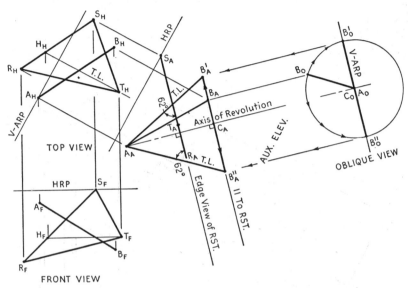

Fig. 87.—Angle Between a Line and a Plane. Revolution Method.

Revolve the line AB by revolving B_o to B'_o or B''_o, thereby generating a right circular cone whose outline elements in the auxiliary elevation show the true angle that AB makes with the plane.

Note that the base of the cone of revolution must be parallel to the edge view of the plane in the auxiliary elevation.

110. Assignments.—See Chapter XIV, Group 5T.

THE INTERSECTION OF PLANES

111. The intersection of two planes is a straight line. It may be found by any of the following three methods:

1. By finding the edge view of one of the planes, Principle 9. This method is preferable in cases where one plane intersects several planes.

2. By means of piercing points. This method makes use of Principle 12.

3. By means of cutting planes. This method makes use of Principle 11.

The following problem gives an example of each method.

112. Problem 26.   *To find the intersection of two oblique planes.*
Example of the First Method.—Edge view method.

Analysis.—A view which shows an edge view of one of the planes shows the points where it intersects the lines which represent the other plane. The

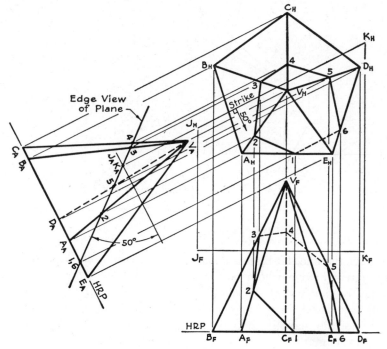

Fig. 88.—Intersection of an Oblique Plane and a Pyramid.   Edge View Method.

line joining these points is the line of intersection of two planes. If the lines of intersection of a given plane and several planes are desired, the solution may be obtained by using only the edge view of the given plane.

Construction.—Fig. 88. *Given* a right pentagonal pyramid and the plane which is represented by the strike-line *JK*, and has a dip of 50° forward. *Required* to find the intersection of the plane and the faces of the pyramid.

In the auxiliary elevation locate the end view of *JK* and lay off the dip angle to obtain the edge view of the given plane. Draw the pyramid in this view. The edge view of the plane cuts the edges of the pyramid at the points 1, 2, 3, 4, 5, and 6. Locate these points in the principal views and connect them by straight lines to obtain the intersection of the plane with the faces and base of the pyramid.

This is the most satisfactory solution for this type of problem.

113. Example of the Second Method.—Piercing point method.

Analysis.—Find the point at which a line of one plane pierces the other plane. Find a second point in the same way. The line joining these two points is the line of intersection of the planes.

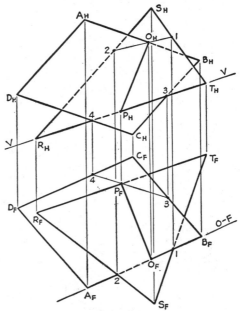

Construction.—Fig. 89. *Given* the planes *ABCD* and *RST* as two pieces of sheet metal. *Required* to find the line of intersection of *ABCD* and *RST* and to show the two pieces of metal as a unit.

The point *O* at which *AB* pierces *RST* is found by Principle 12. The orthofrontal cutting plane *O–F* containing *AB* cuts *ST* at 1 and *RS* at 2. Locate 1 and 2 in the top view. The line 1–2 intersects *AB* at the point *O*. Find the point *P* at which *RT* pierces the plane *ABCD*, using the vertical cutting plane *V–V*. The line joining *O* and *P* is the line of intersection of the given planes.

Fig. 89.—Intersection of Oblique Planes. Piercing-Point Method.

By application of the rules for visibility, determine the visibility of the edges of the two pieces of metal.

114. Example of the Third Method.—Cutting plane method.

Analysis.—A cutting plane cuts each given plane in a straight line, Principle 11. These lines intersect in a point which is common to both planes. A second cutting plane locates the second point common to both planes. A straight line drawn through these two points is the line of intersection of the two planes.

Construction.—Fig. 90. *Given* the oblique planes ABC and PQR. *Required* to find the intersection of ABC and PQR.

The most favorable location for the cutting plane $O–F_1$ is through points B and P. This plane cuts AC at 2 and QR at 1. Locate these points in the top view. Draw the lines $B2$ and $P1$. They intersect at N. Locate

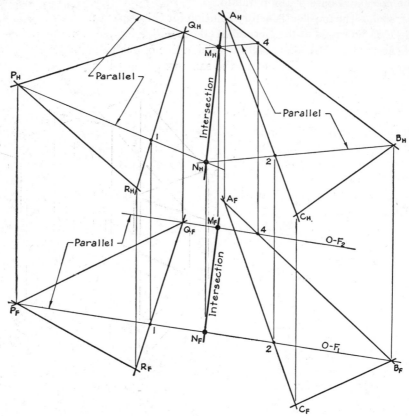

FIG. 90.—Intersection of Oblique Planes. Cutting-Plane Method.

N in the front view. In the front view of the cutting plane $O–F_1$ note that the cutting plane coincides with its lines of intersection $B2$ and $P1$. Draw the second cutting plane $O–F_2$ parallel to the first through the point Q. It cuts AB at 4. Locate 4 in the top view. Since parallel planes cut a third plane in parallel lines, draw a line through Q parallel to $P1$ in the top view and a line through 4 parallel to $B2$. These lines intersect at M_H. Locate M_F on $O–F_2$. The line MN is the line of intersection of the given planes.

These planes are unlimited in extent and the intersection is a line of infinite length.

115. Assignments.—See Chapter XIV, Group 5U.

DIHEDRAL ANGLES

116. A dihedral angle is the opening between two intersecting planes. The two planes are the faces of the angle, and their line of intersection is its edge. A dihedral angle is measured by the plane angle between the two lines in which the faces are cut by a plane perpendicular to the edge.

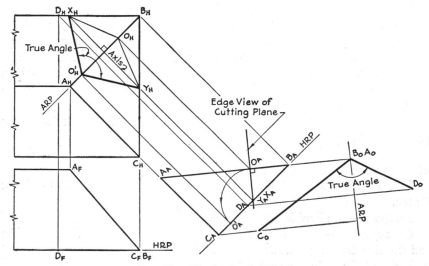

FIG. 91.—Hip Angle of a Roof.

117. Problem 27. To find the angle between two planes of a hip roof.
118. First Method.—Revolution.

Analysis.—Draw an auxiliary elevation which is a normal view of the hip line. Cut the planes by a cutting plane which is perpendicular to the hip line. The plane angle obtained is a measure of the dihedral angle. Find the true size of the plane angle by Principle 14.

Construction.—Fig. 91. *Given* the roof planes *ABC* and *ABD*. *Required* to find the dihedral angle between them.

Draw an auxiliary elevation which is a normal view of the hip line *AB*. Draw a cutting plane in edge view perpendicular to *AB*. It intersects the roof planes in the lines *OX* and *OY*. *XY* is a horizontal line. Revolve the angle *XOY* into a horizontal position about *XY* as an axis. Then *XO'Y* in the top view is the true angle and is equal to the dihedral angle.

119. Second Method.—Edge view of both planes.

Analysis.—In a view which is the end view of the line of intersection of two planes, the dihedral angle may be seen in its true size. Obtain a normal view of the line of intersection and an end view as an oblique view. One other point in each plane should be located in these views. The oblique view is an edge view of both planes and shows the angle in its true size.

Construction.—Fig. 91. After finding the auxiliary elevation as in the first method, draw an oblique view which is an end view of BA and an edge view of both planes. The true dihedral angle is $C_O A_O D_O$.

120. Third Method.—Supplementary angle method.

Analysis.—From any point, drop a perpendicular to each face of the dihedral angle. The angle between the perpendiculars is the supplement of the angle between the planes. This can be seen to be true in the oblique view of Fig. 91 by assuming a point and dropping perpendiculars to $A_O B_O C_O$ and $A_O B_O D_O$. The angle between the perpendiculars is the supplement of the dihedral angle $C_O A_O D_O$.

This method may be used in cases where the line of intersection of the planes is not given.*

Construction.—No figure. Let the construction be made in accordance with the above analysis.

121. *Problem 28. To find the dihedral angle between two oblique planes.*

Analysis.—See Problem 27, first method.

Construction.—Fig. 92. *Given* the planes QRS and RST. *Required* to find the dihedral angle between them. Note that these planes are not cut off horizontally as in the case of the roof, Fig. 92.

Draw an auxiliary elevation of the planes which is a normal view of RS. Through some point O draw a cutting plane perpendicular to RS. It intersects the given planes in the lines AO and OT. About a horizontal axis TX through T revolve the angle AOT into a horizontal position, Principle 14. The true size of the angle is shown in the top view.

Note.—If space on the drawing is available, the second method may be preferable. By looking in the direction SR, an edge view of both planes can be obtained in an oblique view.

122. Assignments.—See Chapter XIV, Group 5V.

* The intersection of two unlimited planes divide space into four dihedral angles. The opposite angles are equal; the adjacent angles, supplementary. The angle obtained by the third method depends upon the location of the point, and it may be difficult to ascertain which dihedral angle has been measured.

123. Problem 29. To draw a line of given length making specified angles with two planes.

Analysis.—The pictorial drawing in Fig. 93A illustrates the basic idea used in the solution of this problem. The locus of a line which passes through a point and makes a constant angle with a plane is a right circular cone. Both nappes of two locus cones with their vertices at V and

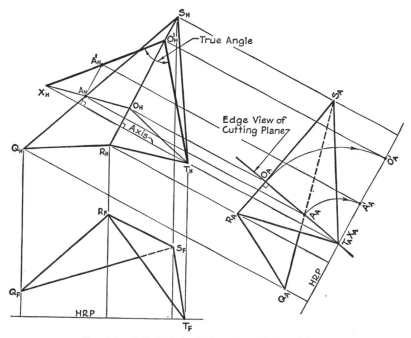

Fig. 92.—Dihedral Angle Between Oblique Planes.

their bases on the planes H and R are shown. The common elements of these cones are AB and CD, each of which makes specified angles with H and R. To determine which are the common elements it is best to conceive of the locus cones as being constructed inside a sphere with their vertices at the center of the sphere and the circles of their bases on its surface. The circles intersect at the points A, B, C, and D, thereby locating the two elements common to both cones.

If the angle between the axes of the cones should be increased or the base angles of the cones reduced so that the base circles would be larger, there may be a greater number of points of intersection, thereby increasing the number of common elements to three or four. The orthographic drawing shows a special case in which the planes of the bases are perpendicular.

Construction.—Fig. 93A. *Given* the point V, the angle H (30°), the angle F (40°), and the length of line.

With V as center in the orthographic views, draw a sphere with its radius equal to the given length of line. Draw both nappes of the cone with angle F equal to 40°. Draw the lower nappe of the cone with angle

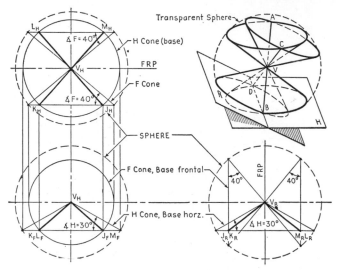

FIG. 93A.—Line Making Specified Angles with Two Planes.

H equal to 30°. The bases of the cones must be on the surface of the sphere. Then, the bases will be circles and the slant heights of the cones will be equal. In this case it can be seen, in the front and top views, that the base circles intersect in the points J, K, L, and M, thereby giving as four solutions the common elements VJ, VK, VL, and VM. However, a much clearer construction is shown in the right side view, in which the bases of both cones are shown edgewise. If the planes of the bases are not mutually perpendicular, a view showing both bases edgewise must be drawn.

Note.—By using two locus cones, each having elements which make a specified vertex angle with its axis, a similar construction can be used for finding a line which makes specified angles with two lines. The given lines may be used as the axes of the cones, or the axes may be drawn parallel to the lines, which may be skew lines.

124. Assignments.—See Chapter XIV, Group 5W.

125. *Problem 30.* To draw through a given point a plane which makes specified angles with two planes.

Analysis.—The angle a plane makes with any given plane is the complement of the angle which a line perpendicular to the plane makes with the given plane. Therefore, this problem may be solved by drawing the required plane perpendicular to a line which makes the complementary angles with the given planes.

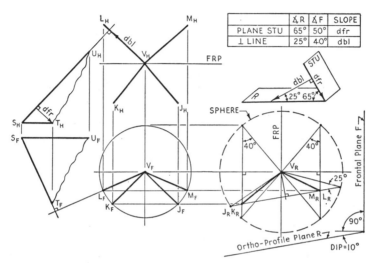

		∢R	∢F	SLOPE
PLANE STU		65°	50°	dfr
⊥ LINE		25°	40°	dbl

FIG. 93B.—Plane Making Specified Angles with Two Planes.

Construction.—Fig. 93B. *Given* the point *S*, an angle of 50° with *F*, and an angle of 65° with an ortho-profile plane *R* that dips forward 10°. *Required* to pass a plane through *S* making these angles and sloping downward, forward, and to the right (*dfr*).

The table and the sketch show the complementary data for a line perpendicular to the required plane.

At any convenient location for V_R draw a sphere and the locus cones for the perpendicular line. It is found that there are four lines making an angle of 25° with *R* and 40° with *F*. These are shown in the front and top views. One of them, *VL*, slopes *dbl*. Through *S* draw the plane *STU* perpendicular to *VL* by the principal line method.

Evidently, there are three other planes that make the specified angles, but they have different directions of dip.

126. Assignments.—See Chapter XIV, Group 5X.

127. *Problem 31. Through a given line to pass a plane which makes a given angle with a horizontal plane.*

Analysis.—Construct a right circular cone with its vertex at any point on the given line, and having a horizontal base and the required base angle. The required plane contains the given line and is tangent to the cone along one of its elements. A tangent to the base circle from the point at which the given line pierces the plane of the base locates the point of tangency through which the element of contact passes.

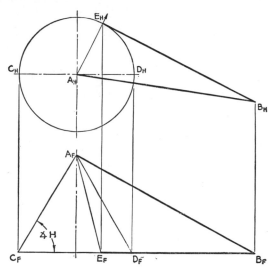

Fig. 94.—Plane Through a Line and Making a Given Angle with a Horizontal Plane.

Construction.—Fig. 94. *Given AB* and the angle *H* which the required plane makes with a horizontal plane. *Required* to draw the plane.

With its vertex at *A* and its base in the horizontal plane through *B*, draw a right circular cone with base angle *H*. From *B* draw a line tangent to the circle of the base at *E*. *AE* is the element of tangency on the cone. *ABE* is the required plane. *BE* is its strike-line and *AE* is its dip-line.

By drawing the tangent to the other side of the circle another solution may be obtained.

128. Assignments.—See Chapter XIV, Group 5Y.

129. *Problem 32. Through a given point on the surface of a cone to pass a plane tangent to the cone.*

Analysis.—The tangent plane contains the element through the given point and a tangent to a curve of the surface at its point of intersection with the element. These two intersecting lines represent the plane.

Construction.—Fig. 95. *Given* C_H on the oblique cone with the center line AB. *Required* to draw the tangent plane through C.

The element AD through C is one line of the required plane. At D draw a tangent to the circle of the base. Then ADF represents the tangent plane.

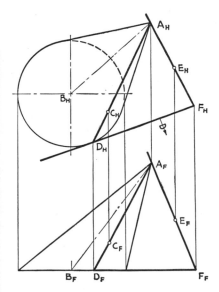 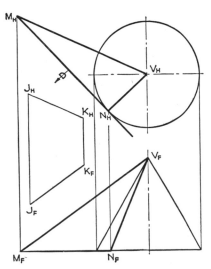

FIG. 95.—Plane Through a Point and Tangent to a Cone.

FIG. 96.—Plane Parallel to a Line and Tangent to a Cone.

130. Problem 33. *Through a given point outside the surface of the cone, to pass a plane tangent to the cone.*

Analysis.—The required plane contains a line joining the given point and the vertex of the cone, and a tangent from a point on this line to a curve of the surface. Two planes satisfy this condition.

Construction.—Fig. 95. *Given* the cone with center line AB and the point E. *Required* to draw the tangent plane through E.

Draw the line AE and find where it pierces the plane of the base of the cone at F. From F draw the line FD tangent to the base circle. Then AFD represents the required plane. It contains the element AD. By drawing a line from F tangent to the opposite side of the circle, the second plane, not shown, will be determined.

If the conditions are such that it is not convenient to find the point F, some plane parallel to the base and nearer the vertex A of the cone may be used. Find where AE pierces this plane, and draw a tangent to the circle cut from the cone.

131. Problem 34. Parallel to a line to pass a plane tangent to a cone.

Analysis.—If a plane is parallel to a line, it contains a line that is parallel to the given line. Therefore, through the vertex of the cone draw a line parallel to a given line and follow the method of Problem 33.

Construction.—Fig. 96. *Given* the line JK and the right circular cone whose vertex is V. *Required* to show a plane parallel to JK and tangent to the cone.

Through V draw VM parallel to JK. It pierces the plane of the base of the cone at M. From M draw the line MN tangent to the base circle at N. Then VMN is the required plane. It contains the element VN and the tangent MN. If the point M falls outside the limits of the drawing, cut the cone with a plane parallel to its base and nearer its vertex. On the opposite side of the cone there is another plane that satisfies the conditions.

132. Problem 35. Through a point on the surface of a cylinder to pass a plane tangent to the cylinder.

Analysis.—The required plane is determined by an element on the cylinder and the tangent to any curve of the cylinder at the point of its intersection with the element.

Construction.—Fig. 97. *Given* the oblique cylinder with axis AB and the point C on its surface. *Required* to show the tangent plane containing C on the surface of the cylinder.

Through C draw the element RS. At S draw the line ST tangent to the circle of the upper base. RST represents the tangent plane.

133. Problem 36. Through a point outside the surface of the cylinder to draw a tangent plane to the cylinder.

Analysis.—Through the given point draw a line parallel to the axis of the cylinder. From the point where it pierces the plane of either base, draw a tangent to the curve of that base. The tangent and the line through the given point determine the plane.

Construction.—Fig. 97. *Given* the oblique cylinder with axis AB and the point D. *Required* to show the plane containing D and tangent to the cylinder.

Through D draw DT parallel to AB, and find the point T where it pierces the plane of the upper base. From T draw a line tangent to the circle of the base. The required plane, represented by *STD*, is tangent to the cylinder along the line *RS*.

A tangent from *T* to the other side of the circle will determine a second plane.

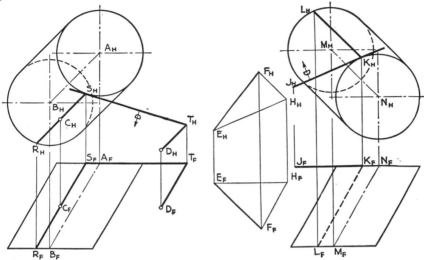

FIG. 97.—Plane Through a Point and Tangent to a Cylinder.

FIG. 98.—Plane Parallel to a Line and Tangent to a Cylinder.

134. *Problem 37. Parallel to a given line to pass a plane tangent to a cylinder.*

Analysis.—A plane that is parallel to the required plane is determined by the given line and a line which intersects it and is parallel to the axis of the cylinder. The tangent plane may be represented by two lines parallel to this plane; *i.e.*, a tangent to a curve of the cylinder, and the element through the point of tangency.

Construction.—Fig. 98. *Given* the line *EF* and the oblique cylinder whose axis is *MN*. *Required* to show a plane parallel to *EF* and tangent to the cylinder.

Through *F* draw *FH* parallel to *MN*. *EFH* is a plane parallel to the required plane. Draw *EH* parallel to the planes of the bases of the cylinder. Draw *JK* parallel to *EH* and tangent to the circle of the upper base at *K*. Draw the element *LK*. *JKL* represents the required plane. Another plane satisfying the conditions may be drawn on the opposite side of the cylinder.

135. Assignments.—See Chapter XIV, Group 5Z; Group 5AA, Miscellaneous.

CHAPTER VI

SURFACES AND DEVELOPMENTS

SURFACES

136. There are four classes of surfaces: plane surfaces, single-curved surfaces, double-curved surfaces, and warped surfaces. All except double-curved surfaces are generated by the motion of a straight line called the generatrix and are called ruled surfaces. Each position of the generatrix is an element of the surface.

Plane Surfaces.—A plane surface is one generated by a straight line which moves so as to touch two intersecting straight lines. Objects having only plane faces are known as polyhedrons. Prisms and pyramids are examples of such objects.

Single-curved Surfaces.—A single-curved surface is one generated by the motion of a straight line which touches a curved line and in which any two consecutive elements are parallel or intersecting. Examples of this type of surface are cylinders, cones, and convolutes.

Double-curved Surfaces.—A double-curved surface can be generated by moving a curve, or a variable curve, so as to produce a surface that is not ruled. The methods of generation include revolving a curve about an axis, moving a curve along another curve, and varying a curve while it is moving. A great variety of surfaces can be generated by these methods, but only a few of them which have definite geometrical properties have been named. There are two classes of double-curved surfaces: (1) Double-curved surfaces of revolution; (2) All other double-curved surfaces.

The most important double-curved surfaces belong to the first class and will be considered as a sub-division of surfaces of revolution.

137. Surfaces of Revolution.—The revolution of any line about an axis generates a surface of revolution. Actually, they may be produced by turning in a lathe or spinning on a potter's wheel. The surface produced may be single-curved, warped, or double-curved.

Single-curved Surfaces of Revolution are generated by revolving a straight line about an axis that is in the same plane. If the line and the

96

axis are parallel, the surface is a cylinder of revolution or a right circular cylinder; if they intersect, the surface is a cone of revolution or a right circular cone.

A Warped Surface of Revolution is generated by revolving a straight line about an axis that is not in the same plane. This is the hyperboloid of revolution of one nappe, the only warped surface of revolution. It may be generated also by the revolution of a hyperbola about the perpendicular bisector of the line joining the foci.

Double-curved Surfaces of Revolution.—The revolution of any plane curve about an axis generates a double-curved surface of revolution, with the exception of the warped surface named above. In the following discussion the generatrix and the axis are considered to be in the same plane. This is not a required condition; but, if they are not in the same plane, the identical surface may be produced by revolving some other curve which is in the same plane; and that curve may be considered to be the generatrix.

The Sphere is generated by the revolution of a circle about one of its diameters.

The Annular Torus is generated by the revolution of a circle about an axis outside the circle. It is used for pipe bends and for fillets on other surfaces of revolution. A torus may be generated by revolving other closed curves.

The Ellipsoids of Revolution.—The revolution of an ellipse about either axis generates this type of surface which is called a spheroid. If the ellipse is revolved about its major axis, the surface is a prolate spheroid; if about its minor axis, an oblate spheroid.

A Paraboloid of Revolution is generated by revolving a parabola about its axis. This surface is used for reflectors. If accurately constructed, light from the focus is reflected in parallel rays.

Hyperboloid of Revolution of Two Nappes.—The revolution of the hyperbola about its transverse axis generates this surface which has two separate nappes. Revolution about the other axis of symmetry generates the hyperboloid of one nappe which is a warped surface.

138. Sections of Surfaces of Revolution.—There are two important types of plane sections of surfaces of revolution.

(1). Right Sections.—Any plane perpendicular to the axis cuts a surface of revolution in a circle.

(2). Meridian Sections.—A plane containing the axis of a surface of revolution is a meridian plane, and it cuts the surface in a line called a meridian line which is identical in form with the outline in a view taken normal to the axis. A meridian section is considered to be the generatrix.

139. Other Double-curved Surfaces.—The **Serpentine** is generated by a sphere whose center moves along a helix.   The common example of this surface is that of a helical spring made of cylindrical material.

The Ellipsoid may be conceived of as being generated by revolving a variable ellipse about its constant axis in such a manner that all the right sections and all the meridian sections are ellipses.

Double-curved Surfaces Without Names may be conceived of as being generated by moving along a curved directrix a curved generatrix which may or may not be variable in form.   Such surfaces are very common and are shown on a drawing by their outlines and sections.

140. Warped Surfaces.—Warped surfaces are discussed in Chapter VIII.

DEVELOPMENTS

141. The development of a surface may be conceived to be the unrolling of the surface onto a plane.   Only surfaces which are made up of plane or single-curved surfaces can be developed.   Double-curved surfaces and warped surfaces are non-developable, but in some cases they can be approximately developed.

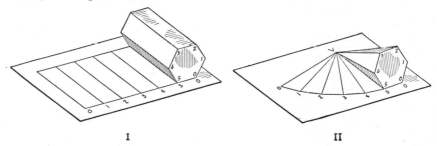

I   II

Fig. 99.—Development of Prism and Pyramid.

An object to be made of sheet metal is developed to obtain a pattern. The material is cut according to the shape of the pattern and rolled or bent to form the object.   All lines in the development are in true length, and the surfaces bounded by them are in true size.   The development usually is cut on the shortest line of the surface so that the joint which is fastened by welding, seaming, riveting, or soldering will be as short as possible.   It is customary to draw the development with the inside surface as the visible surface.

Figure 99-I shows the imaginary unrolling of the surface of a right hexagonal prism onto a plane.   Figure 99-II shows the imaginary unrolling of the surface of a right hexagonal pyramid onto a plane.   Note that in each case the inside of the surface is turned toward the observer.

Objects whose surfaces are commonly developed are prisms, pyramids, cylinders, cones, and others which are combinations of these.   A surface formed as a convolute can be developed.

142. Prisms.—A prism is a polyhedron having parallel polygons, either regular or irregular, for two of its surfaces called the bases, and parallelograms for the others.   The surfaces which are parallelograms are known as the lateral faces and their lines of intersection are called lateral edges.   A prism whose lateral faces are rectangles is known as a right prism; others are oblique.   If the base is a regular polygon, it has a definite center.   The axis is a straight line connecting the centers of the bases.   A truncated prism is that portion of a prism which is between its base and its intersection with a plane which cuts all of its lateral edges.

143. *Problem 38.   To develop the surface of a truncated right hexagonal prism.*

Analysis.—Lay off on a straight line the perimeter of the base of the prism.   This is called the stretchout.   Lay off the true shapes of the lateral faces of the prism on this line adjacent to each other.   This is the development of the lateral surface.   Attach to it a regular hexagon the size of the base.   Find the true shape of the cut surface and attach it to the development of the lateral surface.   Every line in a development must be shown in its true length.

Construction.—Fig. 100.   *Given* the truncated right hexagonal prism whose base is *ABCDEF*.   *Required* to draw the complete development.

To obtain the stretchout, lay off in succession on a straight line *AB*, *BC*, *CD*, etc., equal to the corresponding edges of the base.   Draw the lines *A*1, *B*2, *C*3, etc., perpendicular to the stretchout and equal to the lateral edges.   Connect the points 1, 2, 3, etc., in succession to complete the development of the lateral surface.   Then each face such as *A–B–*2*–*1 is shown in its true shape in the development, with the inside toward the observer.   Make a normal view of the cut surface or section, turn it over, and transfer it to the development.

144. To Make a Model of the prism use heavy drawing paper and cut out the pattern, leaving tabs along edges of the development—one tab for each joint.   Score the lines on which the pattern is to be bent.   Apply paste or rubber cement to the tabs and the inside surfaces to which they are to be attached.   Place all tabs inside the model.

145. Assignments.—See Chapter XIV, Group 6A.

146. *Problem 39. To develop an oblique prism.*

Analysis.—The stretchout for an oblique prism is equal to the perimeter of a right section. All the edges of the prism must be shown in true length in the development. Draw a view which is a normal view of the lateral

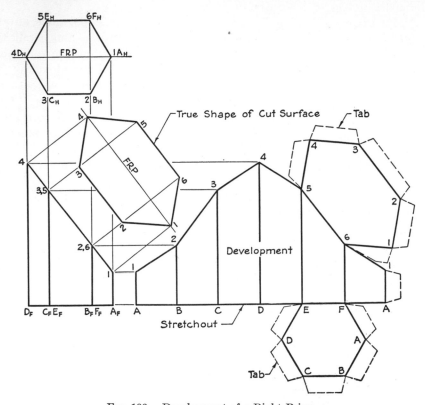

Fig. 100.—Development of a Right Prism.

edges, and draw an end view of the prism. Make the development from these two views.

Construction.—Fig. 101. *Given* the oblique pentagonal prism whose upper base is *ABCDE*. *Required* to draw the entire development.

Draw the normal auxiliary elevation and the end view of the prism. The end view is also a true view of the right section 1–2–3–4–5. Draw the stretchout line equal to the perimeter of the right section by setting off the lengths of its five sides. Lines drawn parallel to the stretchout line from the end points of the edges in the auxiliary view will locate the various points required for the development.

147. Assignments.—See Chapter XIV, Group 6B.

Pyramids.—A pyramid is a polyhedron of which one surface, called the base, is any polygon; and the other surfaces are triangles having a common

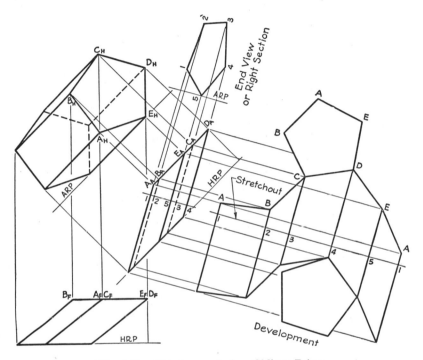

Fig. 101.—Development of an Oblique Prism.

vertex. The triangular faces are called the lateral faces, and their intersections are called the lateral edges. If the base is a regular polygon, and the line joining the vertex and the center of the base is perpendicular to the base, the pyramid is a right pyramid; if inclined, it is an oblique pyramid. A truncated pyramid is that portion of a pyramid which is between its base and the intersection of the pyramid with a plane cutting all the lateral edges. The portion between the base and a section parallel to the base is a frustum.

148. Problem 40.　To develop the surface of a truncated right pyramid.

Analysis.—Develop the lateral surface of the entire pyramid as a series of isosceles triangles placed adjacent to each other in proper order.　Remove the vertex portion.

Construction.—Fig. 102.　*Given* the truncated right pyramid with pentagonal base $ABCDE$.　*Required* to develop the surface of the truncated pyramid.

By Principle 13 find the true length of VA as $V_FA'_F$.　This is the true length of all the lateral edges.　Draw an arc with radius equal to $V_FA'_F$.

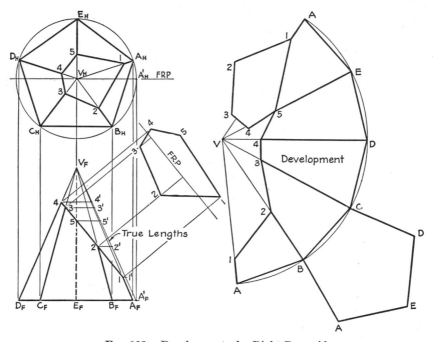

Fig. 102.—Development of a Right Pyramid.

Step off the chords AB, BC, etc., equal to the edges of the base, which are shown in true length in the top view; and lay out five isosceles triangles. This is the development of the entire lateral surface of the pyramid.　Now find the true length of each edge from V to the cutting plane.　As a short cut to the revolution method of finding these true lengths draw a horizontal line from each point across to the true length line $V_FA'_F$.　These true lengths are $V1'$, $V2'$, etc.　Lay off these true lengths on the proper lines in the development so as to obtain the line of the cut section 1–2–3–4–5–1.

Find the true shape of the cut section and turn it over in the development. Attach the base as shown.

149. Assignments.—See Chapter XIV, Group 6C.

150. *Problem 41. To develop the lateral surface of a truncated oblique pyramid.*

Analysis.—Develop the entire lateral surface of the pyramid and discard the part not needed. Find the true length of all the edges and construct a triangle for each face in the proper sequence.

Construction.—Fig. 103. *Given* the truncated oblique pyramid with the heptagonal base *ABCDEFG*. *Required* to develop the lateral surface.

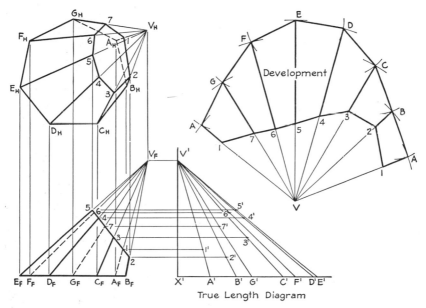

Fɪɢ. 103.—Development of an Oblique Pyramid.

The true lengths of the lateral edges are shown in the true length diagram, which is explained below, and the true lengths of the edges of the base appear in the top view. To make the development use true lengths to construct triangles *VED* and *VEF*, and complete the drawing by adding the true shapes of the other faces. From *V* in the development lay off *V'1'*, *V'2'*, *V'3'*, etc., and discard the portion *V*–1–2–3–4–5–6–7–1.

The drawing shows the characteristic form of the development of the entire lateral surface opened on its shortest edge *VA*. For the surface of the truncated pyramid, however, a workman may prefer to make the seam on edge $B2$, which is the shortest.

The most satisfactory method of finding the various true lengths required for the development is to construct a true length diagram. This diagram is based upon the construction shown in Fig. 104, which shows a simplified method of finding the true length of a line. At A_H lay off the height dimension h perpendicular to A_HB_H. $A'B_H$ is the true length of the line. This construction is equivalent to an auxiliary view joined to the top view. The true length is the hypotenuse of a right triangle which has one view of the line as its base and the orthographic dimension of the other view as its altitude.

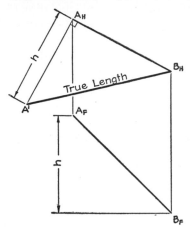

Fig. 104.—True Length of a Line.

151. To Construct the True Length Diagram.—Since all the height dimensions of the lateral edges of the pyramid are equal, the true length diagram is drawn in horizontal alignment with the front view. From the vertical line $V'X'$ lay off the length of the top view of each lateral edge by measuring horizontally to the right of X'. Then, $V'A'$, $V'B'$, $V'C'$, etc., are the true lengths of the lateral edges. To find the true lengths of $V1$, $V2$, $V3$, etc., draw horizontal lines from the front view to the true length diagram in which they are $V'1'$, $V'2'$, $V'3'$, etc.

152. Assignments.—See Chapter XIV, Group 6D.

153. Cylinders.—A cylindrical surface is a single-curved surface generated by a straight line which moves parallel to itself and touches a fixed curved line. The various positions of the generating line are known as elements of the surface.

A cylinder is a solid bounded by a cylindrical surface and two parallel plane surfaces called the bases. If the elements are perpendicular to the bases, the cylinder is a right cylinder; otherwise, it is oblique. The axis is the line joining the centers of the bases.

154. Problem 42. To develop a truncated right circular cylinder.

Analysis.—The cylinder may be developed by the same method used for developing a prism. If sixteen equally spaced points are selected on the circle of the base, the development of the cylinder is equivalent to the development of a sixteen-sided prism. The stretchout is equal to πd, the circumference of a circle. Greater accuracy may be obtained by dividing the calculated stretchout into sixteen equal parts.

Construction.—Fig. 105. *Given* a right circular cylinder and a plane *RST*, which truncates it. *Required* to find the intersection of the plane

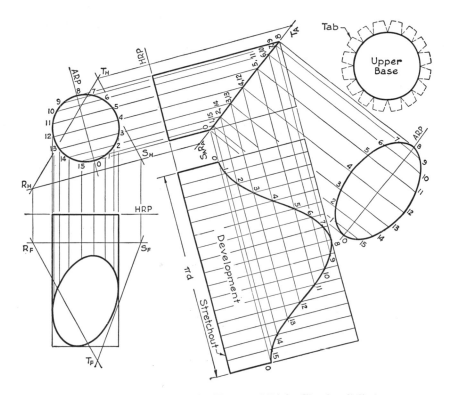

Fig. 105.—Development of a Truncated Right Circular Cylinder.

and the cylinder and the development of that portion of the cylinder that is above the plane.

Draw the auxiliary elevation which is an edge view of the plane and find the points where the plane cuts the sixteen elements. Make the development adjacent to the auxiliary elevation.

Tabs which may be used in making a model are indicated on the development of the upper base.

155. Assignments.—See Chapter XIV, Group 6E.

156. Problem 43. *To develop an oblique cylinder.*

Analysis.—This cylinder is developed like an oblique prism of sixteen sides. It is difficult to obtain an accurate length for the stretchout, which is the perimeter of the ellipse at a right section. A sufficient number of parts should be used so that the polygon very closely approximates the ellipse.

Construction.—Fig. 106. *Given* the oblique cylinder which has AB for its axis and frontal circles for its bases. *Required* to develop the lateral surface.

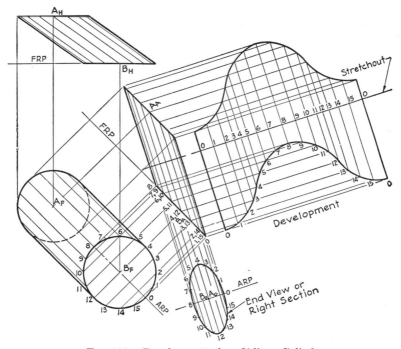

Fig. 106.—Development of an Oblique Cylinder.

Draw the right-auxiliary view which shows the normal view of the axis. The oblique view or end view is found by using sixteen equally spaced points on the circle of the base. Note that on this ellipse the spacing of the points is not uniform. These spaces are set off along the stretchout to obtain the development.

157. Assignments.—See Chapter XIV, Group 6F.

158. Cones.—A conical surface is a single-curved surface generated by a straight line which moves so as to touch a given curved line and pass through a given fixed point called the vertex. The various positions of the generating line are elements of the surface. A cone is a solid bounded by a

conical surface and a plane cutting all the elements.   The conical surface
is the lateral surface, and the plane surface is the base.   The line of centers
of a circular or elliptical cone is a straight line connecting the vertex to the
center of the base.   If the line of centers is perpendicular to the base, the
cone is a right cone; if inclined, it is an oblique cone.   Only in a right cone
is the line of centers the axis.

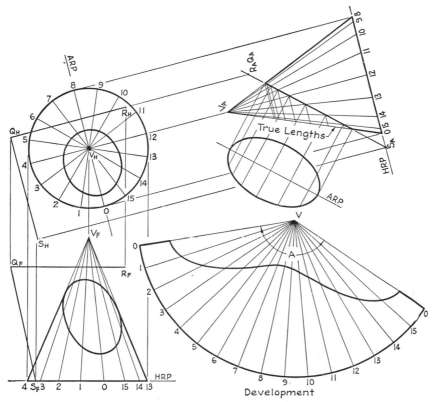

Fig. 107.—Development of a Right Circular Cone.

A truncated cone is that portion of a cone between its base and its
intersection with a plane cutting all the elements.

159. *Problem 44.*   *To truncate and develop a right circular cone.*

Analysis.—A cone may be developed as a many-sided pyramid.   In the
case of a right circular cone the angle A of the development may be calculated by the formula:

$$\text{Angle } A \text{ in degrees is } \frac{360r}{s}$$

in which r is the radius of the base and s is the slant height of the cone.

Construction.—Fig. 107. *Given* the right circular cone and the plane QRS. *Required* to find the plane section of the cone and to develop the portion below the cutting plane.

Draw the auxiliary elevation showing the cone and the edge view of the cutting plane. To draw the plane section locate in the top and front views the points where QRS intersects the elements as found in the auxiliary elevation. Use the auxiliary elevation and the top view for making the development. Draw an arc with radius equal to the outline element which represents the true length of all the elements of the cone. Set off sixteen equal steps on this arc, making it equal to the circumference of the circle, or lay off the angle A and divide the arc into sixteen equal parts. This is the development of the entire lateral surface of the cone. To discard the upper portion lay off the true length of each element from the vertex to the cutting plane. These true lengths are found by drawing horizontal lines parallel to the base of the cone, in the auxiliary elevation.

160. Assignments.—See Chapter XIV, Group 6G.

161. *Problem 45. To develop the lateral surface of a truncated oblique cone.*

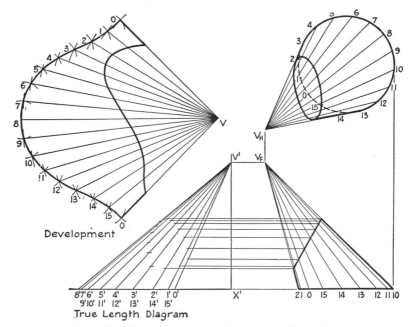

FIG. 108.—Development of a Truncated Oblique Cone.

Analysis.—This cone is developed like a many-sided oblique pyramid. Enough sides must be used to approximate the cone very closely.

Construction.—Fig. 108. See Problem 41 for construction which is similar to the construction required in this case.

The development of the cone shows the characteristic symmetrical form of the development of the whole lateral surface opened on its shortest edge $V0$. For the surface of the truncated cone, however, a workman may prefer to make the seam on element $V2$.

162. Assignments. See Chapter XIV, Group 6H.

163. Transition Pieces.—A transition piece is one used for connecting an opening of one shape with an opening of another shape. It usually consists of plane surfaces and portions of oblique cones, but may have only plane surfaces. Convolutes are also used for transition pieces.

164. Problem 46. *To draw and develop a transition piece, one end of which is a circle and the other a square.*

Analysis.—To draw the transition piece use portions of four oblique cones whose vertices are at the corners of the square. The portions between these conical parts are triangular plane surfaces. Develop the surface by the method used for developing an oblique cone.

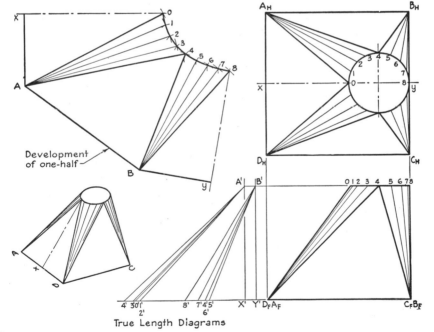

FIG. 109.—Development of a Transition Piece.

Construction.—Fig. 109. *Given* the horizontal circle and the horizontal square *ABCD*. *Required* to draw the transition piece connecting these openings and to make its development.

Divide the circle into sixteen equal parts. Draw the conical parts using one quarter of the circle for each cone, the vertices being at *A*, *B*, *C*, and *D*. The portions *AD* 0 and *AB* 4, etc., between the conical parts are plane surfaces. Usually the elements of the cones should appear on a drawing of a transition piece. Construct true length diagrams and lay out the development as a series of large and small triangles.

165. Problem 47. To develop a conical reducing piece connecting two offset pipes.

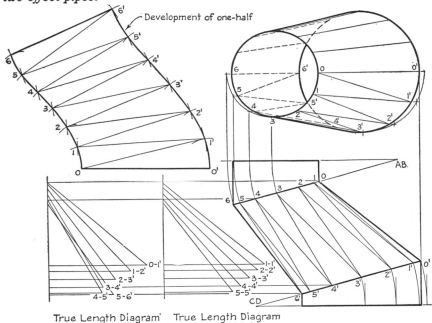

FIG. 110.—Development of a Conical Reducing Piece.

Analysis.—Assume that the vertex of the cone is not available. Then this piece must be developed by triangulation. Divide the surface into a large number of quadrilaterals by drawing elements, and divide each of these into two triangles by drawing a diagonal. Make the development of each triangle.

Construction.—Fig. 110. *Given* two cylindrical pipes of different diameters connected by a conical piece. *Required* to develop the conical piece.

Draw twelve elements as shown, and draw the diagonals 0-1', 1-2', 2-3', etc. Draw a true length diagram for the elements and another diagram for the diagonals. Since the elliptical ends of the conical piece are not shown in true shape in the top view, the quarters 0'-1'-2'-3' of the lower ellipse and 3-4-5-6 of the upper ellipse are revolved to a horizontal position to obtain the true length of the chords. The true lengths of the other symmetrically located chords are equal to these.

Having found the true length of all sides of each small triangle, such as 0'-0-1', construct the triangles in systematic order for the development of the conical piece.

166. Assignments.—See Chapter XIV, Group 6I.

167. Elbows.—An elbow is a connection between two pipes whose axes intersect. The longer the bend of the elbow and the greater the number of

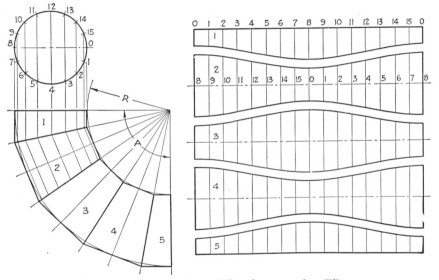

Fig. 111.—Construction and Development of an Elbow.

pieces it contains the smaller will be the friction loss through it and the greater will be the cost of making it. Elbows having a polygon for a right section are known as prismatic elbows. Other elbows are round or elliptical in section.

The sheetmetal worker, when making the elbow, makes a development for one of the inner pieces and uses it as a pattern for laying out the others. Seams are made on alternate sides of the various pieces of the elbow in order to minimize the waste of material. Figure 111 shows how this is done.

Elbows of thick metal pipe usually are made by cutting sections from the pipe and welding them together.

168. Problem 48. To draw and develop an elbow.

Analysis.—Each portion of the elbow is a part of a right cylinder. The seams are made alternately on the shortest and the longest elements of the several pieces.

Construction.—Fig. 111. *Given*: The elbow is to have five pieces. The angle of bend A is 90°, and the least radius of bend R is given. *Required* to draw the elbow and develop each piece.

Divide the angle A into eight equal parts; the number of parts being found by the formula $2N - 2$, where $N =$ the number of pieces in the elbow.

Two of these parts are used for each piece except the end pieces, which require only one part. Develop each piece and arrange the developments adjacent to each other so as to show the development in rectangular form.

169. Problem 49. To make the layout for a pipe connection using right cylindrical and conical pipes and to show the joints.

Analysis.— Two cylinders, two cones, or one of each, that circumscribe a sphere intersect each other in an ellipse which appears as a straight line in the view that is a normal view of both center lines of the intersecting surfaces. Two cones also may intersect in a parabola or a hyperbola.

First Example.

Construction.—Fig. 112. *Given* the center line ABD and center line EC for a branch pipe and the diameters at A, B, D, and E. *Required* to lay out the pipe connections and show the joints.

At B draw a sphere, and draw the cylindrical pipe tangent to the sphere.

From D draw the outlines of the conical pipe tangent to the sphere. These pipes intersect in an ellipse represented by the line 1–2. At C draw a sphere tangent to the conical pipe BD, and from E draw the outlines of a cone tangent to this sphere. The cones intersect in ellipses shown by the lines 3–4 and 5–6. Then, 3–7–5 represents the joint for the branch pipe EC.

Second Example.

Construction.—Fig. 113. *Given* the center lines $ABCD$ and $ABEF$; and the diameters at A, B, C, D, E, and F for a Y-pipe connection. *Required* to lay out the pipe connections and show the joints. Draw spheres at B, C, and E. Tangent to the spheres draw the outlines of all the pipes. The pipes AB and BC intersect in the ellipse shown by the line 1–2. The pipes AB and BE intersect in the line 3–4, and the pipes BC and BE intersect in the line 6–7. The actual intersections for the Y are 8–1, 8–4, 8–7—all portions of ellipses.

170. Problem 50. To make the layout for a reducing elbow.

Analysis.—The reducing elbow can be laid out by the use of inscribed spheres as in Problem 49. In a properly designed elbow of any number of pieces, whether cylindrical or conical, the alternate pieces can be revolved through 180° about their axes, and then all of the pieces can be fitted together to form a continuous cylinder or a frustum of a cone. On the

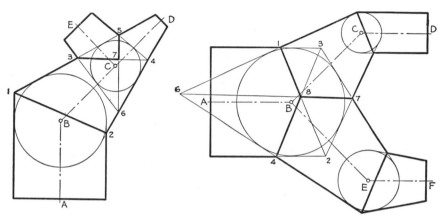

FIG. 112.—Pipe Connections.   FIG. 113.—Y-Pipe Connections.

other hand, a piece of pipe can be sawed into pieces in planes which alternately slope to the right and left at the same angle with the axis; and the pieces can be put together to form the elbow.

Construction.—Figs. 114 and 115. *Given* the diameter of the elbow at B and at E, the angle of bend A, and the radius of the center line of the bend. *Required* to make the lay-out for a three-piece reducing elbow and show how to cut or develop it from the frustum of a right cone.

Lay out the divisions for the elbow as shown in Problem 48, and draw tangents to the arc BE to find the center line $BCDE$. In Fig. 115 lay off on center line BE of the frustum of the cone the lengths BC, CD, and DE equal to those in Fig. 114, and make the end diameters d_1 and d_2. The perpendiculars R_1 and R_2 to the left element of the cone from C and D are the radii of construction spheres drawn at C and D in Fig. 114. Draw the cones tangent to these spheres and show their intersections. The lengths of the center lines for these three pieces of the elbow are X, Y and Z. In Fig. 115 lay off on BE these distances, and draw JK through F and LM through G making the angle a as shown for the joints of the elbow which is to be made from the frustum of the cone by cutting on these lines. If the elbow is to be made from sheet metal, the frustum of the cone can be developed in one piece with the joint lines JK and LM on it.

This construction is worked out to produce an elbow that will connect accurately the points B and E.   In case the relative location of the points B and E is not important, the conical pipe may be cut at other points along the center line BE; and the length BE may be assumed.

171. Assignments.—See Chapter XIV, Group 6J.

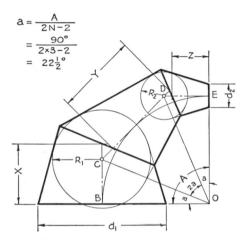

$$a = \frac{A}{2N-2}$$
$$= \frac{90°}{2\times3-2}$$
$$= 22\tfrac{1}{2}°$$

Fig. 114.—Conical Elbow.

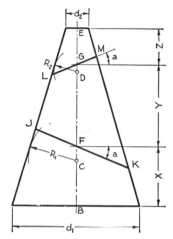

Fig. 115.—Pipe Cuts for Elbow.

172. The Helix.—The cylindrical helix is a double-curved line generated by the revolution of a point around an axis while moving parallel to it, the rate of advance around the axis having a constant ratio to the rate of advance along the axis.   In a right-hand helix the motion is clockwise for an advance along the axis away from the observer.   The advance of the point along the axis for one revolution is the lead of the helix.

In a conical helix the point travels on the surface of a right circular cone.   The ratio of the rate of advance along the axis to the rate of advance around the axis is constant.

173. *Problem 51.   To draw a right cylindrical helix of given diameter and lead.*

Construction.—Fig. 116.   *Given* an opaque cylinder and the lead of a right-hand helix.   *Required* to draw the helix on the surface of the cylinder.

Divide the circle into sixteen equal parts and divide the lead into the same number of equal parts.   The intersection of the elements of the cylinder with horizontal lines drawn through the points of division of the lead locates sixteen points on one turn of the helix. The helix starts at 0, and advances downward in a clockwise direction. Therefore, the first half of the turn of the helix is visible. The drawing shows one and one-half turns.

174. Assignments.—See Chapter XIV, Group 6K.

175. The convolute is a single-curved surface generated by the motion of a straight line which remains tangent to a double-curved line. It is a single-curved surface because two consecutive elements which are infinitesimally close together intersect. The third consecutive element does not intersect the first. The straight line is the *generatrix* and the double-curved line is the *directrix*.

176. *Problem 52. To draw and develop the surface of a helical convolute that is limited by a cylinder.*

Analysis.—In this convolute the straight-line generatrix is limited in length, and remains tangent to a helix. There are two nappes of the surface; one is generated by

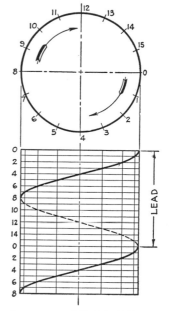

FIG. 116.—Cylindrical Helix.

the upper half of the line; the other, by the lower half of the line. The surface may be represented by the helical directrix, the elements, and the helices generated by the ends of the line.

Construction.—Fig. 117. *Given* a cylindrical helix drawn on an opaque cylinder. *Required* to draw the convolute generated by the frontal line *KJP*.

Through the points *K* and *P* draw large helices which have the same lead as the small helical directrix. In the top view use the same number of divisions of both circles starting at J_H and K_H. Lines joining corresponding points on the small helix and the large helix are elements of the surface and are used to represent the surface in a drawing. In this drawing each convolute is considered to be made of a thin piece of metal, and the elements are on the upper side of the lower nappe and the lower side of the upper nappe. The line *KJP* is tangent to the small helix in the "*V*" between the two nappes of the convolute at point *J*. A right section of the surface is an involute of a circle.

Development.—Since the convolute is a single-curved surface, it can be developed.   Three consecutive elements divide a portion of the surface into two small triangles.   One of these triangles can be revolved about the common element as an axis so that it will lie in the plane of the other triangle.   The development of the helical convolute, however, is accomplished

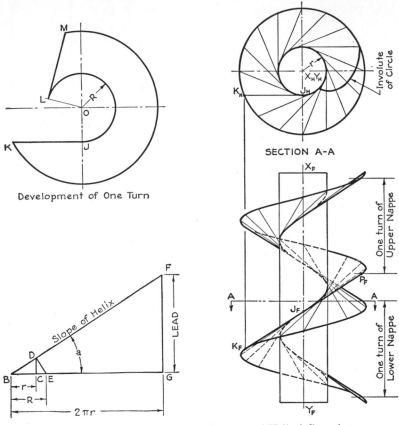

Development of One Turn

SECTION A-A

Fɪɢ. 117.—Construction and Development of Helical Convolute.

by an easier method.   If this convolute is made of sheet metal, a portion of it can be moved along the axis so as to become a circular ring, Fig. 117. To find the inside radius of this ring use the formula for the radius of curvature of a helix:

$$R = \frac{r}{\cos^2 a}$$

in which R is the radius of curvature of the helix, r is the radius of the cylinder on which it is wound, and a is the angle of slope of the helix, equivalent to the slope of JK. The construction for R and the angle a is made graphically. Draw a right triangle whose base BG is $2\pi r$ and whose altitude FG is the lead of the helix. The hypotenuse shows the slope of the helix. The graphical construction for finding R is as follows: Lay off $BC = r$. Draw DC perpendicular to BC. Then draw DE perpendicular to BD. $BE = R$. Use R for the inside radius of the development. Make the arc JL equal to the length of one turn of the helix, which is equal to the hypotenuse of the triangle BFG. Draw JK and LM tangent to the arc and equal to $J_F K_F$.

The helical convolute is used for some screw conveyors. Other convolutes are used in the design of automobile hoods, pontoons, transition pieces, and other objects made of sheet metal.

177. Problem 53. *To draw and develop the surface of a helical convolute that is limited by a plane and to draw a tangent plane to the convolute.*

Analysis.—Only the lower nappe of this convolute is to be shown, and it is to be limited by a horizontal plane which it intersects in the involute of a circle. This involute and the helix may be used in drawing the elements that represent the convolute.

Construction.—Fig. 118. *Given* the cylindrical helix ACB and the plane H. *Required* to represent the convolute, to draw a tangent plane, and to develop the portion ACE of the surface of a convolute.

The tangent to the helix at A intersects the horizontal plane at D. To locate D make $A_H D_H$ equal to the circumference of the cylinder of the helix. Divide the circle representing the top view of the helix and the line $A_H D_H$ each into sixteen equal parts. For elements in the top view of the convolute, draw a tangent to the circle at each division point, and make each tangent one division shorter than the last, beginning with $A_H D_H$. Join these points to obtain the involute $D_H S_4 A_H$. Locate the points of the involute in the front view, and join to corresponding points on the helix.

Draw a horizontal plane through C midway between A and B. Its intersection with the convolute is another involute $E_H T_4 C_H$.

To pass a plane tangent to the convolute through the point S_1 draw the tangent $R_1 S_1$ to the involute. This tangent and the element $G_H S_1$ represent the plane. Also draw a tangent to the other involute at T_1. Since both of the tangents are perpendicular to the element, they are parallel to each other; and these tangents represent the tangent plane. Another tangent plane is $R_4 S_4 T_4$.

If it is desired to represent a convolute surface connecting the given curves, $E_H T_1 T_4$ and $D_H S_1 S_4$, a tangent drawn to $E_H T_1 T_4$ at any point N and a parallel tangent drawn to $D_H S_1 S_4$ will locate point of tangency M. Then MN is an element of the surface. Any number of elements can be located in this manner.

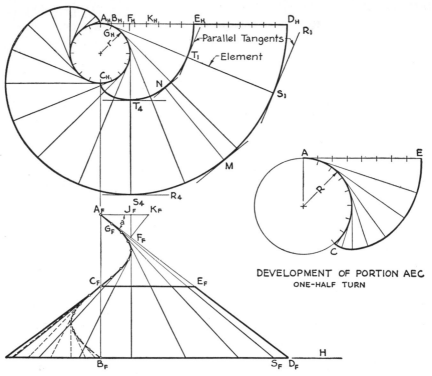

Fɪɢ. 118.—Helical Convolute and Tangent Planes.

To develop the portion AEC, first find the radius for the development of the helix as a circle in the following manner: Draw the horizontal line AK, which is tangent to a horizontal circle of the theoretical cylinder of the helix. Make $A_F J_F$ equal to r. Draw the vertical line $J_F F_F$ to the element AD. Then draw $F_F K_F$ perpendicular to $A_F D_F$. $A_F K_F$ is the radius of curvature R. This graphical construction is in accordance with the formula given in Prob. 52. For the development, draw a circle with radius R equal to $A_F K_F$ and make the length of the arc of this circle from A to C

equal to $A_F E_F$, which is the true length of the helix from A to C. Draw AE equal to $A_F E_F$, divide it into eight equal parts which are each equal to the parts on the arc AC. The involute of the arc AC is CE, and the development of this portion of the convolute is ACE.

178. Problem 54. To design a convolute-type automobile hood.

Analysis.—In many cases two plane curves can be connected by a surface of the convolute type made up of one or more convolutes or combination of convolutes and cylinders or cones. Elements of the surface can be found by the method of tangent planes. If the surfaces are in parallel planes, two parallel lines, one tangent to each curve, determine a tangent plane of the required surface. The line joining their points of tangency is an element of the surface.

Construction.—Fig. 119. *Given* the curve of the hood at the radiator with center A and the curve of the hood at the cowl with center B. *Required* to represent a surface of single curvature connecting these end curves.

At any point S on the curve with center B, draw a tangent. Then draw a line parallel to it tangent to the other curve and find the point of tangency T. The line ST is an element of the surface. Repeat the operation for a sufficient number of elements to represent the surface.

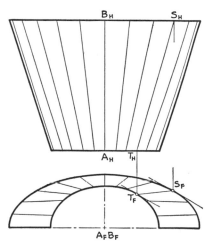

FIG. 119.—Convolute-type Automobile Hood.

The surface is one of single curvature because the tangent planes are tangent to the surface along the entire length of each element. Depending upon the form of the given curves, any certain portion of the surface may be a convolute, a cone, or a cylinder. If all the elements produced meet at one point, the surface is conical. If they are parallel, the surface is cylindrical. Otherwise, it is a convolute.

If the planes of the given curves are not parallel, each pair of tangents must intersect on the line of intersection of planes of the curves.

179. Assignments.—See Chapter XIV, Group 6L.

180. Double-curved Surfaces.—Double-curved surfaces cannot be developed. The sphere, however, may be approximately developed by dividing it into a large number of parts.

181. Problem 55.   To make an approximate development of a sphere by the gore method.

Analysis.—The meridian lines of a sphere intersect at two opposite poles and divide the surface into gores.   The development of the octagonal dome in Fig. 120 inscribed in the hemisphere will serve to explain the gore method.   An examination of the figure shows that each section of the dome touches the sphere along its edges and being of cylindrical form can be used for the approximate development of a gore of the hemisphere.

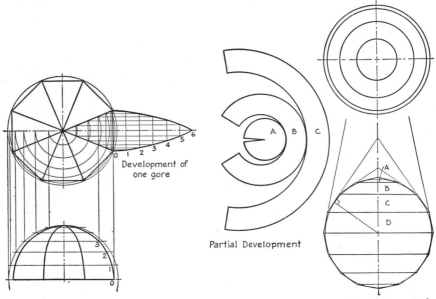

Fig. 120.—Approximate Development of   Fig. 121.—Approximate Development of a
a Hemisphere by the Gore Method.   Sphere by the Zone Method.

Construction.—Fig. 120.   *Given* the hemisphere.   *Required* to develop one gore.

To develop one gore of the hemisphere, note that the corresponding face of the dome is cylindrical.   Draw the horizontal elements of the cylinder 1, 2, 3, etc.   Use the spaces 0-1, 1-2, 2-3, etc., of the front view in making the stretchout which is adjacent to the top view.   Draw the elements 1, 2, 3, etc., at right angles to the stretchout and of the same length as shown in the top view.

Note.—A similar construction may be made for the approximate development of a sphere by circumscribing the dome about the sphere.

182. *Problem 56.   To make an approximate development of a sphere by the zone method.*

Analysis.—Enclose the sphere by means of a number of short frustums of right circular cones which fit the sphere very closely.   Develop each frustum as an approximate development of that portion of the sphere.

Construction.—Fig. 121.   *Given* a sphere.   *Required* to make the approximate development of the surface by the zone method.

Draw a regular polygon of sixteen sides which circumscribes the great circle of the sphere in the front view.   Pass horizontal planes through the corners of the polygon dividing the sphere into eight zones.   Portion *A* is a flat cone; portions *B*, *C*, and *D* are very short frustums of cones.   The development of the portions *A*, *B*, and *C* is shown.

In case the metal is to be stretched, the polygon should be inscribed in the great circle of the sphere.   The conical pieces may be stretched or hammered into a spherical form.

183. Assignments.—See Chapter XIV, Group 6M.

CHAPTER VII

SURFACES AND INTERSECTIONS

184. A great many objects of modern design and manufacture are composed of parts which have various kinds of surfaces. These parts may be prismatic, cylindrical, conical, or of other forms. Drawings for the manufacture of these articles should show the lines of intersection of the surfaces of the various parts in order to represent the object completely. If the object is to be made of sheet metal, the intersections of the surfaces must be found before developments can be made for patterns.

185. There are five methods of finding the intersection of surfaces. They are as follows:

1. *The Edge View Method.*—The edge view is a straight line in the case of a plane or it is a curved line in the case of a cylinder. The edge view may be given in one of the principal views; if not, an auxiliary view will be required.

2. *The Piercing Point Method.*—This method is an application of Principle 12. The line joining all the piercing points which are necessary is the line of intersection of the surfaces.

3. *The Cutting Plane Method.*—This method is an application of Principle 11. A series of cutting planes are used which cut simple lines from each surface. The intersection of these lines are points on the required line of intersection. Simple lines are straight lines or circles which appear in true form. Generally it is not practical to use cutting planes which will cut the surfaces in any other type of lines.

4. *The Cutting Sphere Method.*—Cutting spheres are used to find the intersection of two surfaces of revolution whose axes intersect. A sphere that has its center at the intersection of the axes cuts both surfaces in circles. The intersection of the circles locates points common to both surfaces.

5. *The Cutting Cylinder Method.*—Cutting cylinders may be used to find the intersection of a cylinder or prism with a surface of revolution. The axes of the given surfaces may or may not be parallel or intersecting. The base of each cutting cylinder is a circle of the surface of revolution, and its axis is parallel to the axis of the given cylinder or prism. The cut-

ting cylinder cuts one surface in a circle and the other in straight lines. The circle and the lines intersect at points on the required line of intersection.

Example of First Method.—Edge View Method.

186. *Problem 57. To find the intersection of two prisms.*

Analysis.—The end view of either prism shows the points at which the edges of the other prism pierce its faces. If an end view of each prism is not shown, draw the necessary view.

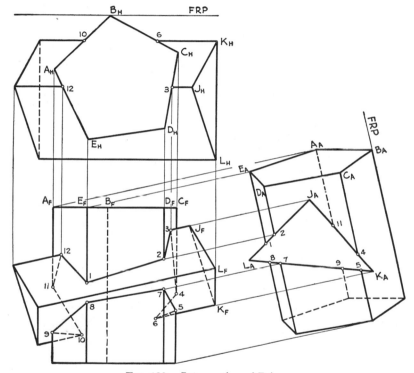

Fig. 122.—Intersection of Prisms.

Construction.—Fig. 122. *Given* the front and top views of the prisms as shown. *Required* to find the intersection.

The top view is an end view of the pentagonal prism; and inspection will show that the edges of the triangular prism pierce its faces at points 3, 6, 10, and 12. Draw a right-auxiliary end view of the triangular prism, and show the other prism in this view. The edges of the pentagonal prism pierce the faces of the triangular prism at the points 1, 2, 11, 4, 5, 9, 7, and 8.

Sight-lines from the numbered points in the top view and the auxiliary view intersect the corresponding edges of the two prisms in the front view locating all the points necessary for the intersection. Begin by connecting the front points which are known to be visible, such as 1–2, and 7–8; and continue until the complete intersection is shown.

187. Assignments.—See Chapter XIV, Group 7A.

188. Types of Intersections.—After locating a sufficient number of points along the intersection of the surfaces of two objects, the points are connected by straight or curved lines which make up the complete intersection of the surfaces. In the case of two curved surfaces the intersection

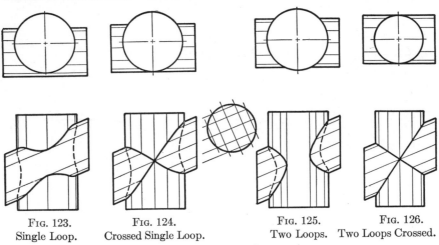

| Fig. 123. | Fig. 124. | Fig. 125. | Fig. 126. |
| Single Loop. | Crossed Single Loop. | Two Loops. | Two Loops Crossed. |

Types of Intersections.

may consist of (1) a single loop, (2) a crossed single loop, (3) two loops, or (4) two loops crossed, depending upon the relative sizes and locations of the surfaces. These types of intersections are illustrated in Figs. 123, 124, 125, and 126. In the case of two polyhedrons, there are four similar types of intersections made up of straight lines instead of curves.

189. The Visibility of the Intersection of Surfaces.—The task of connecting the various points of an intersection is materially simplified by visualizing the possible form of the intersection and by beginning with the visible points. Some rules for determining the visibility of the points and lines follow.

In this statement the visibility of edges, surfaces, elements, or lines cut from the surfaces is considered to be that for each of the objects considered alone in that view.

In the case of polyhedrons:

1. If two edges which intersect are visible, the point of intersection is visible.

2. If either or both of the edges are hidden, the point of intersection is invisible.

3. If the edge and the plane surface intersecting it are visible, the point of intersection is visible.

4. If either the edge or the surface, or both, are hidden, the point of intersection is invisible.

5. If two plane surfaces are visible, their intersection is visible.

6. If either or both of two plane surfaces are hidden, their intersection is invisible.

In the case of two single-curved surfaces:

7. If two elements are visible, their point of intersection is visible.

8. If either or both of the elements are hidden, their point of intersection is invisible.

In the case of double-curved surfaces or single-curved surfaces in which the cutting plane cuts circles from the surfaces:

9. If both circles or the portions of them at the intersection are visible, the point of intersection is visible.

10. If either or both circles or the portions of them at the intersection are hidden, the point of intersection is invisible.

Examples of Second Method.—Piercing Point Method.

190. *Problem 58. To find the intersection of a prism and an oblique plane.*

Analysis.—Find where the edges of the prism pierce the plane by application of Principle 12.

Construction.—Fig. 127. *Given* an oblique pentagonal prism and the plane $QRTS$. *Required* to find the line of intersection of the prism and the plane.

Pass five orthofrontal cutting planes through the edges of the prism. Locate the line 1–1′ in the top view. Locate points 2, 3, 4, and 5 on $Q_H R_H$ and draw lines parallel to 1–1′. They are parallel because the lines of intersection of a plane and parallel planes are parallel. The intersections of these lines with the edges of the prism determine the points A, B, C, D, and E of the line of intersection. Note that in such a case this is an easier solution than a solution by the edge view method.

191. Problem 59.   To find the intersection of two pyramids.

Analysis.—Solve this problem by the second method. Find all the points at which the edges of one pyramid pierce the faces of the other pyramid and connect them in the proper order. There is a large number

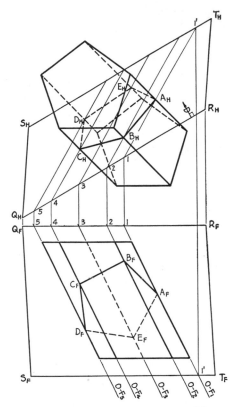

Fig. 127.—Intersection of Prism and Plane.

of points to be found, two for each edge which pierces the other pyramid. This solution requires careful and systematic work.

Construction.—Fig. 128. *Given* the two pyramids. *Required* to find their line of intersection and to show them as one piece.

To find the points (if any) at which the edges *VB* and *VD* pierce the other pyramid, assume the vertical cutting plane *V–V*. The cutting plane intersects the other pyramid in the quadrilateral 1–2–4–3 of the front view. *VD* intersects 3–4 at *a* and 2–4 at *b*. This edge pierces *TPS* at *a*, and

TPQ at *b*.   The edge *VB* does not intersect 1–2–4–3, which shows that it does not pierce the pyramid.

To find where the edge *PS* pierces the other pyramid, assume an ortho-frontal cutting plane *O–F*.   The cutting plane intersects the pyramid

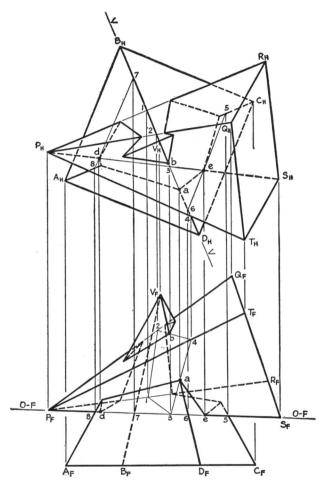

Fig. 128.—Intersection of Pyramids.

in the lines 5–6 and 7–8.   In the top view *PS* intersects these lines at the points *e* and *d*.   *PS* intersects *VDC* at *e* and *VAB* at *d*.   Continue this process until all the required piercing points are found, join the points by straight lines, determine the visibility, and draw the object as one piece. It should not appear as one object pushed through the other.

192. Assignments.—See Chapter XIV, Group 7B.

Examples of Third Method.—Cutting Plane Method.

193. *Problem 60.   To find the intersection of two right cylinders.*

Analysis.—Use the cutting plane method, Principle 11.   The cutting planes are taken parallel to both axes so as to cut straight lines from each surface.   The pictorial sketch of Fig. 129 shows the section made by a cutting plane.

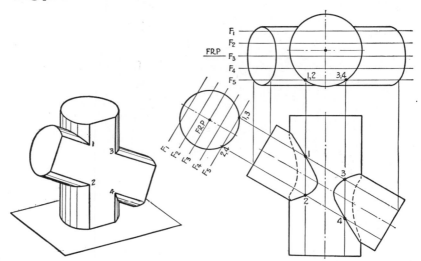

Fig. 129.—Intersection of Right Cylinders.

Construction.—Fig. 129.   *Given* a vertical cylinder and a cylinder with inclined frontal axis.   *Required* to find the intersection.

Use five frontal cutting planes.   They are parallel to the axes of both cylinders and cut straight line elements from both cylinders.   The elements are shown for cutting plane No. 5.   They intersect at the points 1, 2, 3, and 4.   Find a sufficient number of points to give a smooth curve and connect them.

In this case there are two curves of intersection.

Depending upon the relative sizes of the cylinders and the location of the axes, various forms of intersection are produced.   If the front elements intersect, the intersection crosses on the front of the combined cylinders. If the inclined cylinder is moved forward a little, there is one continuous line of intersection.

194. Assignments.—See Chapter XIV, Group 7C.

195. *Problem 61.   To find the intersection of two right circular cones whose bases are parallel.*

Analysis.—Use the third method.   Cutting planes parallel to both bases cut circles from each surface.

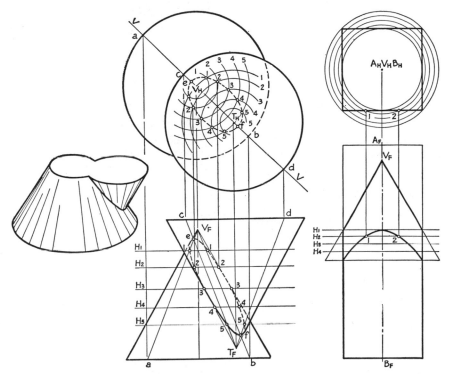

FIG. 130.—Intersection of Cones.   FIG. 131.—Intersection of Cone and Prism.

Construction.—Fig. 130.   *Given* the right circular cones with vertices V and T.   *Required* to find the line of intersection and show the cones as one piece.

Since both bases are horizontal, horizontal cutting planes are used. H_2 cuts a circle from each cone indicated by the arcs marked 2 in the top view.   These arcs intersect at the points marked 2.   Locate the points in the front view by drawing sight-lines.   Two points for each cutting plane are located in like manner.   To determine the highest and lowest points on the curve of intersection use one vertical cutting plane passing through both vertices. It cuts the cones in the elements aV, bV, cT, and dT. These elements intersect at the points e and f. Draw a smooth curve through the points obtained, and brighten the outline elements outside of the intersection.

196. Problem 62. *To find the intersection of a square prism and a right circular cone whose axes are parallel or coincide.*

Analysis.—Use cutting planes which are perpendicular to the axes. Each cutting plane cuts the cone in a circle and the prism in a square. All the squares are the same size.

Construction.—Fig. 131. *Given* the square prism whose axis is AB and the right circular cone whose vertex is V. *Required* to find the intersection of the cone and the prism and to show the prism as a pointed object.

The horizontal cutting planes shown cut the cone in the circles shown in the top view. The intersection of these circles with the square section of the prism gives points on the required curved lines of the intersection.

Note.—The form of the curve on each face of the prism is hyperbolic.

197. Assignments.—See Chapter XIV, Group 7D.

198. Problem 63. *To find the intersection of a cone and a cylinder whose axes are skew lines.*

Analysis.—The cutting planes should cut straight lines from both surfaces. To do so, these planes must pass through the vertex of the cone and must be parallel to the axis of the cylinder.

Construction.—Fig. 132. *Given* the right circular cone with vertex V and the open cylindrical pipe whose axis is AB. *Required* to find the line of intersection and to show the cone and pipe as if made of sheet metal.

Through the vertex V of the cone draw a line parallel to the axis of the cylinder. This line pierces the plane of the base of the cone at C. Since every cutting plane must contain the line VC, the cutting planes may be set up in a right auxiliary view which is an end view of both VC and the cylinder. All of them will appear edgewise and will pass through $V_A C_A$.

Instead of taking cutting planes at random, or equally spaced, select those which will give critical points on the required curve of intersection. Use the following cutting planes: planes $VC1$ and $VC9$ tangent to the cylinder at elements 1 and 9; planes $VC2$ and $VC8$ through elements 2 and 8, which are outline elements of the cylinder in the top view; planes $VC4$ and $VC5$ through elements 4 and 5 which are outline elements of the cylinder in the front view; and frontal plane $VC6$ through an outline element of the cone in the front view. In this case cutting planes $VC3$ and $VC7$ are used to give additional points on the curve.

It is not necessary to draw the base of the cone in the auxiliary view. To avoid this time-consuming and inaccurate construction of an ellipse, draw the horizontal-profile line, JK, which is the intersection of the plane of the base of the cone and a plane perpendicular to the axis of the cylinder.

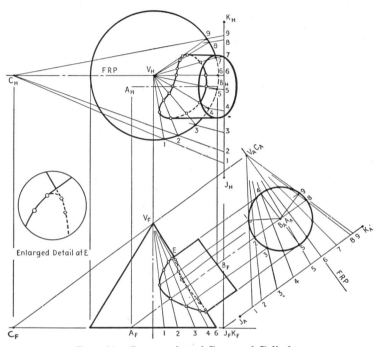

Fig. 132.—Intersection of Cone and Cylinder.

The cutting planes intersect $J_A K_A$ at the points 1, 2, 3, ... 9. Transfer them to $J_H K_H$, and draw the lines $C1$, $C2$, $C3$, ... $C9$ in the top view. Then, the cutting planes are represented accurately in the top view as $VC1$, $VC2$, $VC3$, ... $VC9$. These planes cut the cone in elements $V1$, $V2$, $V3$, ... $V9$, shown in both the top view and the front view.

Draw in the front and top views the elements of the cylinder shown as points 1, 2, 3, ... 9 in the auxiliary view, and draw the other elements cut from the cylinder, but not numbered. The corresponding elements of the cone and cylinder intersect in points on the required curve of intersection.

199. Assignments.—See Chapter XIV, Group 7E.

200. *Problem 64.* *To find the intersection of two oblique cones whose bases are parallel.*

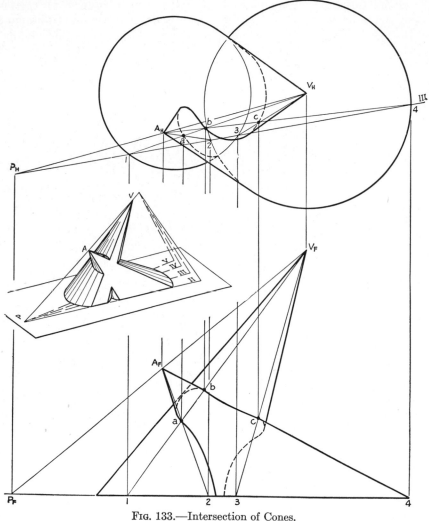

Fig. 133.—Intersection of Cones.

Analysis.—Two methods of selecting the cutting planes are possible:

1. Cutting planes parallel to the bases may be used. They cut circles from both cones.

2. Cutting planes which pass through both vertices may be used. They cut straight-line elements from both cones. This is the method used in this solution.

Construction.—Fig. 133. *Given* the oblique cones whose vertices are *A* and *V* and whose bases are horizontal circles. *Required* to find the intersection and show the cones as one piece.

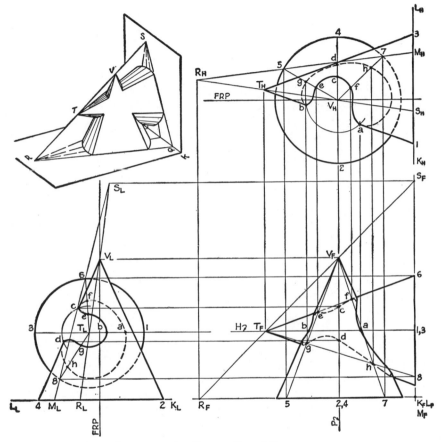

FIG. 134.—Intersection of Cones.

Draw the line *VA* and find the point *P* at which it pierces the horizontal plane of the bases. Every cutting plane used contains the line *PAV*. In the top view No. III cutting plane is *VP*-III. The line *P*-III is horizontal and cuts the bases at the points 1, 2, 3, and 4. The elements *V*1 and $V3$, cut from the cone whose vertex is V, intersect the elements $A2$ and $A4$, cut from the other cone, at the points a, b, and c.   Draw the elements in the front view and locate the points a, b, and c.   Use a sufficient number of cutting planes to find enough points for a smooth curve.

Note.—In case the bases are not in the same plane either extend one of the cones or cut off one of them to obtain this condition.

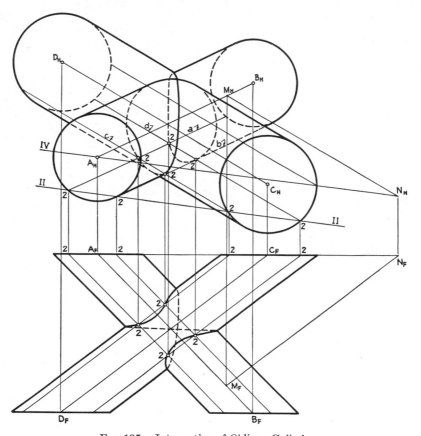

Fig. 135.—Intersection of Oblique Cylinders.

201. Assignments.—See Chapter XIV, Group 7F.

202. *Problem 65.   To find the intersection of two cones whose bases are in perpendicular planes.*

Analysis.—Use cutting planes which pass through both vertices. These planes cut straight-line elements from both cones.

Construction.—Fig. 134. *Given* the two right circular cones whose vertices are V and T. *Required* to find the line of intersection of the cones and to show them as one piece.

Draw the line TV which intersects the planes of the bases of the cones at the points R and S. Obtain the line of intersection KL of the planes of the bases. Every cutting plane contains the line RS and intersects KL. Draw the line RM in the top view. Locate M in the side view. MS is a line of the cutting plane MRS. In the top view the cutting plane intersects one cone in the lines $V5$ and $V7$. In the side view the cutting plane intersects the other cone in the elements $T6$ and $T8$. Draw both sets of the elements in the front view. These elements intersect in the points e, f, g, and h. Use several such planes. A horizontal plane through T and a profile plane through V determine critical points. The horizontal plane passes through the outline elements $T1$ and $T3$ and cuts from the other cone a horizontal circle. The outline element $T1$ and the circle intersect at the points a and b. In like manner the profile plane locates the points c and d in the left-side view.

203. Assignments.—See Chapter XIV, Group 7G.

204. *Problem 66. To find the intersection of two oblique cylinders having parallel bases.*

Analysis.—Although it is possible to use cutting planes parallel to the bases, the planes used in this solution are parallel to both axes and cut straight-line elements from each cylinder.

Construction.—Fig. 135. *Given* the two oblique cylinders whose axes are AB and CD. *Required* to find the intersection and show the cylinders as a one-piece unit.

Through any suitable point M on AB draw MN parallel to CD. AMN is a plane through AB parallel to CD. N is a point in the horizontal plane of the bases A and C. Locate N in the top view. AN is the horizontal line of one cutting plane AMN. All other cutting planes are parallel to this one. Draw the line II-II parallel to AN in the top view to represent a horizontal line of No. II cutting plane. This line intersects the bases of the cylinders at the points marked 2. Through these points draw the elements a and b parallel to AB and the elements c and d parallel to CD. They interesct in four points marked 2. Use a sufficient number of cutting planes to find the curved line of intersection.

Note.—If the bases of both cylinders are parallel but are not in the same plane, either extend or cut off one of them to obtain this condition.

205. Assignments.—See Chapter XIV, Group 7H.

Example of Fourth Method.—The Cutting Sphere Method.

206. Problem 67. *To find the intersection of two right circular cones whose axes intersect.*

Analysis.—If the center of a sphere is on the axis of a surface of revolution, the intersection is a circle. Since the axes of the cones intersect, a cutting sphere whose center is at the intersection of the two axes is used. If the sphere has a suitable diameter, it will intersect each cone in two circles. If these circles, which lie on the surface of the sphere, intersect, the points of intersection are common to both cones.

Construction.—Fig. 136. *Given* the right circular cones whose axes are *AC* and *BC*. *Required* to find the intersection of the two cones and to show them as a unit.

The cutting sphere I intersects the cones in the circles *a* and *b* shown in edge view in the front view. They intersect in two points marked 1. The cutting sphere II intersects the two cones in the circles *d* and *f*. They intersect in two points marked 2 in the front view. Draw the circles *a* and *d* in the top view and locate the points 1 and 2 on them.

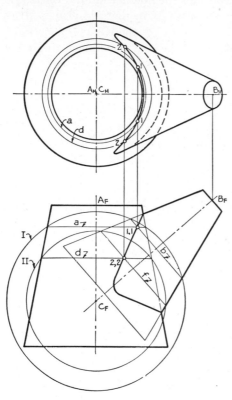

Fig. 136.—Intersection of Right Circular Cones.

Note.—By this method the line of intersection can be found in the front view without reference to the top view. The method can be used only for surfaces of revolution whose axes intersect. The cutting spheres must be drawn in a view which is taken normal to both axes; therefore, if such a view is not given, it will have to be made before proceeding with the solution, and some other method may be preferable. If both cones are designed to be tangent to a sphere with center *C*, the intersection consists of plane curves as shown in Fig. 112, Chapter VI.

207. Assignments.—See Chapter XIV, Group 7I.

Example of the Fifth Method.—Cutting Cylinder Method.

208. *Problem 68.   To find the intersection of a cone of revolution and a cylinder, the axes of which are neither parallel nor intersecting.*

Analysis.—Any right section of the cone is a circle and within reasonable limits may be used as the base of a cutting cylinder.   The cutting cylinder must have its axis parallel to the axis of the given cylinder, so that they

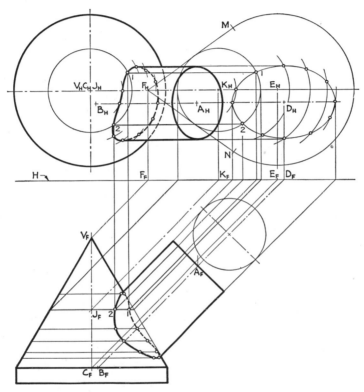

Fig. 137.—Intersection of Cone and Cylinder.

intersect in straight lines which are elements of both.   These elements intersect the circular base of the cutting cylinder at two points which are on the surface of the cone and on the required line of intersection.

Construction.—Fig. 137.   *Given* the right circular cone with axis *VC* and the right circular cylinder with axis *AB*.   *Required* to find the intersection of the surfaces, and to show a construction for controlling the selection of cutting cylinders to give critical points.

Let JK parallel to AB be the axis of an oblique cutting cylinder. It intersects the cone in the horizontal circle, center J, that is shown in the top view, and it intersects a horizontal plane H located a suitable distance above the cone in a circle whose center is K, also shown in the top view. The given cylinder intersects H in the ellipse shown in the top view. The circle with center K intersects the ellipse at points 1 and 2. The cutting cylinder intersects the given cylinder along elements 1–1, and 2–2, and they intersect the circle with center J at points 1 and 2. Usually it is best to locate 1 and 2 on the cone in the top view and draw sight-lines to the front view.

A random selection of cutting cylinders is not entirely satisfactory. It is much better to use a smaller number of cutting cylinders which will give critical points. To control the selection of cutting cylinders make the following construction: Consider the first cutting cylinder to have the base of the cone for its base; then the circle with center E represents the intersection of this cylinder with H. The cutting cylinder at V has zero diameter, and its intersection with H is F. Draw the tangents F_HM and F_HN. Then the upper base of any cutting cylinder is a circle tangent to these straight lines. By trial, a circle can be found that is tangent to these lines and intersects the ellipse at the end of an axis. Four such circles intersect it in eight well-distributed points, and only two others are required. Practically the entire construction is made at the location of the ellipse. One frontal cutting plane through VC should be used.

Instead of a right circular cone, a double-curved surface of revolution may be given. The other object may be a prism instead of a cylinder. A desirable feature of this method is that the construction can be made almost entirely in the clear.

209. Assignments.—See Chapter XIV, Group 7J.

210. *Problem 69.   Having been given one view of a point on the surface of a sphere, to locate the point in an adjacent view.*

Analysis.—A cutting plane through the point cuts a circle from the surface of the sphere. The adjacent view of the point is located on the circle.

Construction.—Fig. 138. *Given* the sphere with center O and the front view of point N on the surface of the sphere. *Required* to find the adjacent view of the point N.

Pass the horizontal cutting plane H through N_F. Draw the top view of the circle cut from the sphere. Draw a sight-line to the top view and locate the point at N_H or N'_H. Unless specified, the point may be on the front or the back of the sphere.

214. Assignments.—See Chapter XIV, Group 7K.

215. *Problem 73. To find the intersection of a surface of revolution and a plane which is parallel to its axis.*

Analysis.—In a view which is an end view of the axis the plane is shown as an edge view. Cutting planes perpendicular to the axis of the surface of revolution cut circles from the surface. Their intersections with the given plane are located first in the view which is an edge view of the plane.

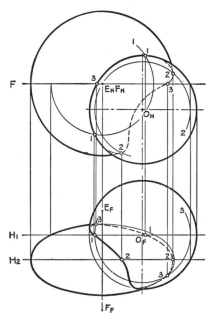

Fig. 141.—Intersection of Double-Curved Surfaces of Revolution.

Construction.—Fig. 142. *Given* a circular base block which is made up of two surfaces of revolution, a torus and a scotia somewhat similar to those used for the base of a column; and a vertical plane *V–V*. *Required* to find the intersection of the plane and the block.

Seven horizontal cutting planes are used in a symmetrical arrangement so that one circle in the top view usually represents two circles in the front view. The points at which these circles intersect the plane *V–V* in the top view locate points on the required curved lines of intersection. Locate the points in the front view by drawing sight-lines. Critical points 2 and 3 are found by drawing a circle in the top view tangent to $V-V$. This circle represents the sections made by cutting planes H_2 and H_3. To locate the critical points 6 take cutting plane H_6 through the center of the torus. Cutting planes H_1 and H_4 are selected so as to cut the scotia in two circles of equal size, and planes H_5 and H_7 are spaced equidistant from H_6. A greater number of cutting planes may be desirable.

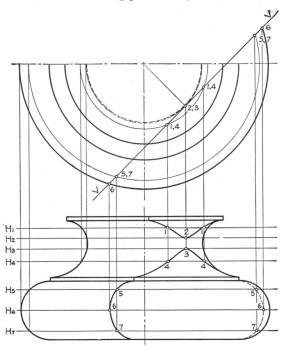

FIG. 142.—Plane Section of a Surface of Revolution.

Note.—This method is used to find the curved intersection whenever a prismatic piece is partly turned to form a surface of revolution. A connecting rod end is an example. The junction of the turned portion and the prismatic portion is a fillet which is a part of the inner surface of an annular torus. If $V-V$ represents a plane face of the rod end, the curve 4–3–4 would be its intersection with the fillet. This method is also used in finding shades and shadows by the slicing method.

216. Assignments.—See Chapter XIV, Group 7L; Group 7M, Miscellaneous.

CHAPTER VIII

WARPED SURFACES

DEFINITIONS

217. **A warped surface** is a ruled surface generated by the continuous motion of a straight line according to conditions which are such that no two consecutive positions lie in the same plane.

The generatrix is the moving straight line which generates the surface.

A directrix is a straight or curved line which the generatrix continuously touches.

The director is a surface to which the generatrix remains parallel.

Warped surfaces are shown by drawing the directrices and a number of elements indicating successive positions of the generatrix. They are interesting surfaces which have considerable practical value and would be more generally used if they were more fully understood.

The classification of warped surfaces given below does not cover all the possible methods of generation, but includes those which are of practical value. Some of the surfaces which may be generated by more than one method are mentioned only under the method most generally used.

CLASSIFICATION OF WARPED SURFACES ACCORDING TO THE METHOD OF GENERATION

218. The motion of the straight-line generatrix is controlled by:

1. Two linear directrices and a plane director.
    - *a.* Two straight directrices. **The hyperbolic paraboloid.**
    - *b.* Two curved directrices. **The cylindroid.**
    - *c.* One straight and one curved directrix. **The right conoid and the oblique conoid.**
2. Two linear directrices and a constant angle.
    - A helix, its axis, and a constant angle with the axis. **The right helicoid and the oblique helicoid.**
3. Three linear directrices.
    - Two curved directrices and one straight directrix. **The warped cone and the cow's horn.**

143

4. Revolution about an axis.

One skew line revolved about the other as an axis. **The hyperboloid of revolution of one nappe.**

THE HYPERBOLIC PARABOLOID

219. The hyperbolic paraboloid is a warped surface generated by the continuous motion of a straight line which touches two other non-parallel, non-intersecting straight lines and remains parallel to a plane director.

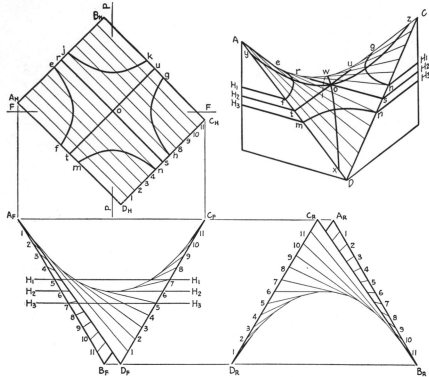

Fig. 143.—Hyperbolic Paraboloid with Plane Sections.

220. Problem 74. To draw the hyperbolic paraboloid.

Analysis.—The plane director usually is not shown, but the first and last positions of the generatrix are given. The plane director is parallel to both of these lines. A series of equally spaced parallel planes cut a straight line in a number of equal parts. Therefore, to draw the elements of a hyperbolic paraboloid divide each directrix in the same number of equal parts and join them in proper order.

Construction.—Fig. 143. *Given* the directrices AB and DC and the elements AD and BC. *Required* to show eleven other equally spaced elements of the surface.

Divide AB and DC each into twelve equal parts and number them consecutively from A to B and from D to C. Draw the elements 1–1, 2–2, 3–3, etc. Consider the surface to be made of an opaque piece of metal with the elements on each side of the metal. Draw the front and side views without using any hidden lines.

221. Problem 75. To show the plane sections of the hyperbolic paraboloid.

Analysis.—The plane sections of this surface are a straight line, two intersecting straight lines, a parabola, and a hyperbola.

Construction.—Fig. 143. *Given* the hyperbolic paraboloid $ABCD$. *Required* to find the horizontal sections H_1, H_2, and H_3; the frontal section F–F; and the profile section P–P.

Locate in the top view the points of intersection of each horizontal cutting plane and the elements of the surface found in the front view. Plane H_1 intersects the warped surface in the curves ef and gh, which are two branches of a hyperbola. Plane H_3 intersects the warped surface in the curves jk and mn, which are two branches of another hyperbola. The plane H_2 intersects the warped surface in two straight lines rs and tu. The frontal plane F–F intersects the warped surface in a parabola shown in the pictorial drawing as yoz, and in the front view as the parabolic outline. The profile cutting plane P–P intersects the warped surface in a parabola shown in the pictorial view as wox and in the side view as the parabolic outline.

The pictorial drawing shows the hyperbolic paraboloid as a surface modeled on a rectangular block.

222. Problem 76. To draw a view of the hyperbolic paraboloid which shows the elements of one generation parallel to the plane director.

Analysis.—Since the elements are parallel to the plane director, a view which is an edge view of the plane director shows them so that they appear parallel.

Construction.—Fig. 144. *Given* the hyperbolic paraboloid $ABDC$. *Required* a view which shows an edge view of the plane director.

The first generation of this warped surface is made with AB and DC as the directrices. The second generation of the same surface is made with AD and BC as the directrices. These two generations form the same surface. Through any point on the surface two straight lines can be drawn. For this solution use AB and DC as the directrices. To find the plane director, pass a plane through AD parallel to BC by drawing the line AE parallel to BC. ADE is the plane director. Draw the auxiliary elevation as an edge view of the plane director. In this view BC is drawn parallel to AD, and all the other elements of this generation are drawn parallel to these two elements.

223. Uses of the Hyperbolic Paraboloid.—This surface is found on some concrete walks and floors. If the opposite edges of the form are not

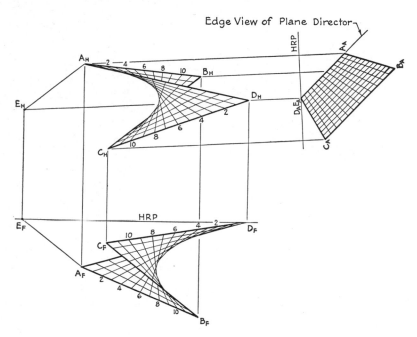

FIG. 144.—Hyperbolic Paraboloid and Plane Director.

in the same plane, an approximate hyperbolic paraboloid may be generated by the movement of a straight-edge board along the edges of the form. Other concrete work such as the wing walls for abutments may have this surface. The forms can be built entirely of straight material.

224. Assignments.—See Chapter XIV, Group 8A.

THE CYLINDROID

225. The cylindroid is a warped surface generated by the continuous motion of a straight line which touches two plane curves and remains parallel to a plane director. The conditions must be such that a conoid is not generated. The cylindroid is used for joining arches which are not in parallel planes or which are offset.

226. *Problem 77. To draw a cylindroid.*

Analysis.—Draw the elements parallel to the plane director in the view which shows it as an edge view.

Construction.—Fig. 145. *Given* the semicircles, whose centers are C and K, and a vertical plane director through CK. *Required* to draw the warped surface.

Divide the semicircle, whose center is C, into twelve equal parts. Locate the division points in the top view and draw all the elements parallel to the vertical plane of which CK is an edge view. Show these elements in the front view.

227. Assignments.—See Chapter XIV, Group 8B.

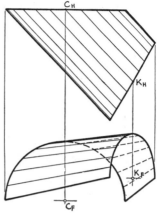

Fig. 145.—Cylindroid.

THE CONOID

228. The conoid is a warped surface generated by the continuous motion of a straight line which touches a circle, an ellipse, or a plane curve

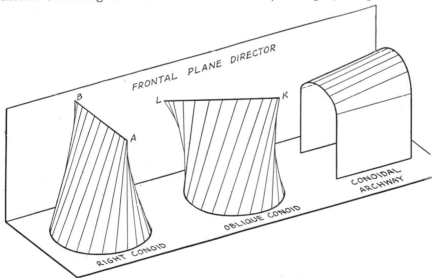

Fig. 146.—Conoidal Surfaces.

and a straight line and remains parallel to a plane director.   If the straight
line is perpendicular to the plane director, the surface is a right conoid.
See line AB, Fig. 146.   If the straight-line directrix is inclined to the plane
director, the surface is an oblique conoid.   See LK, Fig. 146.

**229. Problem 78.   To draw a right conoid and find a right section of
it.**

Analysis.—The plane director is at right angles to the straight-line
directrix.   All the elements appear perpendicular to this directrix in a
view which is the normal view of it.

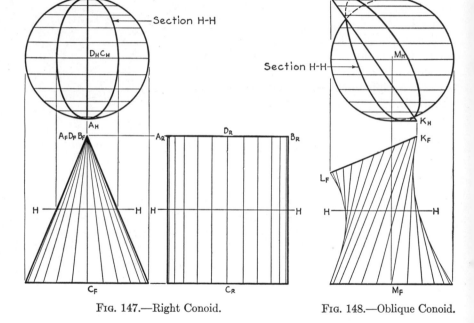

FIG. 147.—Right Conoid.   FIG. 148.—Oblique Conoid.

Construction.—Fig. 147.   *Given* the circle whose center is C for one
directrix, and AB for the other.   *Required* to draw the conoid and find
a right section H–H.

In the top view divide the circle into twenty-four equal parts and
draw through the points thus obtained elements which are perpendicular
to AB.   Draw these elements in the front view and the right-side view.
Note that the surface has the appearance of a cone in the front view and
of a cylinder in the side view.   To find the right section find the inter-

section of the elements and the edge view of the cutting plane *H–H* and locate them in the top view by Principle 2. This section is an ellipse.

230. Assignments.—See Chapter XIV, Group 8C.

231. *Problem 79. To draw an oblique conoid and to find a section parallel to its base.*

Analysis.—Draw the elements parallel to the plane director and intersecting the directrices.

Construction.—Fig. 148. *Given* as directrices the line *KL*, a circle whose center is *M*, and a frontal plane director. *Required* to draw the elements of the surface and the section *H–H*.

Divide the circle into twenty-four equal parts. Through the points thus obtained draw elements which are parallel to the frontal plane. Locate the intersection of each of these elements with the cutting plane *H–H*, and draw the curve in the top view.

232. Uses of the Conoid.—The conoid is used for transition pieces and for archways. Figure 146 shows the conoidal archway which connects a semicircular arch with a semi-elliptical arch. The conoid may be used to connect a flat ceiling with an arch.

233. Assignments.—See Chapter XIV, Group 8D.

THE RIGHT HELICOID

234. The right helicoid is a warped surface generated by the continuous motion of a straight line which touches a helix and its axis and remains parallel to a plane perpendicular to the axis of the helix. The helix may be right- or left-hand. Another type of right helicoid is one in which the elements are tangent to a coaxial cylinder instead of intersecting the axis.

235. *Problem 80. To draw a right helicoid.*

Analysis.—Through equally spaced points on the helix draw elements which are perpendicular to and intersect the axis.

Construction.—Fig. 149. *Given* a right cylindrical helix on the surface of an opaque cylinder. *Required* to draw a right helicoid whose elements are of a stated length.

Draw the element ending at 0 at the top of the helix, and draw the large helix having the same lead as the small helix on the cylinder. Draw the elements as radial lines in the top view and connect the corresponding points on the two helices by horizontal lines in the front view. Consider that the helicoid is a thin opaque surface with the elements drawn on the upper side. Then the visibility is as shown.

236. Uses of the Right Helicoid.—Right helicoids are used for screw conveyors.   The working surfaces of square screw threads are right helicoids.   Circular stairways are constructed on the basis of this surface.

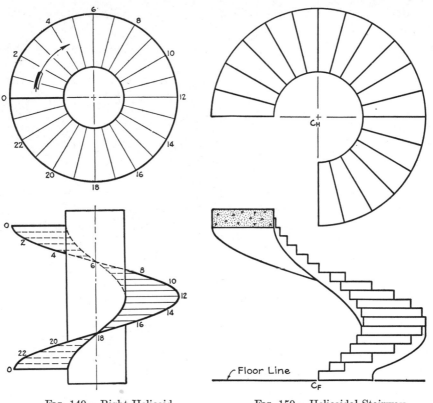

FIG. 149.—Right Helicoid.   FIG. 150.—Helicoidal Stairway.

Figure 150 shows a circular stairway of concrete.   The lines formed by the intersection of the treads and the risers are elements of a right helicoid. The underneath surface of the stairway is a right helicoid.

237. Assignments.—See Chapter XIV, Group 8E.

THE OBLIQUE HELICOID

238. The oblique helicoid is a warped surface generated by the continuous motion of a straight line which touches a helix and its axis and makes a constant angle, other than 90°, with the axis.   The helix may be right-hand or left-hand. The helicoid may have elements which slope downward or upward from the helix.

239. Problem 81. To draw the oblique helicoid.

Analysis.—The surface is usually limited between two helices. It may be drawn by connecting corresponding points on the two coaxial helices which have the same lead.

Construction.—Fig. 151. *Given* a right-hand helix on the surface of an opaque cylinder for the upper helicoid. Given one element *JK*. *Required* to draw two oblique helicoids which partly form a large V-type screw thread.

Through the point *K* draw one and one-half turns of the outer helix having the same lead as the given helix. Draw elements through the corresponding points of the two helices for one turn. These elements are drawn as lines on the upper surface of an opaque helicoid. At point 12 on the upper helicoid draw the front view of a line which is parallel to *JK*. At the point where it intersects the cylinder, start a second small helix having the same lead as the first one. The corresponding points on this helix and the outer helix are connected as elements on the lower surface of the lower helicoid. The two helicoids join along the large helix to form the surfaces of a large screw thread of the V-type at the central portion of the front view. This drawing represents one thread of a double screw thread; that is, another thread like this one can be drawn between the successive turns of this thread.

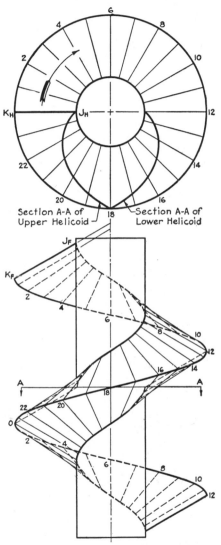

FIG. 151.—Oblique Helicoids.

Section A–A shows the form of the curve cut from the helicoid by a plane perpendicular to its axis, a horizontal plane in this case. These curves are spirals of Archimedes, and the two together show the form of this section of the screw thread.

240. Assignments.—See Chapter XIV, Group 8F.

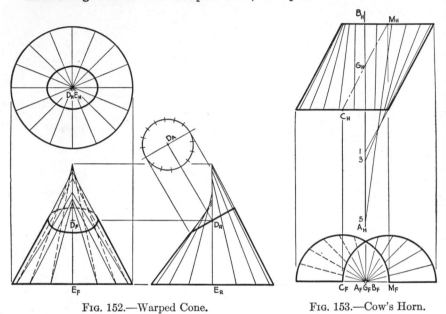

FIG. 152.—Warped Cone.   FIG. 153.—Cow's Horn.

THE WARPED CONE

241. The warped cone is a ruled surface generated by the continuous motion of a straight line which touches two circles or two ellipses or one of each not in parallel planes and intersects the straight line joining their centers. If an ellipse and a circle are used as directrices, the conditions must be such that a cone is not generated. This surface is used for transition pieces.

242. Problem 82. To draw a warped cone.

Analysis.—The elements can be drawn as radial lines in the view which is an end view of the straight-line directrix.

Construction.—Fig. 152. *Given* the circles whose centers are at E and D. *Required* to draw the warped cone.

DE is the straight-line directrix. The top view is an end view of DE. Divide the large circle into sixteen equal parts. Connect the division points with $D_H E_H$. Note where they cross the ellipse which is the top view of the small circle. Locate the points on the large circle and the small circle in both the front view and the side view. Connect corresponding points and continue the elements to their intersection with DE produced. The surface has an upper nappe which is not shown. For practical purposes only the portion between the two circles is used.

243. Assignments.—See Chapter XIV, Group 8G.

COW'S HORN (CORNE DE VACHE)

244. The cow's horn is a warped surface usually generated by the continuous motion of a straight line which touches two circles located in parallel planes and a straight line which is perpendicular to the planes of the circles and intersects their line of centers. This surface is used for archways.

245. Problem 83. To draw the cow's horn.

Analysis.—In the view which shows the straight-line directrix as a point, draw the elements as radiating lines and note their intersections with the circular directrices.

Construction.—Fig. 153. *Given* the semicircles whose centers are C and M and the straight-line directrix AB which passes through the midpoint G of CM and is perpendicular to the plane of the semicircles. *Required* to draw the warped surface.

In the front view AB appears as a point, and the semicircles appear in true form. Draw the elements as radiating lines preferably spaced at equal angles. Locate the points where the elements intersect the circles and join corresponding points in the top view.

246. Assignments.—See Chapter XIV, Group 8H.

THE HYPERBOLOID OF REVOLUTION

247. The hyperboloid of revolution of one nappe is a warped surface which may be generated by any of the following methods:

1. By the revolution of a line about an axis which it does not intersect and to which it is not parallel. It is capable of two generations by this method.

2. By the revolution of a hyperbola about an axis in the plane of the curve and which is the perpendicular bisector of a line joining the foci. It is the only surface which is both a warped surface and a surface of revolution.

3. By the motion of a straight line so that it touches three straight-line directrices.

4. By the motion of a straight line so that it touches three circles whose centers are on an axis perpendicular to the planes of the circles.

248. Problem 84.   To draw the hyperboloid of revolution and locate a point on its surface.

Analysis.—According to the first method of generation show a number of equally spaced elements of the surface.   To locate a point on the surface, cut the surface by a plane perpendicular to the axis and locate the point on the circle thus obtained.

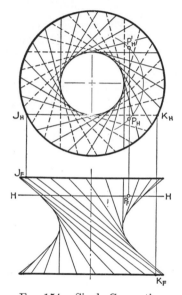

Fig. 154.—Single Generation.

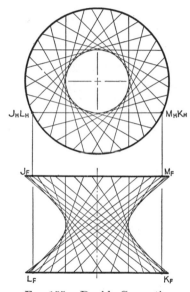

Fig. 155.—Double Generation.

Hyperboloids of Revolution.

Construction.—Fig. 154.   *Given* the axis, the generating frontal line *JK*, and a point P_F on the surface.   *Required* to represent the surface in two views and to find the adjacent view of the point *P*.

In the top view draw a circle tangent to *JK*.   This is called the circle of the gorge.   Divide the gorge circle into twenty-four equal parts and draw the elements representing the successive positions of *JK* tangent to the gorge circle at these points.   Note that these are fifteen-degree divisions of the circle.   Consider that the warped surface is made of thin opaque metal and that the lines are on both sides of the surface. Then the upper half of each element is visible in the top view. In the front view locate the ends of all elements on the lines which represent the upper and lower circles. Join these points by drawing only the visible portions of the elements. Only one generation of the surface is shown.

To locate the top view of the point P cut the surface by the horizontal plane H. The section is a circle which is shown by the arc in the top view. Locate P on this arc at P_H or P'_H.

Figure 155 shows the elements for the double generation of the hyperboloid of revolution; first, by the revolution of the line JK; second, by the revolution of the line LM. These lines slope at the same angle in opposite directions as shown. The elements of one generation intersect the elements of the other generation. This figure shows that it is possible to generate this surface by using three of the elements of one generation as directrices and an element of another generation as the generatrix.

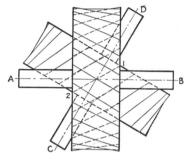

FIG. 156.—Skew Gearing.

249. Uses of the Hyperboloid of Revolution.—If straight pieces of material are located along the elements of both generations and fastened together at their points of intersection, a light, strong, graceful structure is obtained. Some pieces of reed furniture are built in this manner.

Hyperboloids of revolution are used for the pitch surfaces of skew gearing, which is used for connecting two shafts which are neither parallel nor intersecting. Figure 156 indicates skew gearing for the shafts AB and CD. The pitch surfaces for the gears are shown with elements drawn on each. Since the elements are straight lines, the gears can be designed so that they will touch along the common element 1–2. The line 1–2 is revolved about AB to generate one pitch surface, then about CD to generate the other. The teeth are cut along the lines of the elements.

The pitch surfaces of hypoid gears for automobiles are based on hyperboloids of revolution.

250. Assignments.—See Chapter XIV, Group 8I.

CHAPTER IX

GEOLOGY AND MINING PROBLEMS

251. The principles of descriptive geometry by the direct method are used for the rapid solution of problems in geology and mining. In many cases a stratum of rock, a seam of coal, or a vein of ore has practically plane surfaces for limited areas. The deposits are usually inclined and are treated as oblique planes.

Most problems in geology and mining may be analyzed as line, plane, and surface combinations or relations. Some of the problems are as follows:

The location of a vein of ore or a stratum of rock by use of the meager information obtainable.

The intersection of veins with each other or with a fault. This intersection has an important bearing on mining operations and valuations.

The intersections of shafts, tunnels, or inclines with each other or with the vein.

The location of excavations and dumps.

The leveling of building sites for the surface plant.

DEFINITIONS

252. *Strike* is the direction of a horizontal line on a surface of a stratum of rock or vein of mineral. It is usually expressed as a bearing.

Dip is the inclination of the stratum or vein measured downward at right angles to the strike. It is measured in degrees as the dihedral angle below a horizontal plane.

The hanging wall is the surface of rock above a vein of mineral.

The foot wall is the surface of rock below the vein.

The upper bedding plane is the upper surface of a stratum.

The lower bedding plane is the lower surface of a stratum.

The outcrop is the intersection of a vein or stratum with the surface of the earth. Usually the vein is partly or mostly covered by loose material.

156

A fault is a fracture in the earth's crust along which there has been a dislocation of the walls.

Striae are scratches or small grooves on a surface which has moved in contact with the adjoining surface during faulting.

A shaft is a vertical or slightly inclined opening made for finding or mining ore.

An incline is an inclined shaft usually following the vein.

A tunnel is a horizontal or nearly level passage in a mine and opening to the surface.

A drift is a horizontal passageway driven on the course of the vein.

A crosscut is a working driven across to a vein or to another working.

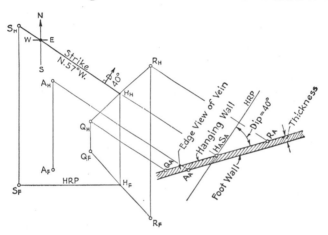

Fig. 157.—Strike and Dip of a Vein.

253. Problem 85. *To find the strike and dip of a vein of mineral when three points in one of the walls are known.*

Analysis.—Assume that the wall of the vein is practically a plane. Obtain an edge view of this plane in an auxiliary elevation.

Construction.—Fig. 157. *Given* the points Q, R, and S in the hanging wall of a vein of ore and a point A in the foot wall. *Required* to find the strike, dip, and thickness of the ore.

Connect Q and R and draw a horizontal line HS in the plane QRS. The top view of this line is the strike, and its bearing is N 57° W. Find an edge view of the plane QRS. Measure the dip angle, which is 40°. Locate the point A in this view and draw an edge view of the foot wall parallel to QRS. Measure the thickness of the ore shown in edge view.

APPARENT DIP

254. The apparent dip is the angle below the horizontal of any line on the surface of a stratum other than the true dip-line. If two apparent dip-lines are known, it is possible to determine the strike and true dip of the stratum.

255. Problem 86. *To find the strike and true dip of a stratum when the bearing and inclination of two apparent dip-lines are known.*

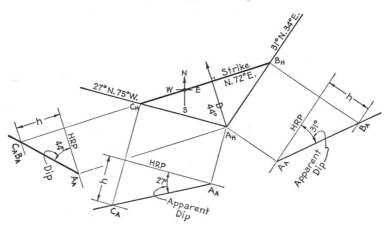

Fig. 158.—Strike and Dip from Two Apparent Dips.

Analysis.—Two intersecting lines determine a plane. Solve the problem on this theory.

Construction.—Fig. 158. *Given* 27° N 75° W and 31° N 34° E as two apparent dips of a stratum. *Required* to find the strike and true dip.

Assume A_H and draw $A_H C_H$ N 75° W and $A_H B_H$ N 34° E for the top view of two intersecting lines of a plane parallel to the stratum.

Draw sight-lines perpendicular to $A_H C_H$ and $A_H B_H$ for auxiliary elevations. Lay off $A_A C_A$ 27° below HRP and $A_A B_A$ 31° below HRP. Make C_A and B_A the same distance h below HRP. Locate C and B in the top view. Line CB is the strike, since both C and B are at the same level. The bearing of the strike is N 72° E. Now draw an auxiliary elevation which is an edge view of the plane ABC. Measure the true dip in this view. It is found to be 44°. Note that a front view is not used in the solution of this problem.

256. Short Method of Solving Problem.—Fig. 159. Lay off the apparent dip angles with HRP at AC and AB, and locate the points C_A and B_A a distance h below HRP. Locate C_H and B_H. Draw $C_H B_H$, the strike-line. $A_H E_H$ is the dip-line. Set off the distance h perpendicular to the dip-line to find the true dip. Note that this is the same as Fig. 158 with the auxiliary views joined onto the apparent and true dip-lines. It makes a compact construction and does not violate any of the principles of descriptive geometry.

257. *Problem 87. To draw the shortest vertical shaft, the shortest possible incline, the shortest level tunnel, and the shortest*

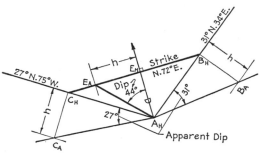

Fig. 159.—Strike and Dip from Two Apparent Dips.

tunnel on a 15% up-grade from a given point to a vein.

Analysis.—Draw an auxiliary elevation which is an edge view of the vein. In this view draw all the required lines as normal views.

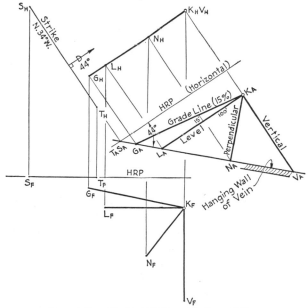

Fig. 160.—Shaft and Tunnels for a Mine.

Construction.—Fig. 160. *Given* the strike ST (N 34° W), the dip (44° NE), and the point K from which the lines representing the shaft and tunnels shall be drawn. *Required* to draw three views of the specified lines

Find in an auxiliary elevation the edge view of the vein and locate K_A. From K draw the vertical line KV, the perpendicular line KN, the level line KL, and the grade line KG. All these lines appear as normal views in the auxiliary elevation, where their lengths may be measured. In the top view draw KN, KL, and KG perpendicular to ST, and locate the lines in the front view.

258. Assignments.—See Chapter XIV, Group 9A.

259. Problem 88.   *To find the shortest connection which can be made on a required grade line connecting two workings in a mine.*

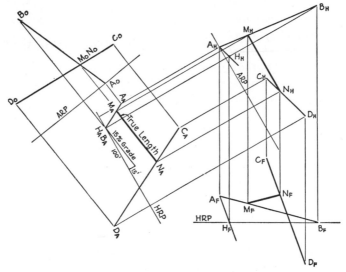

FIG. 161.—Shortest Crosscut on Given Grade.

Analysis.—These mine workings are represented by two non-intersecting, non-parallel straight lines. Pass a plane through one of them parallel to the other, and draw an auxiliary elevation of the lines which is an edge view of the plane. The grade line should be drawn in this view, although its location is not yet known. Make an oblique view by looking in the direction of the grade line. The point where the given lines intersect in this view is the proper location for the end view of the grade line.

Construction.—Fig. 161. *Given AB as an incline in one part of the mine, and CD as a steep shaft in another part of the mine. Required to locate the shortest crosscut on a 15% upgrade from AB to CD.*

Pass a plane through AB parallel to CD by drawing AH parallel to CD. HB is the strike of this plane. Draw the auxiliary elevation by looking in the direction HB. $A_A B_A$ and $C_A D_A$ are parallel.   At B_A lay off a line on a 15% upgrade toward CD.   Look in the direction of this line and draw the oblique view in which $A_O B_O$ crosses $C_O D_O$ at $M_O N_O$, the end view of the required crosscut connection.   Locate MN in all views.

Note.—The shortest level line is parallel to HRP in the auxiliary elevation.   The shortest line is perpendicular to AB and CD in the auxiliary elevation.   Otherwise, the solution for either of these lines is like that for the grade line.

260. Assignments.—See Chapter XIV, Group 9B.

261. Problem 89.   To find the intersection of a vein of ore and a fault.

Analysis.—A horizontal cutting plane cuts a horizontal line from each of the given planes.   Their intersection is one point on the required line of

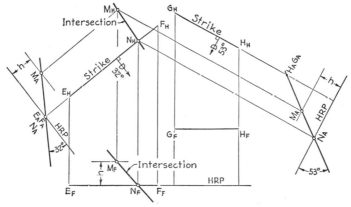

Fig. 162.—Intersection of a Vein and a Fault.

intersection.   A second horizontal cutting plane will locate a second point on the intersection.   The line joining these points is the required intersection.

Construction.—Fig. 162.   *Given* EF as the strike of the vein of ore, which dips forward 32°, and GH as the strike of the fault plane, which dips forward 53°.   *Required* to find the intersection.

Draw as an auxiliary elevation an edge view of each plane.   Use HRP for one cutting plane.   It cuts EF from one plane, and a new strike-line parallel to GH from the other.   These lines intersect at N_H.   At distance h above HRP draw another horizontal plane which cuts new strike-lines from the given planes.   These lines intersect at M_H. MN is the required line of intersection of the vein of ore and the fault plane.

Figure 163 is a pictorial drawing showing the given planes, the horizontal lines cut from them by two cutting planes, the intersection points M and N, and the line of intersection MN.

RELOCATION OF A FAULTED VEIN

262. If a fault is reached in the workings of a mine, the vein may be lost on account of its displacement by faulting. The fault plane which cuts off the vein may appear as the striated surface of a wall of rock. The striae, or scratches, indicate that the lost portion of the vein has been moved an unknown distance in one of two opposite directions. Some other information, such as that given in Problem 90, is necessary for the relocation of the vein or a rich streak of ore.

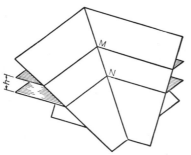

FIG. 163.—Intersection of a Vein and a Fault.

263. *Problem 90. To relocate a rich streak of ore which has been displaced by a fault.*

Analysis.—The vein can be shown in an edge view; and, if any point in the displaced ore is known, the dislocated portion of the vein can be found. In a normal view of the fault plane, striae show the direction of movement and make it possible to find the new position of any part of the ore.

Construction.—Fig. 164. *Given* in the hanging wall a point A in a rich streak of ore that strikes N 60° E and dips 45° NW, also the fault plane through point A, which strikes N 50° W and dips 60° NE. One point in the hanging wall of the ore beyond the fault is found at C. The striae are straight lines that make 75° with a horizontal line of the plane and slope *dbr*, looking NE. *Required* to find the location of the vein beyond the fault and the point at which the rich streak of ore lost at A may be found.

By the method of Problem 89, the line of intersection is AB. Locate C in the edge view of the ore vein and draw DE through C parallel to AB. This is the hanging wall of the vein beyond the fault plane. Next draw a normal view of the fault plane and on it the direction of the striae, which is 75° below horizontal line AD of the fault plane and toward the right. The point A has moved to F, a point in the ore on the opposite side of the fault. Locate F in all the views. AF in the normal view is the true amount of dislocation, and the direction from A to F is shown in the top view. The slope of AF may be found if desired.

264. Assignments.—See Chapter XIV, Group 9C.

265. Contour Maps.—*A contour line* is a level line on the surface of the earth. All points on a contour line are theoretically at the same elevation. Actually, the elevations of only a few points are determined, and the contours are approximated by the surveyor.

A contour map is a map showing the top view of the surface of the ground by means of contours. In descriptive geometry each contour line

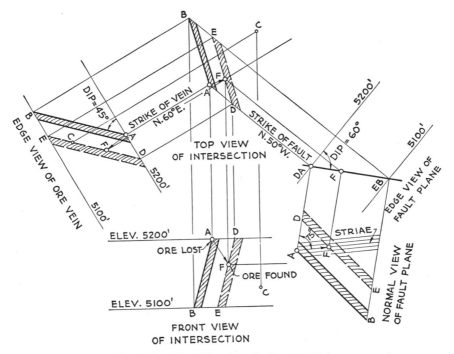

Fig. 164.—The Relocation of a Faulted Vein.

is considered as a horizontal section of the earth's surface. A relief map, or model of the earth's surface, can be made by placing upon each other thin sheets of wall board which are cut out along successive contour lines. The thickness of the wall board should represent to scale the vertical interval between the contours.

266. *Problem 91.* *To locate the probable outcrop of a stratum of rock on a contour map.*

Analysis.—Draw an edge view of the stratum and show horizontal cutting planes at the various levels of the contours. They cut horizontal lines from the stratum.   For any level the horizontal straight line on the bedding plane of a stratum intersects the contour line at the outcrop.

Construction.—Fig. 165.   *Given* the contour map; and three points *A*, *B*, and *C* in the upper bedding plane; and one point *D* in the lower bedding plane.   *Required* to find the strike, dip, and thickness of the stratum, and its outcrop.

Draw the strike-line *CH*.   The auxiliary elevation taken in the direction of the strike is an edge view of the upper bedding plane *ABC*.   Locate

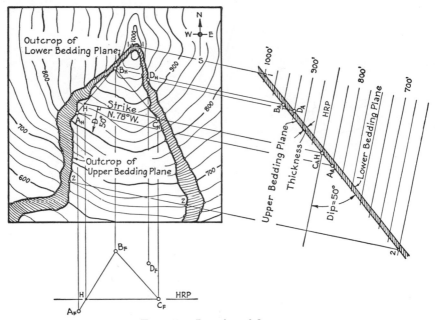

Fig. 165.—Location of Outcrop.

point *D* in the auxiliary view and draw the lower bedding plane parallel to the upper bedding plane.   Measure the dip and the thickness of the stratum in this view.   Draw the edge view of a horizontal plane for each contour level.   At the 1000 foot level 1–1 is a horizontal line in the lower bedding plane.   It intersects the 1000 foot contour in the two points marked 1. In the same way locate points on each contour for the line of outcrop of the lower bedding plane.   At the 650 foot level 2–2 is the line of intersection of the horizontal cutting plane with the upper bedding plane.   It intersects the 650 foot contour at two points marked 2.   Repeat this to locate points on each contour for the outcrop of both bedding planes.

267. Assignments.—See Chapter XIV, Group 9D

CUTS, FILLS, AND MINE DUMPS

268. Rock or other loose material when dumped from a point onto a horizontal plane will take the general shape of a right circular cone. The base angle of the cone is known as the *angle of repose* of the material. It varies with the kind of material, size of the particles, and the moisture content. The average angle of repose is: sand, 33°; gravel or earth, 36°; rock, 36°–45°.

269. Problem 92. *To locate on a hillside the line of cut and the line of fill required for a level area.*

Analysis.—Horizontal cutting planes at the given contour levels intersect the surfaces of the proposed cut and fill in contours that can be drawn.

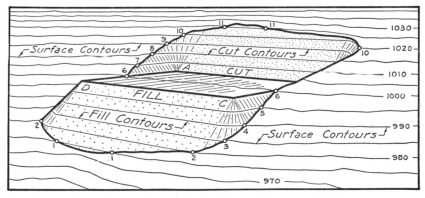

FIG. 166.—Cut and Fill for a Level Area on a Hillside.

The intersection of a given contour and a proposed contour usually locates two points on the required line of cut or fill.

A perspective view of a level area $ABCD$ to be made by a cut and fill similar to that of Fig. 167 is shown in Fig. 166. The area in the picture has a more uniform slope, but otherwise the conditions are approximately the same. The elevation of the level area $ABCD$ is 1000 feet above sea level, and the 1000 foot contour is the line of no cut and no fill between the points marked 6. The required fill, the lower boundary of which is not known, is a portion of the frustum of a pyramid, the corners of which are rounded to a conical form. Assumed contours on the slope of the fill intersect the corresponding surface contours at points on the line of the toe of the fill. The points obtained are as follows: the 975 foot contours intersect at points 1 and 1; the 980 at 2 and 2; the 985 at 3, 990 at 4, and the 995 at 5.

The form of the required cut in the hillside is similar to that for the fill, but inverted. The imaginary contours for the cut intersect the surface contours as follows: the 1005 foot contours intersect at 7, the 1010 at 8, the 1015 at 9, the 1020 at 10 and 10, and the 1025 at 11 and 11. The line joining these points is the line of the cut.

Construction.—Fig. 167. *Given* the contour map and 40° for the angle of repose for the cut and 33° as the angle of repose for the fill. *Required* to find the line of cut and the line of fill for a level area *ABCD* at the 600 foot level.

Draw the right-side view showing section *P–P* made by a profile cutting plane. *ABCD* is the required level area. Show the cut in edge view

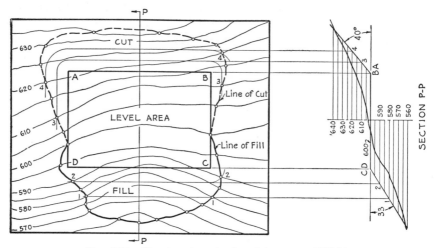

Fig. 167.—Construction of a Level Area on a Hillside.

extending upward from *BA* and the fill in edge view extending downward from *CD* at the given angles of repose. Draw horizontal cutting planes at the elevations of the contours. At the 580 foot level the cutting plane cuts the horizontal line 1–1 from the surface of the required fill. It intersects the 580 foot contour at the points marked 1. At the 590 foot level a horizontal plane cuts a horizontal line from the surface of the fill which intersects the 590 foot contour at the left-hand point 2. At the corner *C* the fill is conical. With center at *C* strike an arc intersecting the 590 foot contour at 2. This arc represents the base of a right cone with vertex at *C*, altitude of 10 feet, and a base angle of 33°. At the 610 foot level the line cut from the surface of the required excavation follows around three sides of the rectangular area and intersects the 610 foot contour at two points marked 3. In the same way find two points marked 4 at the 620 foot level. Continuing in this manner, find points on all contours which will be intersected by the cut or covered by the fill. The 600 foot contour is the line of no cut and no fill.

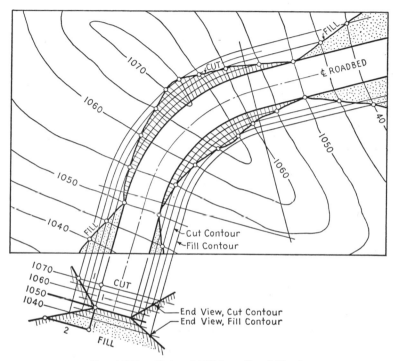

Fig. 167A.—Cut and Fill for a Level Road.

270. Problem 92A. To find the cut and fill for a level road.

Analysis.—Since both the cuts and fills will have uniformly sloping surfaces the contour planes will intersect these surfaces in lines which are parallel to the edges of the roadbed. These lines (cut and fill contours) will intersect the ground contours of corresponding elevations at points which determine the outlines of the cuts and fills.

Construction.—Fig. 167A. *Given* a contour map of an area on which a level road is to be constructed at elevation 1050. *Required* to find the outlines for a 1 to 1 cut and a 2 to 1 fill.

In an auxiliary elevation at one end of the road draw a combined typical right section showing the slopes of the specified cut and fill surfaces. From the points at which the contour planes intersect the sloping cut and fill surfaces draw the contours for these surfaces on each side of the roadbed. Note their intersection with the corresponding ground contours on the map. Draw lines through these points to show the outlines of the cut and fills.

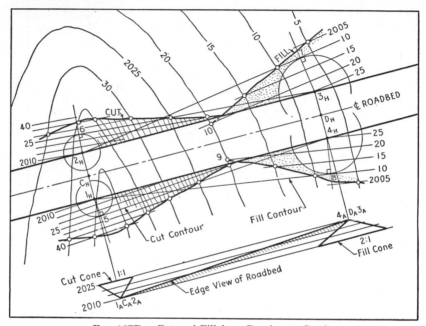

FIG. 167B.—Cut and Fill for a Road on a Grade.

271. *Problem 92B. To find the cut and fill for a road on a grade.*

Analysis.—The solution of this problem is based on Problem 31, Fig. 94, in which the plane ABE corresponds to a surface of a fill with AB as an edge of the roadbed, AE as the slope of the fill, and the strike line BE as a fill contour for the surface. By drawing an inverted cone at B, a plane corresponding to a surface of a cut may be obtained. Therefore, by using a cone for cut and a cone for fill on each side of the roadbed it is possible to draw cut and fill contours for the required cut and fill surfaces. These contours will not be parallel to the center line of the road, but otherwise they are used as explained for a level road.

Construction.—Fig. 167B. *Given* a contour map of an area on which a road is to be constructed having an elevation of 2010 at C and 2025 at D.

Required to find the outlines for a 1 to 1 cut and a 2 to 1 fill. Lay out the rectangle 1–2–3–4 with *CD* as its length. Use an auxiliary elevation which shows the roadbed edgewise. In the auxiliary elevation and top view construct inverted cut cones at points 1 and 2, and fill cones at points 3 and 4. Then 4–5 and 3–6 are the 2025 cut contours (strike-lines) for the surfaces of the cut, and all cut contours must be parallel to them. Similarly, 1–8 and 2–7 are the 2010 fill contours (strike-lines) for the fill surfaces, and all fill contours must be parallel to them. Note that 5, 6, 7, and 8 are points of tangency, and the cone elements 1–5, 2–6, 3–7, and 4–8 each may be equally divided into three parts to locate points for the cut and fill contours at elevations 2015 and 2020. These spacings, continued along the elements of tangency, may be used to locate as many other cut and fill contours as desired.

The intersection of these contours with the ground contours of corresponding elevations gives points on the outlines of the required cut and fill. In order to determine the points at which the cut and fill outlines intersect the edges of the roadbed, two imaginary points such as 9 and 10 should be located.

272. Mine Dumps.—If the material is dumped from one point, the form of the dump is a cone, as stated in Art. 268. Figures 166 and 167 show a portion of such a cone having vertex *C*. Draw a cone having its vertex at the dumping point, and the proper base angle; cut it by the horizontal planes of the contours; and through the intersections of the contours and the circles so obtained, draw the line of fill for the dump. If a level area having a certain diameter at the top of the dump is desired, take the vertex of the construction cone at the proper height above the area. Other dumps may be similar to the fill in Fig. 167.

273. Profiles.—The line of intersection of any vertical cutting plane and the surface of the ground is called a *profile*, and it is shown in a normal view of that plane. On a contour map the intersections of the cutting plane with the contours locate the points to be used for making a profile of the surface. In Fig. 167 Section *P–P* shows an edge view of all the horizontal planes of the contours. The points of intersection of the cutting plane and the contours were located in this view by sight-lines, not shown, and the profile or section of the surface was drawn through these points.

274. Assignments.—See Chapter XIV, Groups 9E and 9F.

CHAPTER X

ENGINEERING PROBLEMS

275. Although descriptive geometry was originally devised to simplify the solution of specific engineering problems, its functions have increased to include more varied types too numerous to discuss. Among these, however, might be mentioned the following: timber framing, details of steel connections, pulley layouts, force diagrams, determination of clearance, location of roads on contour maps, location of drainage pipes and street intersections.

TIMBER FRAMING

276. Figure 168 shows the framing for a small hip roof. The common forms of roofs are the gable roof and the hip roof. A gable roof slopes two

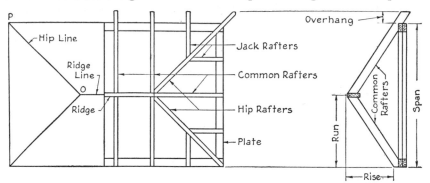

Fig. 168.—Framing for a Hip Roof.

ways from the ridge. A hip roof slopes downward over the four sides of a building. In a gable roof there is only one kind of rafter, the common rafter. The sectional view in Fig. 168 is the same as for a gable roof. The inclination of a roof is given in two ways:

1. As pitch, which is a fraction equal to the total rise of the roof divided by the total span. The result is a common fraction such as one-quarter, one-third, or one-half. A one-half pitch roof is one which has a slope of 45°.

2. As the number of inches of rise which correspond to a run of twelve inches. For example, the statement might be that a roof has a rise of eight inches in a run of twelve. Evidently this system is much more flexible.

In Fig. 168 three kinds of rafters are shown for a hip roof. At the rear side of the house the rafters are shown with an overhang. The rafters in the drawings which follow do not have an overhang, but it is evident this is merely an addition which may be made at the end of the rafter as drawn. The left portion of the roof plan in Fig. 168 shows imaginary planes corresponding to the underneath side of the sheathing which covers the rafters. *PO* is a theoretical hip line of the roof.

277. Problem 93. To make a detailed drawing of a jack rafter.

Analysis.—The face view and edge view show all the cuts necessary to frame this rafter.

Construction.—Fig. 169. *Given* the pitch of the roof and the size of the rafter. *Required* to draw the details of a short jack rafter.

In the plan draw a short portion of the hip rafter and the plate. In the front view draw a face view of the rafter having the required pitch. The points 1, 5, 4, and 10 are obtained by drawing sight-lines from the top view. 1–5, 4–10, 2–7, and 7–6 are lines for cuts on the faces of the rafter. Draw an auxiliary view by looking normal to the edge of

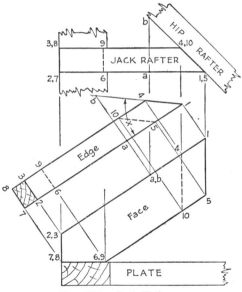

Fig. 169.—Jack Rafter.

the rafter. This view shows the lines for the cuts on the edges of the rafter. To increase the accuracy of the construction for the angles at the upper end use the line *ab*. The point *b* is on the edge of the hip rafter. Obtain the point *b* and the angle *a1b* in the auxiliary view.

278. Problem 94. To make a detailed drawing of a hip rafter.

Analysis.—An auxiliary view may be drawn as a face view of the rafter showing all cuts on the face of the rafter. An oblique view which shows the edge of the rafter will show the cuts on the edge.

Construction.—Fig. 170. *Given* the pitch of the roof and the size of the rafter. *Required* to make a detailed drawing of the rafter.

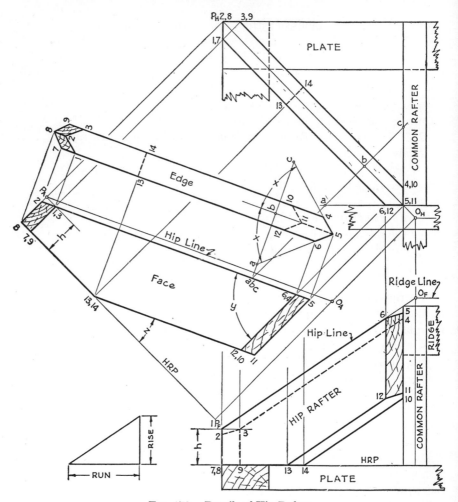

Fig. 170.—Details of Hip Rafter.

In the top view lay out the intersection of the ridge and common rafters and draw the hip rafter to fit into this construction. In the front view lay out the slope of the roof plane. $O_F P_F$ is the hip line in the front view, and it coincides with the slope of the roof. Then find the auxiliary elevation $O_A P_A$ of the hip line. Since the hip rafter used in this case is not beveled on top, it does not touch the hip line. Draw a horizontal line through P_A to locate points 1 and 3. Draw the top edge of the rafter through these points, parallel to the hip line, and finish the face view. To show the edge of the rafter draw a view by looking normal to the edge of the rafter. To obtain greater accuracy for the angle 4–5–6 draw the horizontal line abc across the top of the rafter in the top view, a and c being located in vertical planes which pass through the faces of the common rafters. Locate a and c in the edge view of the rafter which gives an accurate determination of the angles x. To draw the rafter in the front view locate points 13 and 14 in the top view; then, using the top view and the auxiliary elevation, draw the front view by Principles 2 and 3.

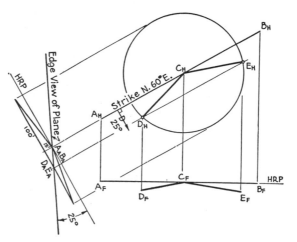

FIG. 171.—Grade Lines in a Plane.

279. Assignments. — See Chapter XIV, Groups 10A and 10B.

280. *Problem 95. To locate a grade line in an oblique plane.*

Analysis.—All the possible directions for a line of given grade are represented by the elements of a right circular cone with horizontal base and the proper base angle. If the vertex of the cone is located in the given plane, the plane intersects the cone in two elements, which are the required grade lines. The slope of the line cannot be greater than the slope of the plane.

Construction.—Fig. 171. *Given* a plane represented by AB whose strike is N 60° E, and which has a dip of 25° southeasterly. *Required* to draw a grade line of the plane which passes through the point C and slopes 15% downward.

In the auxiliary elevation draw an edge view of the plane. With the vertex on AB at the point C construct in the auxiliary elevation and the top view a right circular cone whose elements have a grade of 15%.

The edge view of the plane cuts the edge view of the circle of the base of the cone at D_A and E_A. Locate D and E in the top view and the front view.

The lines CD and CE are lines of the plane which have the required grade.

281. Assignments.—See Chapter XIV, Group 10C.

282. Problem 96.   *To locate a road of a given grade on a contour map.*

Analysis.—A right circular cone whose elements have the given grade and whose altitude is equal to the contour interval intersects the surface in two lines which have the proper grade for that portion of the road.

Construction.—Fig. 172. *Given* the contour map. *Required* to lay out a road from the point A to the house at B on a grade of 10%.

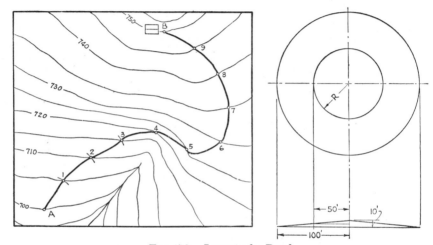

FIG. 172.—Layout of a Road.

Draw a right circular cone whose elements have a 10% grade. Since the contour interval is 5 feet, find the radius R of the base of the cone whose altitude is 5 feet. With the radius R and center A cut the 705 foot contour at point 1, which is used as the most satisfactory of the two possible locations. The line $A1$ is the first portion of the road. With center 1 and the same radius cut the 710 contour at 2. Join 1–2. With 2 as center cut the 715 foot contour at 3. Join 2–3. Continue this process until the point B is reached.

283. Assignments.—See Chapter XIV, Group 10D.

284. Problem 97.   *To draw a guide pulley located so that a belt may run in either direction.*

Analysis.—A belt will run onto a pulley if it is delivered into the central plane of the pulley; that is, into the plane which is perpendicular to the axis of the pulley at its midpoint. In the case of two pulleys with shafts at right

angles the pulleys may be located so that they will drive in one direction
without using a guide pulley. If the rotation is to be in either direction, a

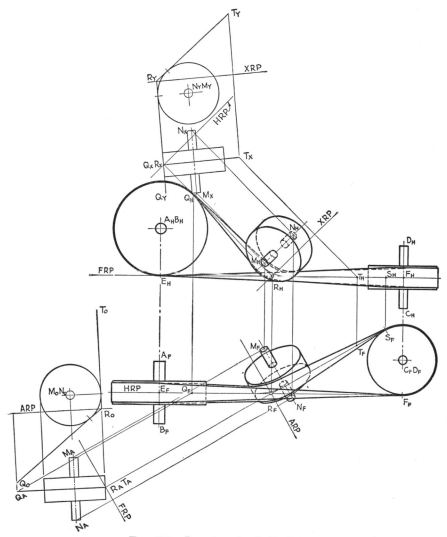

FIG. 173.—Location of a Guide Pulley.

guide pulley is necessary. In this case the pulleys are arranged so that both
of them are tangent to a straight line which is perpendicular to both shafts.
This side of the belt is delivered into the central plane of a pulley for either

direction of rotation.   The other side of the belt must pass around a guide pulley which delivers it into the central plane of either pulley.

Construction.—Fig. 173.   *Given* the pulley on the shaft AB and the pulley on shaft CD.   Arrange them so that EF is tangent to each pulley. *Required* to draw a guide pulley for the other side of the belt.

Select a point R on the line EF.   The lines RQ and RS are tangent to the given pulleys. QRS is the central plane for the required guide pulley. Select a point T on RS to save space.   Find as a left-auxiliary view the edge view and as an oblique view the normal view of QRT, and draw the guide pulley tangent to QR and RT.   Since R is a point on the straight side of the belt, the oblique view shows the amount of clearance between the two sides of the belt at the pulley.   Using these views, draw the front view of the guide pulley.

Find as an auxiliary elevation the edge view and as an oblique view the normal view of QRT.   Draw the guide pulley in these views, and from them draw the top view.

285. Assignments.—See Chapter XIV, Group 10E.

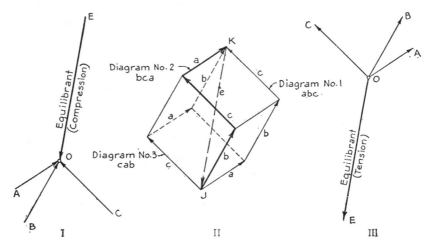

Fig. 174.—Force Diagrams.

FORCE DIAGRAMS FOR CONCURRENT NON-COPLANAR FORCES

286. Vector diagrams or force diagrams can be drawn for concurrent non-coplanar forces in very much the same way as they can be drawn for forces which act in a plane.   The diagram is a space diagram, and the forces are represented by oblique lines.

A vector is a line which represents the magnitude and direction of a force by its length and direction.

A resultant is an imaginary force which has the same effect in amount and direction as all the forces which act on a point.

An equilibrant is the imaginary force required to counteract all the forces which act on a point. The magnitudes of the equilibrant and the resultant are equal, but their directions are opposite.

If the vectors representing all the forces which act on a point are placed end to end so that the arrows follow each other, the closing line of the polygon formed is the equilibrant if the arrow points toward the starting point, and the resultant if it points in the opposite direction.

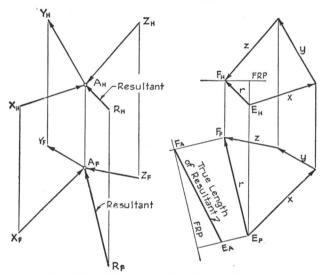

FIG. 175.—Diagram for Resultant of Forces.

Figure 174-I shows a space sketch of three forces *AO*, *BO*, and *CO* acting on the point *O*. Figure 174-II shows a parallelepiped of forces made up of all the possible force diagrams which can be drawn for the forces given in Fig. 174-I. Diagram 1 is for the forces in the order *abc*. Diagram 2 is for forces in the order *bca*. Diagram 3 is for forces in the order *cab*. An inspection of the parallelepiped shows that there are three more possible diagrams which lie on its edges. The diagonal *JK* is the equilibrant, which is shown in the same direction and length in sketch I. All the forces in this case are said to be compressive. Figure 174-III shows parallel and equal forces acting away from the point *O*. The diagrams for the solution of this case are those on the parallelepiped in Fig. 174-II. All these forces, which act away from the point O, are tensile forces.

287. Problem 98. To find the resultant of any number of concurrent non-coplanar forces.

Analysis.—The vector diagram made by drawing all of these forces end to end in two views will have as its closing side the resultant force. These forces are represented by oblique lines, and their magnitudes are found only in true length views.

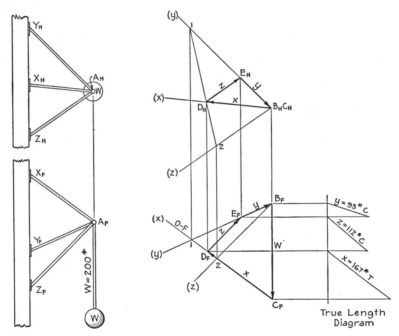

Fig. 176.—Stresses in Members of a Structure.

Construction.—Fig. 175. *Given* the forces AX, AY, and AZ, three oblique forces acting on the point A. *Required* to find the direction and magnitude of the resultant.

Select any point E on the drawing, and draw a force x in the top view and front view represented by an arrow parallel and equal to AX. Draw the arrow y parallel and equal to AY and the arrow z parallel and equal to the force AZ. Close the diagram by joining E and F. The arrow points toward F for the resultant r. Draw RA parallel and equal to EF. Find the true length of the resultant and measure its magnitude.

288. Assignments.—See Chapter XIV, Group 10F.

289. *Problem 99.   To find the forces produced in a structure of three members by a force acting at their intersection.*

Analysis.—This is the reverse of Problem 98.   The parallelepiped in Fig. 174-II suggests the method of solving the problem.   *KJ* corresponds to the given force.   The vectors *a* and *c* at *K* determine a plane, and the vector *b* at *J* pierces this plane at a point from which *K* can be reached by two vectors whose directions are known, thus completing the diagram *bca*.

Construction.—Fig. 176.   *Given* a weight of 200 pounds suspended from the point *A* of the structure *AX*, *AY*, and *AZ* fastened to a vertical wall. *Required* to find the forces in the three members acting on their point of intersection.

Draw *BC* parallel and equal to the force *W*.   At *B* draw in the front view and top view *B* (*y*) and *B* (*z*) parallel to *AY* and *AZ* respectively. At *C* draw *C* (*x*) parallel to member *AX*.   Find where the line *C* (*x*) pierces the plane (*y*) *B* (*z*) by Principle 12.   This construction locates the point *D*. At *D* draw the line *DE* parallel to *B* (*z*), locating the point *E* on *B* (*y*). This closes the diagram which is *BCDE*.   *CD* represents the force in *AX*. *DE* represents the force in *AZ*, and *EB* represents the force in *AY*.   These are oblique vectors.

The true length diagram adjacent to the front view gives the magnitude of each force.   The member *AX* is in tension, and the other two members are in compression.

290. Assignments.—See Chapter XIV, Group 10G;   Group 10H, Miscellaneous.

CHAPTER XI

THE MONGEAN METHOD OF DESCRIPTIVE GEOMETRY

291. This chapter is included in order to present briefly some essentials of the original method of *Gaspard Monge*. The *Mongean Method* of descriptive geometry refers all spatial relationships to two planes of projection at right angles to each other which divide space into four parts called *quadrants*. These planes are known as the vertical and horizontal planes of projection. Since a frontal plane is a special vertical plane that is perpen-

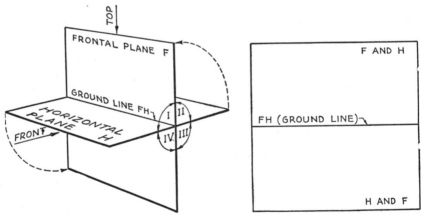

FIG. 177.—Planes of Projection and the Quadrants.

FIG. 178.—Drawing-board Representation of Planes of Projection.

dicular to the direction of sight for the front view, accuracy of expression is gained by using the word "frontal" instead of "vertical" for this plane of projection. A profile plane of projection at right angles to the frontal and horizontal planes, and auxiliary planes of projection at right angles to one of them are used to some extent in the present development of the method.

292. The *frontal plane of projection F* and the *horizontal plane of projection H* are shown in Fig. 177. The four parts into which space is divided

180

by these unlimited planes are known as *angles* or *quadrants*, and they are numbered as shown.

The planes F and H intersect in a line known as the *ground line* or *folding line*, usually designated as GL, although there are some advantages derived from using the letters of the two planes of projection FH. The ground line is a horizontal-frontal line. In order to represent both the F and H planes on a sheet of paper, one of them is conceived to have been revolved about the ground line as an axis so as to coincide with the other. The illustration indicates that H is being revolved into F, which is suitable for blackboard work. The frontal plane F, however, may be revolved

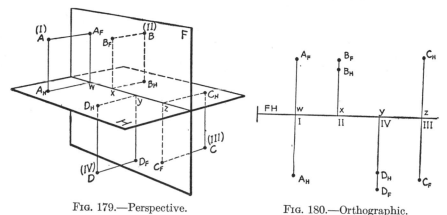

FIG. 179.—Perspective.   FIG. 180.—Orthographic.

Points Located in the Quadrants.

into H, which is more satisfactory for drawing-board work. In either case the first and third quadrants are opened, and the second and fourth quadrants are closed. Figure 178 shows the planes in coincidence on the paper. If an object is placed in the second or fourth quadrant, its front and top views are very likely to overlap. Therefore, for practical purposes, only the first and third quadrant positions are used for objects.

293. The pictorial drawing, Fig. 179, shows one point in each quadrant. A is in the first quadrant, B in the second, C in the third, and D in the fourth. Lines of projection from point A to the planes of projection F and H project the point onto these planes; A_F is the *frontal projection* or *front view* of A, and A_H is the *horizontal projection* or *top view*. The terminology of the first ten chapters is used to some extent in this discussion.

The orthographic drawing, Fig. 180, shows how the projections or views of each of these points appear and their relation to the ground line and to each other.   The line joining the projection A_F and A_H is perpendicular to the ground line, and is called a *projector* or sight-line.   When looking at the front view of a point, whose subscript is F, the observer should consider the paper as the frontal plane, and the directions from FH are up and down; but when looking at the top view of a point, whose subscript is H, the observer should consider the paper as the horizontal plane, and the directions from FH are forward and backward.   The typical arrangements of the projections or views of a point for the various quadrants are as follows: *first quadrant*: A_F is above FH; A_H is in front of FH.   They are on opposite sides of FH.   *Second quadrant*: B_F is above FH; B_H is

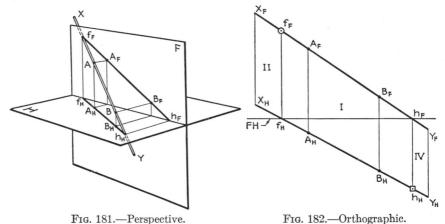

Fig. 181.—Perspective.   Fig. 182.—Orthographic.

Traces of an Oblique Line.

behind FH.   Both are on the same side of FH.   *Third quadrant*: C_F is below FH; C_H is behind FH.   They are on opposite sides of FH.   *Fourth quadrant*: D_F is below FH; D_H is in front of FH.   Both are on the same side of FH.

294. The Mongean Method Includes all Quadrants.—In contrast to the direct method, the Mongean method requires familiarity with constructions in all quadrants.   Although a problem may be stated for one quadrant, the solution may involve others.

295. The Traces of a Line.—The points at which a line pierces the planes of projection are known as its *traces*.   Also, the point at which a line pierces any plane is called its trace on that plane.   In Fig. 181 the horizontal trace, which is its own H-projection h_H, is the point at which AB extended pierces the horizontal plane H; the frontal projection h_F is at the intersection of the ground line and the frontal projection of the line.

The frontal trace, which is its own F-projection, is marked f_F, and its horizontal projection f_H is at the intersection of the ground line and the horizontal projection of the line.

296. Problem 100. To find the horizontal and frontal traces of a line.

Analysis.—The solution of this problem is based on the fact that one projection of a trace is located at the intersection of a projection of the given line and the ground line.

Construction.—Figs. 181 and 182. *Given* the line AB. *Required* to find the F- and H-piercing points or traces.

The pictorial drawing, Fig. 181, and the orthographic drawing, Fig. 182, show the line AB and its traces. To find h_F, extend $A_F B_F$ to intersect FH; to find f_H, extend $A_H B_H$ to intersect FH; draw a projector from each of these points to locate the projection of the trace on the other projection of AB extended. The planes F and H are pierced at f_F and h_H.

Symbols, a square for h_H and a circle for f_F, are useful if the traces of several lines are required, and may replace notation.

The line AB is shown extended to the length XY. All of that portion between the traces is in the first quadrant. From the frontal trace to X is in the second quadrant, and from the horizontal trace to Y is in the fourth quadrant.

The traces of lines are used for finding the traces of planes, the shadows of objects, the vanishing points of lines in perspective, and the intersections of surfaces.

297. Assignments.—See Chapter XIV, Group 11A.

298. The Traces of a Plane.—The line in which any plane intersects a plane of projection is called the trace of the plane, and the trace takes the name of both of the intersecting planes. Figure 183 shows an oblique plane S in the first quadrant. The frontal trace of the plane is AB, which is marked FS; and the horizontal trace is CB, which is marked HS. The traces intersect at B on the ground line. A frontal trace is a special frontal line of a plane. It is its own F-projection, and its H-projection is in the ground line. A horizontal trace is a special horizontal line of a plane. It is its own H-projection, and its F-projection in the ground line. Therefore, FS and HS do not represent the same line. In Fig. 184 point A is in the F-trace of the plane; A_F is in FS, but A_H is in the ground line. The point C is in the H-trace of the plane; C_H is on HS, but C_F is in the ground line.

Figure 184 shows the traces extended so as to form an X. That part of the plane between (HS) and (FS) is in the third quadrant. That part between FS and (HS) is in the second quadrant, and that part between HS and (FS) is in the fourth quadrant. Thus, the appearance of the same oblique plane is quite different if represented by the traces for each of the quadrants separately.   This can be seen more clearly if a part of the drawing is covered by a card for each case.

299. Problem 101.   *Given one projection of a line located in a plane given by its traces, to find the adjacent projection.*

Analysis.—The line, extended if necessary, has its traces in the traces of the plane.   If the F-projection is given, find its intersection with the F-trace of the plane and with the ground line; draw projectors from these points to intersect the ground line and the H-trace respectively, thus finding the H-projection of the traces of the line.   Join them for the H-projection of the line extended.

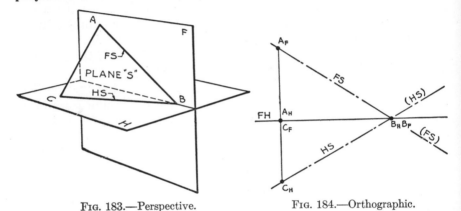

FIG. 183.—Perspective.   FIG. 184.—Orthographic.

Traces of an Oblique Plane.

Construction.—Fig. 185.   *Given* the front projection $A_F B_F$ of the line AB in the plane S.   *Required* to find the horizontal projection of the line.

Extend $A_F B_F$ to intersect FS at 1_F and FH at 2_F.   Draw projectors from 1_F and 2_F to find 1_H on FH and 2_H on HS.   Join 1_H and 2_H, and draw projectors from A_F and B_F to find $A_H B_H$, the required horizontal projection of the line.

The procedure explained above is used for locating a point in a plane. If a point is in a plane, it is on a line of the plane.   Therefore, draw a line of the plane and locate the point on it.   Generally, the most satisfactory line to use is either a horizontal or frontal line as shown for point D or C in Fig. 186.

300. Assignments.—See Chapter XIV, Group 11B.

301. Problem 102.   *To find the traces of a plane given as a plane figure.*

First Method. Analysis.—The required traces pass through the corresponding traces of the lines of the given figure.

Construction.—Fig. 185. *Given* the front and top view of the triangle *ABC*. *Required* to find the traces of the plane of the triangle.

Extend *AB* and *BC* and find the traces marked 1, 2, 3, and 4. Draw *FS* through 1_F and 4_F and *HS* through 2_H and 3_H. The traces of the required plane are *FS* and *HS*. If they intersect on the ground line, the construction is checked.

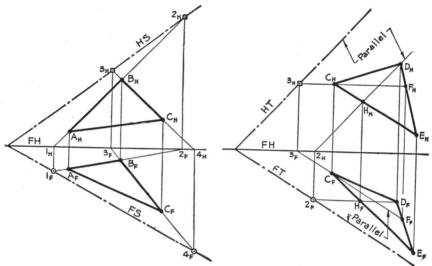

FIG. 185.—Points and Lines in Oblique Plane *S*. Traces of the Plane of Triangle *ABC*.

FIG. 186.—Traces of the Plane of a Given Triangle.

302. Second Method. Analysis.—The required traces of the plane are parallel to principal lines of the plane and pass through the traces of these lines.

Construction.—Fig. 186. *Given* the front and top views of the triangle *CDE*. *Required* to find the traces of the plane of the triangle.

Draw the horizontal line *D H* and find its trace, marked 2; draw the frontal line *CF* and find its trace, marked 3. Through 2_F draw *FT* parallel to C_FF_F, and through 3_H draw *HT* parallel to D_HH_H. The required traces of the plane are *HT* and *FT*, and they intersect on the ground line.

303. Assignments.—See Chapter XIV, Group 11C.

CHAPTER XII

SHADES AND SHADOWS

304. *Shades and shadows* are used to give a sense of depth to a picture made upon a flat sheet of paper or canvas. A knowledge of this subject is an essential part of the training of architects and artists, who use shades and shadows on their rendered drawings or pictures to make them realistic and attractive. Although anyone looking at the drawing gains an impression of the depth and form of the object, a person with training in shades and shadows can visualize it more completely. The shadow may reveal either the form casting the shadow or the form of the surface receiving it.

In this chapter most of the methods used for finding shades and shadows are given and treated from the standpoint of the principles of descriptive geometry upon which they are based. For a complete treatment including short-cuts intended for those who wish to use shades and shadows extensively, the reader is referred to books devoted entirely to this subject.

305. Definitions.—That portion of the surface of an object which is opposite the source of light is said to be in *shade*. In the case of a cylinder or a sphere placed in sunlight, one-half is in shade. The line which separates the lighted portion from the unlighted portion is called the *shade-line*.

That portion of any surface from which the light is excluded by some other object is in *shadow*. It is the area bounded by the shadow of the shade-lines of the object casting the shadow. The distinction between shade and shadow is not easy to make in some cases. A complicated object may be analyzed as being composed of several parts, and one part may cast a shadow on another part just as it would cast a shadow on some independent surface. Shadows usually appear darker than shades, and drawings are rendered accordingly.

The shade and shadow of a square prismatic block are shown pictorially in Fig. 187 and orthographically in Fig. 188. The top and two faces are in the light, and the other two faces are in shade. The shade-lines are AB, BC, CD, and DE. The shadow falls partly upon the ground plane H and partly on the wall plane F, and it is bounded by the shadows of the shade-lines. The shadow of AB and DE bend at FH.

186

Although light from any source may be assumed for finding the shade and shadow of an object, sunlight is generally used, since it is most common and the rays are considered to be parallel. The rays from an electric lamp

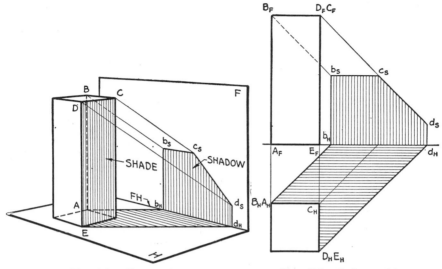

FIG. 187.—Perspective. FIG. 188.—Orthographic.

Shade and Shadow of a Prism.

radiate from practically a point, and produce shadows which are more difficult to draw and which may be unusual in appearance.

306. The Direction of Light.— The standard direction of light is shown in Fig. 189. The rays are assumed to pass over the left shoulder of the observer and to go downward, backward, to the right, parallel to the body diagonal of a cube placed so that its faces are principal planes. Figures 190 and 191 show that the ray is drawn at 45° in all principal views. The actual angle made with the horizontal or other principal planes is

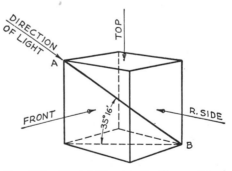

FIG. 189.—Sketch Showing the Conventional Direction of Light.

35° 16′. This direction of light produces shadows approximately like those quite generally observed at the average latitude of the United States.

Furthermore, the constructions are greatly simplified by use of a 45° triangle.

The direction of light, Fig. 190, is shown in three principal views of a cube located in the third quadrant. In Fig. 191 the cube is in the first quadrant; and, although the direction may not at first appear to be the same, a closer examination shows that it is identical, the top view merely being placed below the front view.

307. Location of the Object.—The object may be placed in either the third or the first quadrant, whichever the draftsman is accustomed to use in making his drawing. Many architects still prefer the first quadrant.

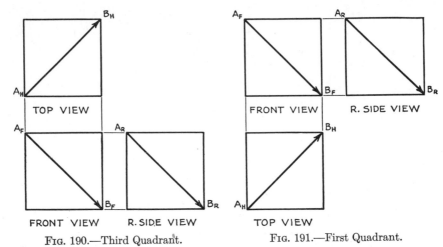

FIG. 190.—Third Quadrant.   FIG. 191.—First Quadrant.

Orthographic Representation of the Conventional Direction of Light.

Figure 192 shows an object in the third quadrant, and Fig. 193 shows the same object in the first quadrant. The shades and shadows are identical in both cases; the only real difference in the two drawings is the placing of the top view.

308. Methods of Finding Shadows.—There are six methods generally used for finding shadows. Although the same constructions may be used to some extent for more than one method, a statement of the methods to be discussed is desirable.

1. The piercing point method	4. The method of tangent surfaces
2. The auxiliary view method	5. The method of sections
3. The slicing method	6. The envelope method

309. The piercing point method consists of finding the shadow of a sufficient number of points by finding where the rays from the points pierce the surface receiving the shadow, or, in other words, by finding the *traces* of these rays. Actually, the point which casts the shadow stops the ray of light, but a line called the ray is drawn for the construction. If the shade-line is known and the shadow falls on a horizontal, frontal, or profile plane,

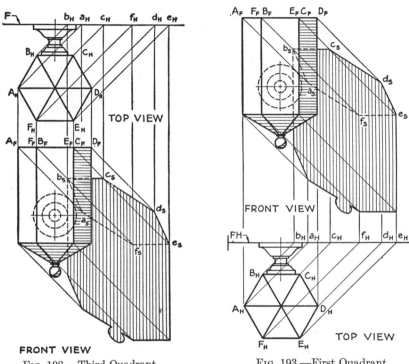

FIG. 192.—Third Quadrant.   FIG. 193.—First Quadrant.

Shade on an Object and Shadow on a Frontal Wall.

the piercing point (trace) is easy to find by the method given in Chapters V and XI, because the plane will appear as an edge view in any view adjacent to that showing the shadow. This method is the only one needed in many cases, and the same principle is used to some extent in all other methods.

310. *Problem 103. To find the shadow of a horizontal pentagonal plate.*

Example of the First Method.

Analysis.—Construction rays drawn through each corner of the pentagon pierce the plane which is to receive the shadow. The lines joining these points bound the shadow of the plate.

Construction.—Fig. 194. *Given* the front and top views of pentagonal plate *ABCDE*. *Required* to find its shadow first on a frontal plane; second, on a horizontal plane, after removing the frontal plane.

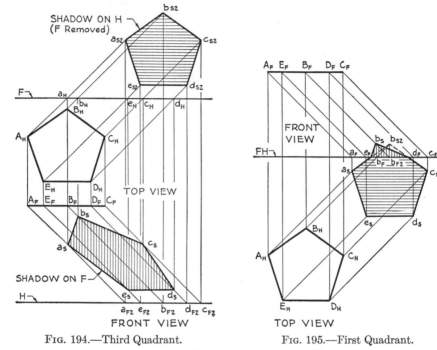

FIG. 194.—Third Quadrant.   FIG. 195.—First Quadrant.

Shadow of a Horizontal Pentagonal Plate.

Draw construction rays from *A, B, C, D,* and *E.* They intersect the edge view of the frontal plane *F* at a_H, b_H, etc. The front view of these points is a_S, b_S, etc. The lines joining these points bound the shadow.

If the frontal plane is removed, the shadow will fall on the horizontal plane *H.* The construction rays intersect this plane at a_{F2}, b_{F2}, etc. These points appear in the top view at a_{S2}, b_{S2}, etc.

One fact demonstrated by the shadow on *H* should be noted. If a line or a plane surface is parallel to the plane receiving the shadow, the shadow is parallel and equal to the line or has the same shape and size as the surface.

If the plate is in the first quadrant, Fig. 195, one line *FH* represents the edge view of both planes. The plate is so located that part of the shadow is on H and part is on F. Since most of the shadow falls on H, find the complete outline of that shadow although b_{S2} is an imaginary shadow on H behind the frontal plane F. Also, find the real shadow of B at b_S on the frontal plane. Join b_S to the points where a_Sb_{S2}, and c_Sb_{S2} intersect FH, which gives the portion of the shadow which falls on F. The location of the plate in the first quadrant has some slight advantage in that the planes receiving the shadow may be thought of as the ground and wall, and both portions of the shadow are shown joined together as they will appear. It should be remembered, however, that the observer of the top view cannot see the shadow on the frontal plane; and the observer of the front view cannot see the shadow on the horizontal plane. In a pictorial drawing, both portions may be seen at the same time.

All of the examples shown in the remainder of this chapter have the object in the third quadrant.

311. *Problem 104. To find the shadow of a circle.*

Analysis.—The shadow of a circle is the line joining the shadow of a number of its points. The shadow is an ellipse, an equal circle, or possibly a straight line. The most satisfactory method of obtaining a smooth curve for an elliptical shadow is to find the shadow of a circumscribing octagon.

Construction.—Fig. 196. *Given* the conical lamp-shade in sunlight, suspended from the wooden beam. *Required* to find the shadow on the wall.

The conical lamp-shade is designed so that is circular rim is the shade-line. Therefore, the shadow is the same as the shadow of a horizontal circular disc. Circumscribe the square $ABCD$ about the circle and draw an octagon inside the square tangent to the circle at the points 1, 2, 3, 4, 5, 6, 7, 8. Find where the rays from these points and A, B, C, D, and O intersect the edge view of wall F, and locate the shadows of these points in the front view. The shadow of the square is $a_Sb_Sc_Sd_S$. Sight-lines through 2 and 6 cut off two corners; and lines through 4 and 8 parallel to b_Sd_S cut off two corners, giving the shadow of the octagon. The ellipse inscribed within the octagon is the shadow of the circular rim. The major axis of the ellipse is more inclined than the diagonal b_Sd_S.

In Fig. 197 the construction for the shadow of a horizontal circle cast upon a frontal wall is considerably simplified. Find the shadows of A, O, and C, and draw horizontal lines through a_S and c_S to complete the shadow of the square. With center o_S, draw arcs from c_S and a_S to locate e and f on line 3–7. Through e and f draw horizontal lines to intersect the diagonals of the square at 2, 4, 6, and 8. Draw lines through these points parallel to the diagonals to complete the octagon.

The upper part of Fig. 197 shows the shadow of a profile circle on a frontal wall. The position of the circumscribing square and octagon is different, but the construction and the lettering are similar.

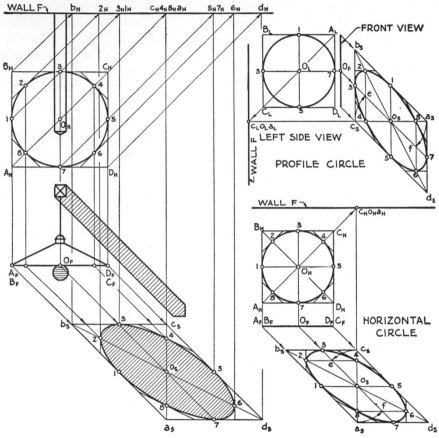

FIG. 196.—Shadow of a Horizontal   FIG. 197.—Constructions for the
Circle on a Frontal Wall.   Shadow of a Circle.

The constructions of Fig. 197 may be called the short-cut method of finding the shadow of a circle, but by comparison with Fig. 196 they are seen to be based upon true constructions.

312. Problem 105. *To find the shadow of a cap on a column and to find the shade on both.*

Analysis.—Determine the shade-lines of the cap and use the first method of finding its shadow on the column, the surface of which is shown as an edge view in the top view.

Construction.—Fig. 198. *Given*, first, a column surmounted by a cap with two faces frontal; second, a column surmounted by a cap with one diagonal frontal; and, third, a column surmounted by a cylindrical cap. *Required* to find the shadow of each cap on its column and the shade areas.

Case I.—The top, left, and front faces of the cap are in light; and the lower, rear, and right faces are in shade. The shade-lines which cast the shadow on the column are AC and CE. The critical points for the shadow

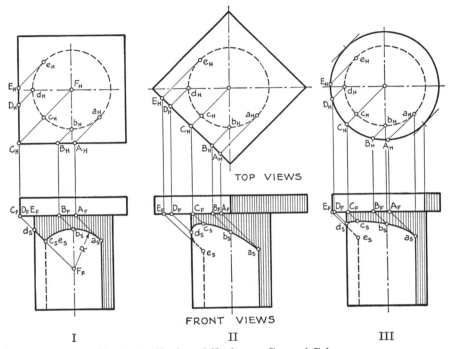

Fig. 198.—Shade and Shadow on Cap and Column.

to be found are a_H, b_H, c_H, d_H, and e_H. Rays drawn backward from these to the shade-line locate A_H, B_H, C_H, D_H, and E_H, the points to be used on the shade-line for casting the shadow. Rays from these points in the front view locate shadows a_S, b_S, c_S, d_S, e_S. A curve through a_S, b_S, c_S, which is the arc of a circle with center F_F, is a part of the outline of the shadow, which continues around to e_S. The right-rear half of the column from a_S to e_S is in the shade.

Case II.—Only the left-front and top faces of this cap are in light, and the shade-line to be used is AE. Construction in this case is carried out in the same manner as in Case I.

Case III.—Tangents are drawn to the circle of the cap which show that its left-front half is in light and the opposite half is in shade. The shadow of the shade-line AE is found as in Cases I and II.

313. Assignments.—See Chapter XIV, Group 12A.

314. The Auxiliary View Method.—The auxiliary view method is not largely used, but it is the best method for explaining the short-cut method of finding the shade and shadow of a sphere.

315. *Problem 106.* *To find the shade-line of a sphere and its shadow on a horizontal plane.*

Analysis.—An auxiliary elevation taken perpendicular to the direction of the light shows an edge view of the shade-line, and an edge view of the shadow of the sphere on the horizontal plane. The shade-line is a great circle whose plane is normal to the direction of the light.

Construction.—Fig. 199. *Given* the sphere with a center A. *Required* to find the shaded area and the shadow on horizontal plane H.

Through A, the center of a sphere, draw a construction ray BA. The imaginary shadow of A is at a_S. Draw an auxiliary elevation of the sphere taken normal to the ray BA. The cylinder of light which circumscribes the sphere is tangent to it along a great circle shown in the auxiliary elevation as 0–6. Find the end view $B_O A_O$ of the ray; draw a normal view of the shade-line, which is a circle of radius R; select twelve points on it; locate these points in the auxiliary elevation and the top view; draw rays through them; find where they intersect H in the auxiliary elevation; and locate their shadows in the top view. These are twelve points on an ellipse which is the shadow of the sphere. The shade-line of the sphere shown in the top view is a similar but smaller ellipse. A line connecting an end of the major axis and an end of the minor axis makes 30° with the major axis in each case.

316. Figure 200 shows the short-cut method of constructing the true shade and shadow of a sphere based upon the results of the method shown in Fig. 199. The outline of the shadow on the horizontal plane and the shade-line in the front and top views are similar ellipses in which two equilateral triangles can be inscribed having the minor axis as the common base. For the shadow, the minor axis 3–9 is the diameter of the sphere. The center of the ellipse is the imaginary shadow of the center of the sphere. For the front and top views of the shade-line the major axis of the ellipses is the diameter of the sphere. Also, in any of the ellipses two squares may be inscribed, each having one-half the major axis as its diagonal. Corners of these squares locate four intermediate points on the ellipse. This is a

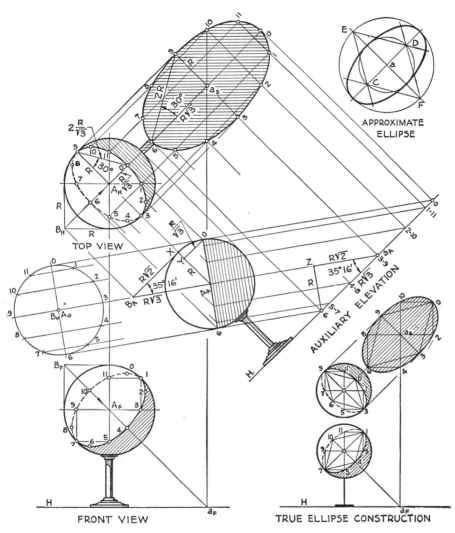

FIG. 199.—Shade and Shadow of a Sphere.

FIG. 200.—Constructions for Shade and Shadow of a Sphere.

short-cut, theoretically sound method of finding eight points on the required ellipse for the shade or the shadow of a sphere.*

The form of the shade-line is the same for any principal view of a sphere, and the form of the shadow on a frontal plane or a profile plane is the same as that on a horizontal plane.

An interesting construction is shown for an approximate ellipse having the same axes as those in Fig. 200. Two equilateral triangles with common base CD equal to the minor axis locate points E and F, which with C and D are the centers for the four arcs used in drawing the approximate ellipse.

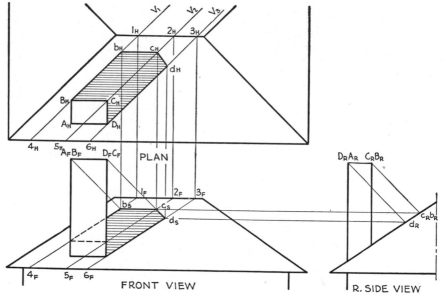

Fig. 201.—Shadow of a Chimney on a Roof.

Proof of Short-Cut Construction

*To prove that the angle a_S–6–9 in the shadow is 30°, study the auxiliary view, Fig. 199. Since B_AX is the diagonal of a square whose sides are R (see top view), $B_AX = R\sqrt{2}$. In the triangle B_AA_AX, $A_AX = R$. ∴ $B_AA_A = R\sqrt{3}$. The triangle $a_A 6 Z$ is equal to A_AB_AX, and $a_A 6 = R\sqrt{3}$. In the shadow $a_S 6 = a_A 6 = R\sqrt{3}$, and $a_S 9 = R$ ∴ 6–9 = $2R$ and angle a_S–6–9 = 30°.

To prove that the angle A_H–9–0 is 30° study the auxiliary view and top view. Triangle $A_A0 Y$ is similar to A_AB_AX, and $A_A0 = R$. ∴ By proportion $0–Y = \dfrac{R}{\sqrt{3}}$. In the triangle A_H–0–9, $A_H0 = \dfrac{R}{\sqrt{3}}$, and $A_H9 = R$. ∴ $0–9 = 2\dfrac{R}{\sqrt{3}}$, and A_H–9–0 = 30°.

317. Assignments.—See Chapter XIV, Group 12B.

318. The Slicing Method.—The slicing method makes use of imaginary slices assumed to be cut by planes of light which are usually either vertical or orthofrontal. The point which casts a shadow is in this plane of light, and its shadow is located on the intersection of the plane of light and the surface that receives the shadow.

319. Problem 107. *To find the shadow of a chimney on a roof.*

Analysis.—The surface that receives the shadow is inclined. Therefore, if the side view is not used, the problem is that of finding where the rays pierce an inclined plane by slicing. This is an application of Principle 12; the cutting planes or slicing planes used in this case are vertical planes of light.

Construction.—Fig. 201. *Given* the chimney with its top at $ABCD$ and the hip roof of a building. *Required* to find the shadow of the chimney on the roof.

The shade-lines are the vertical edges at B and D and the horizontal edges BC and CD. Since the vertical edges intersect the roof, the shadows of the points B, C, and D are sufficient to determine the shadow of the chimney. Pass vertical cutting planes V_1, V_2, and V_3 through these re spective points and containing the ray from each point. These planes cut the roof in the slice-lines 1–4, 2–5, and 3–6. These slice-lines contain the shadows of points B, C, and D, which are found at b_S, c_S, d_S in the front view; and b_H, c_H, d_H in the plan. A study of the direction of the edges of the shadow is interesting and valuable.

If the drawing consists of the front view and a right-side view, the latter shows the edge view of the roof plane on which the shadow falls, and the first method may be used.

320. Problem 108. *To find the shade and shadow of the scotia and torus of a column base.*

Analysis.—A vertical plane of light can be imagined to slice the surface of the object in a line which may be found by the method of Problem 73. At the top of the scotia in each slicing plane there is a point which casts its shadow on the curve cut from the scotia. A ray of light that is tangent to a slice-line on the torus locates at its point of tangency a point on the shade-line of its surface.

Construction.—Fig. 202. *Given* the object shown in the figure. *Required* to find the shade and shadow on the scotia and the shade on the torus.

The vertical cutting planes used are V_1, V_2, V_3, V_4, V_5, V_6, V_7. They slice the surface of the object in the lines shown, which are found by using seven horizontal cutting planes according to the method of Problem 73,

the construction for which is not shown.   The horizontal circle that passes
through A and C is the shade-line that casts a shadow on the scotia. C
casts its shadow at c_S which is on the outline curve of the surface.   Point
A casts its shadow at a_S on the slice-line through A.   Each slice gives one
point on the curve of the boundary of the shadow.   One-half of each cylindrical surface is in shade.

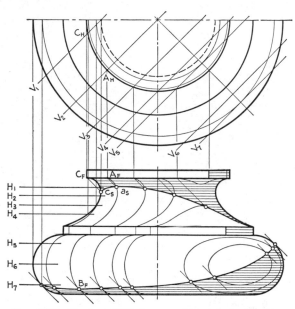

Fig. 202.—Shade and Shadow on a Torus and a Scotia.

Draw a ray tangent at B_F to the curve of the slice, which determines one
point on the shade-line of the torus.   Each slice-line may have one or two
rays drawn tangent to it for determining other points on the shade-line.

321. Assignments.—See Chapter XIV, Group 12C.

322. The Method of Tangent Surfaces.

The shade-line of some double-curved surfaces of revolution can be found
most readily by means of the properties of cones tangent to the surface.
Therefore, before discussing this method it is necessary to learn to find
the shade-lines of a cone.

**323. *Problem 109.   To find the shade and shadow of a right circular
cone.***

Analysis.—Let the base of the cone be horizontal; then the shadow of
the base on H is a circle.   Tangents drawn from the shadow of the vertex

to the shadow of the base complete the outline of the shadow. The tangents are the shadows of the shade-lines of the cone. Therefore, the shade-lines can be determined from the shadow.

Construction.—Fig. 203. *Given* the right circular cone with its base resting on H and its vertex at A. *Required* to find its shadow and the shade-lines.

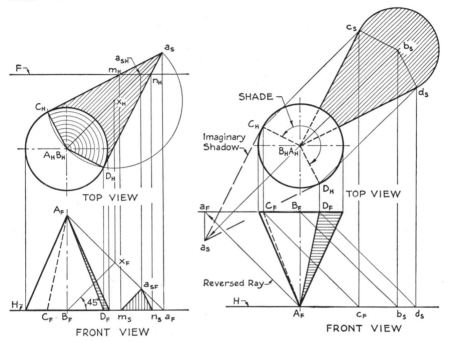

FIG. 203.—Shade and Shadow of a Cone.

FIG. 204.—Shade and Shadow of an Inverted Cone.

The base of the cone is its own shadow. The shadow of the vertex is at a_S. Draw the tangents $a_S C_H$ and $a_S D_H$ to complete the outline of the shadow; only the portion beyond the base of the cone is visible. AC and AD are the shade-lines of the cone. The points C and D can be determined accurately by drawing a semicircle with center X_H on $a_S A_H$ as a diameter; X_F is located by drawing the line $B_F X_F$ at 45°.

If a portion of the shadow is to be shown on a frontal plane F, find the shadow of A on the frontal plane at a_{SF} and the points M and N where F cuts the outline of the shadow on the horizontal plane. This portion of the shadow is shown in the front view, as $m_S a_{SF} n_S$.

If the same cone is inverted with its vertex resting on H, Fig. 204, the shadow is as shown, from which the shade-lines can be determined. The same lettering is used. In this case, however, the shaded area occupies more than one-half the surface of the cone, which is the same amount that is in the light on the upright cone.

The construction for obtaining the shade-lines may be simplified by drawing the reversed ray from A. Locate the imaginary shadow on H at ι_s. The light is imagined to pass in the reverse direction so that the imaginary shadow is on the plane of the base of the cone. This construction saves space and is practically the same as that in Fig. 203.

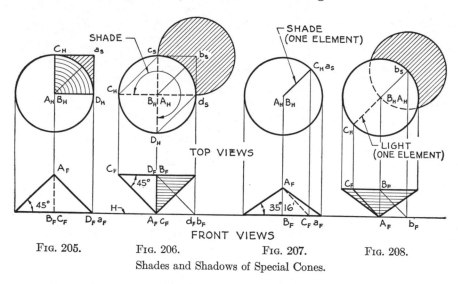

FIG. 205.   FIG. 206.   FIG. 207.   FIG. 208.

Shades and Shadows of Special Cones.

Special Cases of Shades and Shadows of Right Circular Cones. Two special cases are important in the use of tangent cones for finding the shade-line on a double-curved surface. They are the cone whose base angle is 45° and the cone whose base angle is 35° 16′.

Figure 205 shows an upright 45° cone. The shadow of its vertex is at a_S; and its shade-lines are AC and AD, which are seen to include exactly one-fourth of the surface of the cone as the shaded area. Figure 206 shows an inverted 45° cone. The same lettering applies, and the shaded area is exactly three-fourths of the surface of the cone.

Figure 207 shows an upright 35° 16′ cone. The shadow of the vertex falls at a_S, a point on the circle of the base. This is true because the element AC is parallel to the standard direction of light. Therefore, it may be said that the surface of this cone is entirely lighted except for one element AC, which is in shade. Figure 208 shows an inverted $35°$ $16'$ cone and the surface may be said to be entirely in shade except for one element CA, which is in the light.

324. Problem 110.   To find the shade of a double-curved surface of revolution by means of tangent cones.

Analysis.—If a right circular cone whose axis coincides with the axis of a surface of revolution is tangent to the surface, it is in contact along a circle, the plane of which is perpendicular to the axis. The shade-lines of the cone each contain one point on the shade-line of the given surface. By using a number of cones of different base angles a sufficient number of points can be found to draw the shade-line. One tangent cylinder, which is a cone of infinite altitude, is also used.

Construction.—Fig. 209. *Given* the oblate spheroid surmounting the cylindrical shaft. *Required* to find the shade-line and shade on the spheroid and its shadow on the cylinder.

Use one tangent cylinder which gives the points 1 and 2 on the circle of contact at H_O. Then draw tangent to the spheroid the cone with its base on H_1 and its vertex at A. Use the construction

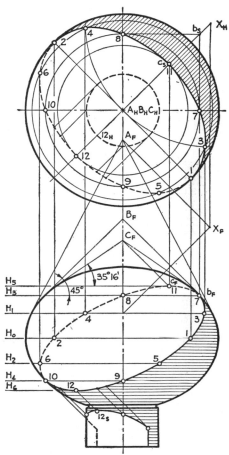

Fig. 209.—Shade-line by Means of Tangent Cones.

of Fig. 203 for finding X, the center of an arc which locates points 3 and 4, which are the lower ends of the shade-lines of this cone, and are on the surface of the spheroid, because the base circle of the cone is entirely on the spheroid. An inverted cone with the same base angle is imagined to be constructed at H_2. It locates points 5 and 6, which are exactly opposite 3 and 4. These points can be located by symmetry without drawing the inverted cone.

Next, draw a 45° cone tangent to the spheroid, its base being at H_3 and its vertex at B. From Fig. 205 it is seen that the lower ends of its shade-lines are at points 7 and 8. Imagine an inverted 45° cone, its base being at H_4. This cone locates the points 9 and 10 opposite 7 and 8.

Finally, use a 35° 16' cone, its base being at H_5 and its vertex at C. By Fig. 207 the end of the shade-line is at point 11. An inverted cone of the same base angle gives point 12, which is opposite point 11.

If the properties of these cones are well understood, this is a rapid method of finding the shade-line on a surface of this type.

The shadow on the cylindrical stem is found by finding the shadow of several points on the shade-line. Point 12 casts its shadow at 12_S. Reversed rays are drawn in the top view from critical points at which it is desired to find shadows, and the points which will cast these shadows are located on the shade-line.

325. Assignments.—See Chapter XIV, Group 12D.

326. The Method of Sections.—In this method sections of the surface that are easy to draw are made by parallel cutting planes. The shade-line is imagined to cast its shadow on each of these planes. The intersection of the outline of the section and the shadow of the shade-line on that cutting plane gives one or two points of the required shadow.

327. *Problem 111. To find the shadow in a niche which has a spherical surface at the head and bottom.*

Analysis.—The analysis is covered in the above explanation.

Construction.—Fig. 210. *Given* the plan and front elevation of a niche. *Required* to find the shadow within the niche.

The frontal cutting plane F_1 cuts the surface of the niche in the line marked 1_X in the front elevation. A and B are the centers of arcs of the shade-line which is $d_S E_F K_F c_S$ in the front view. The imaginary shadows of A and B are at a_S and b_S. Using these points, outline shadow 1_Y is drawn, which is identical with the outline edge of the niche. Section 1_X intersects outline shadow 1_Y in two points, each of which is marked 1_S. These are the shadows of two points on the shade-line which could be found by running rays backward.

The second frontal cutting plane F_2 produces section line 2_X and receives outline shadow 2_Y. These intersect in two points, each marked 2_S. The shadow of critical point E falls at e_S and the shadow of K falls at k_S on the cylindrical surface. The light rays at c_S and d_S in the front view determine two critical points. Only a few well-selected cutting planes are required in this case.

This method could have been used for finding the shadow on the scotia shown in Fig. 202, and the shadow could have been obtained with less effort. In this case, horizontal cutting planes would have been used.

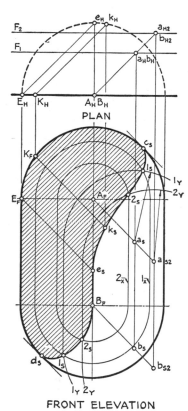

FRONT ELEVATION

Fig. 210.—Shadow in a Niche by the Method of Sections.

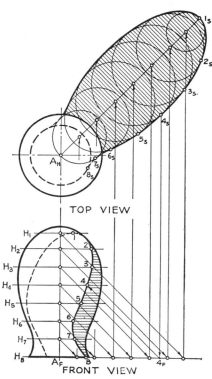

Fig. 211.—Shade and Shadow of a Surface of Revolution by the Envelope Method.

328. Assignments.—See Chapter XIV, Group 12E.

329. The Envelope Method.—In this method the shadow is found first; and if the shade-line is desired, it is obtained from the shadow by using reversed rays. It is suitable for a double-curved surface of revolution, the outline of which is a reversed curve, or which is so slender that the method of tangent cones would be inconvenient. It consists in casting the shadows of a number of right sections (circles) onto the plane that receives the shadow, this plane being perpendicular to the axis of the object. The shadow of each circle is a circle; and the shadow of the object is the line which envelops all of the circles and is tangent to each. The points of tangency are shadows of points on the shade-line which can be obtained from them.

330. *Problem 112. To find the shadow of a double-curved surface of revolution, and the shade-line by means of the envelope method.*

Analysis.—The analysis has been covered in the above explanation.

Construction.—Fig. 211. *Given* the double-curved surface of revolution with a vertical axis. *Required* to find its shadow on the horizontal plane through A and to find its shade-line.

Use eight horizontal cutting planes indicated in front view. Each cuts a horizontal circle from the surface, and its shadow on the horizontal plane will be an equal circle. Find the imaginary shadow of the center of each circle and draw it as a very fine line. Draw a smooth curve that is tangent to all the circles and encloses them. The area within this curve is the shadow of the object. The points of tangency of the enveloping outline and the circles are marked $1_S \ldots 8_S$. These are shadows of points on the shade-line of the object. For instance, draw a sight-line from 4_S to 4_F and a reversed ray to locate point 4 on H_4. Point 4 is the point which casts its shadow at 4_S. This point is not shown in the top view; and the shade-line is omitted in this view, since it is not required in the construction and is not likely to be desired for any purpose.

This method could be used for a sphere or spheroid, but the methods previously given are more satisfactory.

331. Assignments.—See Chapter XIV, Group 12F.

CHAPTER XIII

PERSPECTIVE DRAWING

332. Perspective drawing is the draftsman's method of representing the true appearance of a building, structure, or other object. Other pictorial methods are based upon orthographic projection or oblique projection, both of which use a group of imaginary parallel rays. Perspective uses the natural method in which the rays from the object converge to a point in the eye of the observer. as in Fig. 2 Chapter II.

THE VISUAL RAY METHOD

333. The visual ray method demonstrates the character of a perspective drawing. *A visual ray* is a ray of light from any point of the object to the observer's eye. *The picture plane F* is an imaginary frontal plane usually placed between the eye and the object. *The perspective of a point* is the point at which its visual ray pierces the picture plane. *The perspective of a line* is the line joining the perspective of its two end points. The location of the observer's eye is called the *point of sight S*. The point where a perpendicular from the point of sight intersects the picture plane is the *center of vision C V*.

334. *Problem 113. To draw the perspective of a block by the visual ray method.*

Analysis.—The perspective drawing consists of the perspective of the edges and corners of the object. A visual ray from each corner pierces the picture plane and locates the perspective of that corner. In the top view the picture plane and the perspective on it appear as a line. The width of the picture is shown in this view. In order to obtain the height of the picture, a side view of the object and the picture plane is used. The picture plane and the perspective also appear as a line in this view. Sight-lines from these two edge views locate the perspective front view of the object.

Construction.—Fig. 212. *Given* the rectangular block placed with its base on the horizontal *ground plane G* and turned so that two of its faces are inclined to the picture plane *F*. The plan and the right-side view of the block in this position are shown. The eye of the observer is located at S, which is in front of the picture plane and above the object the distance shown. *Required* to find the perspective drawing of the object as it would appear from this point of sight.

The visual rays from the corners of the object to S_H intersect the picture plane F in the points a_H, b_H, etc. This is an edge view of the perspective picture. The same rays are shown in the right-side view, converging to

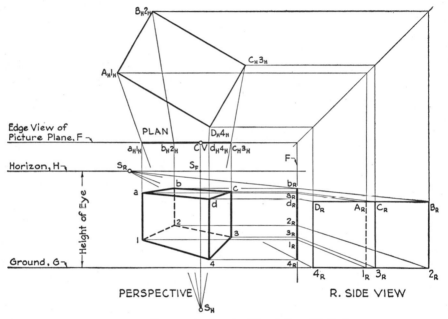

Fig. 212.—Perspective by the Visual Ray Method.

S_R; and they intersect the picture plane F at a_R, b_R, etc., which is also an edge view of the perspective picture. The intersection of the sight-lines from each point of the top and side views of the perspective picture locates it in the perspective front view.

335. In perspective, a group of two or more parallel lines is called a *system of lines*. There are three systems of lines on this object: one system is vertical, and parallel to the picture plane. These lines are parallel in the picture. If produced, the lines of a second system will meet at a point to the right, and the lines of a third system at a point to the left. These points, not shown in the drawing, are known as the *vanishing points* of the lines, and each vanishing point is on the *horizon H*, which is the intersection with F of a horizontal plane that passes through the *point of sight S*. This type is known as *two-point or angular perspective*.

The perspective shown in Fig. 212 was obtained entirely by use of visual rays without making any use of a vanishing point. In this method the object can be placed in any desired position without affecting the construction of the perspective after the orthographic views are drawn. If two systems of lines are parallel to the picture plane, the third system converges to a vanishing point at the *center of vision CV*; and the drawing is known as a *parallel or one-point perspective*. If the object is placed so that all three systems of lines are inclined to the picture plane, the drawing is a *three-point perspective*.

THE VANISHING POINT METHOD FOR ANGULAR PERSPECTIVE

336. The lines of any parallel receding system appear to meet at a point which is infinitely far away. The perspective of this point is known as the *vanishing point* of the lines. It is the point where the ray from that infinite point to the observer's eye pierces the picture plane. This ray is parallel to the lines of the system. There is a vanishing point for every system of receding lines on an object. Since most buildings and structures have many lines on them which correspond to the directions of the edges of a cube and one system of these lines is vertical and two systems are inclined to the picture plane and are horizontal, the most important vanishing points are the *right vanishing point R* and *left vanishing point L* located in the plane of the horizon H. By using vanishing points the direction of the lines in a perspective drawing are determined.

337. Problem 114. *To draw an angular perspective by the vanishing point method.*

Analysis.—Locate the right and the left vanishing points for the horizontal lines of the object. Make use of the visual ray method for finding the width of the picture. If any line lies in the picture plane, its true length is shown in the perspective. The height of the object can be measured on such a vertical line.

Construction.—Fig. 213. *Given* the same block shown in Fig. 212 placed in the same angular position, but with the nearest edge in the picture plane, and the point of sight S at the same distance from the object. *Required* to find the perspective.

Through S draw a line parallel to DC, and all other lines of that system. This line is shown in the top view as $S_H R_H$, and in the front view as $S_F R$. The piercing point of this line is R (its frontal trace), and it is the *vanishing point* for that system of parallel lines. The vanishing point R is the perspective of the point, infinitely far away, at which SR is assumed to meet all the parallel lines of this system.

In the same manner, the *left vanishing point* L is found by drawing a line through S parallel to DA and all lines of that system. In order to

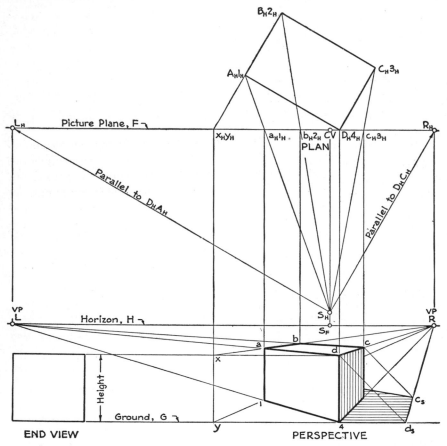

Fig. 213.—Perspective by the Vanishing Point Method, Using an Orthographic Plan.

avoid any confusion of lines in Fig. 213, the *ground plane* G and the *horizon* H are placed on the paper below S_H. In practical work, H and G would be somewhere near F to save space. Draw visual rays from the corners of the object to S_H, and find where they pierce the picture plane as in Prob. 113. From an end view of the object, shown at the left, the true height of edge $d4$ is obtained in the perspective. By drawing lines from d and 4 to the left and right vanishing points and then drawing sight-lines from picture plane, the edges $a1$ and $c3$ are obtained. By drawing lines from a and c to the vanishing points, the corner b is obtained, which should check with the sight-line drawn from the picture plane. Another method of finding the height of point a is shown. Produce the plane A–B–2–1 until it intersects the picture plane in a vertical line shown as point $x_H y_H$. Since this line is in the picture plane, the height of the point A can be measured on it. The line drawn from x to R locates a. By comparing this perspective with that in Fig. 212 they are found to be identical in shape but not in size because in Fig. 212 the picture plane was placed somewhat in front of the nearest edge of the object, which caused the perspective drawing to be smaller.

338. The Shadow.—The shade and shadow of the object are shown in Fig. 213. The direction of light is parallel to the picture plane and passes downward to the right at an angle of 45° with H. Since the rays are parallel to the picture plane, they appear parallel to each other in the perspective. A plane that contains a ray and vertical edge of the object intersects the ground plane in a horizontal line parallel to the picture plane. Therefore, the shadow of d is at d_S, and the shadow of the edge $d4$ is d_S4. In the same way, the shadow of c is found at c_S, and the shadow $d_S c_S$ vanishes at R. The shadow of bc vanishes at L. The right face of the object is shown in shade.

339. *Problem 115. To find the vanishing points of oblique lines.*

Analysis.—The gable roof of a house has oblique parallel lines for each roof plane and the vanishing points for these two systems of lines can be found by the same principle used for finding the left and right vanishing points for horizontal lines.

Construction.—Fig. 214. *Given* the plan of the house and its roof located as shown with reference to the picture plane F and the point of sight S. *Required* to find all vanishing points and draw the perspective.

In order to save space and conform to commercial practice, the ground plane G is located as shown in the figure. The point of sight is about five feet above the ground, the natural level for the observer's eye, and the center of vision CV is approximately at the center of the width of the picture.

First Method, or general method, of finding vanishing points for oblique lines. In order to find the vanishing points for the oblique lines of the roof, draw a front view of the gable lines AB and BC, shown as $A_F B_F$ and $B_F C_F$. Through S draw a line parallel in space to AB. This line is shown as $S_H R_H$ and $S_F K$, which are respectively parallel to $A_H B_H$ and $A_F B_F$. This line pierces the picture plane at K, the vanishing point for AB and FE. In like manner, draw a line through S_F parallel to $B_F C_F$ and locate K', which is the vanishing point for BC and ED. Both K and

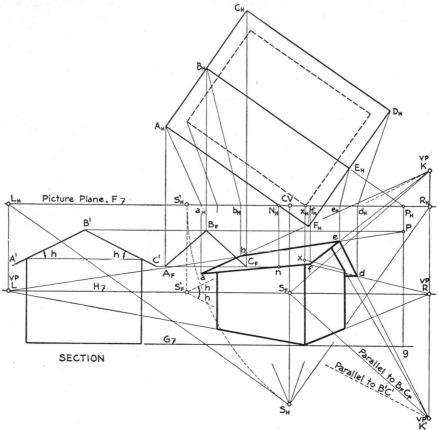

FIG. 214.—Angular Perspective Showing Vanishing Points for Oblique Lines.

K' are on the vertical line through R because the gable lines are in a vertical plane parallel to the end planes of the house. The line KRK' is the vanishing line of these planes.

Second Method of finding the vanishing points K and K'. Although the first method is theoretically sound, an easier and more accurate method is commonly used. The actual horizontal distance from the point of sight to vanishing point R is $S_H R_H$. A line having the actual roof slope drawn from the point of sight will rise the distance RK before reaching the picture plane. Therefore, with the center R_H and radius $R_H S_H$, draw the arc $S_H S'_H$, and draw a sight-line to H to locate S'_F. Then $S'_F R$ is equal to $S_H R_H$. At S'_F draw a line parallel to $A'B'$, the actual roof slope; and it will intersect a vertical line through R at K. This construction may be considered to be the revolution of the triangle SKR about KR as an axis until it lies in the picture plane.

Having all the vanishing points, the perspective is constructed in the same manner as that in Problem 114. One vertical edge of the building is in a picture plane so that the height of the point X can be measured directly. In order to obtain the perspective of EB, produce the vertical plane through $B_H E_H$ until it intersects the picture plane at P_H. In the perspective, Pg is the true height of the ridge; and the line from p to L is the perspective of the line of the ridge. Point N on the eave AF is in the picture plane, and its height is measured directly.

340. Problem 116. To draw a perspective plan by the perspective plan method.

Analysis.—Measurements can be made on any given horizontal line in perspective by using the conception of an isosceles triangle one of whose

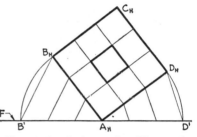

FIG. 215.—Orthographic Plan and Isosceles Triangles.

legs is in the picture plane, and therefore is shown in true length. The perspective of this triangle shows the other leg in its perspective length. The base of the triangle has a vanishing point called the *measuring point,*

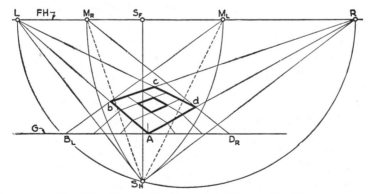

FIG. 216.—Perspective Layout and Perspective Plan.

which is the vanishing point for all lines parallel to the base.   These lines are used for laying off measurements on the perspective of the given line.

Construction.—Figs. 215 and 216.   *Given* the square plate $ABCD$, and S_HL parallel to A_HB_H, and S_HR parallel to A_HD_H.   *Required* to draw the perspective plan.

In Fig. 215 $A_HB_HC_HD_H$ is the orthographic plan of the square plate. Corner A_H is in the picture plane. A_HB_HB' and A_HD_HD' are isosceles triangles which have A_HB' and A_HD' in the picture plane.   The bases are $B'B_H$ and $D'D_H$.   These triangles are used in the required perspective plan to find the perspective lengths of AB and AD.

In Fig. 216 make AB_L and AD_R on the line G equal to A_HB' and A_HD' of Fig. 215.   Draw S_HM_L parallel to $B'B_H$ to find the *measuring point* M_L, which is the vanishing point for lines parallel to the base of the isosceles triangle A_HB_HB'.   Find the right *measuring point* M_R in a similar manner.   By using measuring point M_L, vanishing point L, and line AB_L, the perspective AbB_L of the triangle A_HB_HB' is found. Ab is the perspective of the line shown as A_HB_H.   By using M_R, R and AD_R the perspective Ad of the line AD is found, and the square can be completed.

By comparison of Figs. 215 and 216, the triangle LS_HM_L is seen to be similar to the triangle A_HB_HB', which is isosceles.   Therefore, the point M_L can be located by drawing the arc with center L.

341. The perspective layout construction.—Without making the drawing in Fig. 215, select L and R the desired distance apart on FH, which represents both the picture plane F and the horizon H.   Draw a semicircle on LR, select S_H on the semicircle, and strike arcs from S_H with L and R as centers to locate M_L and M_R.   Be careful to note that M_L, the measuring point for lines that vanish at L, is to the right of S; and that M_R, the measuring point for lines that vanish at R, is to the left of S.

342. Problem 117.   *To make the perspective of an object by the perspective plan method.*

Analysis.—A perspective plan is used in the same manner to make a perspective as an orthographic plan is used to make a front view.

Construction.—Fig. 217.   *Given* the dimensions of a short column and its base.   *Required* to draw the perspective plan and the perspective.

Assume L and R on line FH.   Draw the semicircle LS_HR.   Select the point of sight S_H so that the right and left faces of the object will be shown as desired.   In this case, take one corner of the perspective plan B at S_H through which the line G' is drawn to represent the level of the perspective plan.   From B lay off the measurements of the left-hand face toward A_L

and the measurements for the right-hand face toward C_R. Complete the perspective plan as in Problem 116, using measuring points M_L and M_R.

The ground level G is located about five feet below FH. The line bh in the picture plane is the vertical measuring line on which all heights are

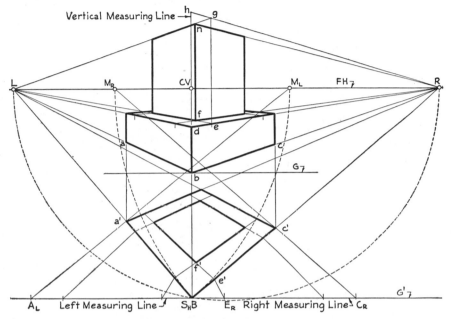

FIG. 217.—Angular Perspective by the Perspective Plan Method.

measured. From this stage the drawing is completed in a manner similar to that used in Problems 114 and 115.

Note.—The perspective plan can be located at any desirable level. In some cases, it is located at the actual ground level on which the object rests so that G' is at G, but usually it is much more satisfactory to have the perspective plan entirely below the perspective; and it may be on a separate sheet of paper. The perspective plan method has advantages over the method of Problems 114 and 115; but, since an architect usually has a complete orthographic plan, he prefers to use it in making the perspective. If the design is to be worked out directly in perspective, the perspective plan method is preferable. The methods may be combined.

343. Problem 118. To find the vanishing points of oblique lines and make a perspective of a house by the perspective plan method.

Analysis.—The vanishing points for the gable lines of a roof can be found by drawing from a measuring point lines having the true slope of the roof as shown in the second method of Problem 115, Fig. 214, in which S'_F corresponds to M_R of Fig. 218.

Construction.—Fig. 218.   *Given* the dimensions of the house.   *Required* to find all vanishing points and make a perspective by the perspective plan method.

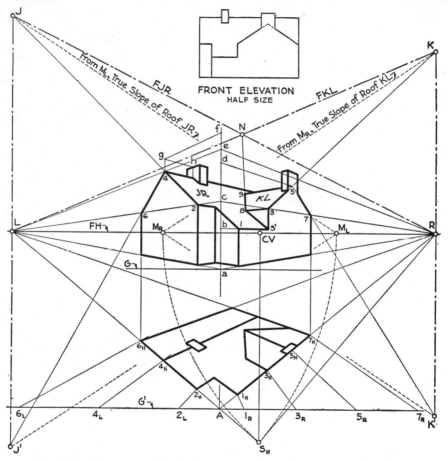

FIG. 218.—Perspective Showing Vanishing Points and Vanishing Lines for
Gables and Roofs.

Assume L, R, and S_H as in Problem 117.   Locate M_L and M_R by striking arcs from S_H with centers L and R.   Since the gable lines are in the faces of the building, their vanishing points are on the vanishing lines of the faces, which are the vertical lines through L and R.   The upper vanishing point J for the gable 2–4 is found by drawing a line from M_L at the true slope of the roof. The upper vanishing point K for the gable line 3–5 is found by drawing a line from M_R at the true slope of the roof. In the same manner, J' and K' are found.

The ground level of the perspective plan is represented by G'. Select A so that the center of vision is at the point of interest or approximately at the center of the total width of the building. Construct the perspective plan in the manner explained in Problem 116. The work is simplified by starting from the point A, the intersection of the left and right base lines of the building. Then the vertical measuring line af is in the plane of two principal faces of the building. Take G a satisfactory distance below the horizon at FH and proceed as in Problem 117, but make use of the vanishing points J, J', K, and K'. These vanishing points are especially useful in drawing an actual house with projecting gables, in which case several lines will be required.

The vanishing line FJR for the roof plane JR is found by joining the vanishing points J and R for two systems of its lines. In like manner, FKL is the vanishing line for the roof plane KL. If point 8 is known, the intersection of these roof planes is the line $8N$. This is an accurate method of drawing the valley 8–9.

The line JJ' is the vanishing line of the left plane of the building, and all others parallel to it. The line KK' is the vanishing line of the right plane of the building and all planes parallel to it.

344. Assignments.—See Chapter XIV, Group 13A.

345. The Selection of a Point of Sight.—The selection of the point of sight is the most important decision to be made in making a perspective. First, it must be taken so that its location in respect to the picture is relatively the same as the observer's location to the object. Second, the distance in front of the object must not be too small or too great. In order that all vanishing points and construction may be shown within the limits of a page, the point of sight has been placed too close to the object to give a pleasing effect in most of these drawings. A good average distance for the point of sight in front of the object is about four to six times the width of the perspective. Third, the center of vision should be somewhere near the center of the width of the picture, or at some point of special interest. The picture plane is perpendicular to the direction of sight which joins the point of sight and the center of vision. To place the point of sight entirely to one side of the object results in a perspective that is unnatural, because the observer may not be able to see the object by looking in the specified direction.

346. Problem 119.　*To draw a perspective plan for a parallel perspective.*

Analysis.—The measuring points are found on the basis of the use of an isosceles triangle as explained in Problem 116. The triangle in this case is a 45° right triangle.

Construction.—Figs. 219 and 220. *Given* the dimensions of a square plate with a square hole at its center. *Required* to draw the perspective plan.

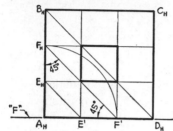

Fig. 219.—Orthographic Plan and 45° Isosceles Triangles.

In Fig. 219 $A_H B_H C_H D_H$ is the orthographic plan of the square plate. Edge $A_H D_H$ is in the picture plane. $A_H F_H F'$ is an isosceles triangle with $A_H F'$ in the picture plane. This triangle is used in drawing the perspective of the square in Fig. 220. The lines of the plate are either parallel or perpendicular to the picture plane; the parallel lines have no vanishing point; and the lines perpendicular to the picture plane vanish at the center of vision, called the *center vanishing point, CVP.*

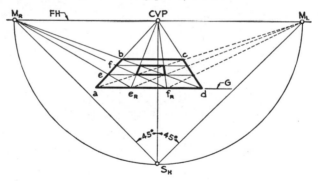

Fig. 220.—Layout and Perspective Plan for One-Point Perspective.

In Fig. 220 draw $S_H M_R$ parallel to $F'F_H$ of Fig. 219 to locate the right measuring point M_R, which is the vanishing point for the system of 45° lines shown as $F'F_H$, $E'E_H$, and $D_H B_H$. On the line G lay off af_R equal to $A_H F'$. Using M_R, CVP, and af_R draw the perspective aff_R of the triangle $A_H F_H F'$. The perspective of the line shown as $A_H F_H$ is af. To locate the points e and b, draw the lines $e_R M_R$ and dM_R. Complete the perspective of the square. In a similar way, if desirable, M_L can be found and used. By comparison of Figs. 219 and 220, the triangle S_H–M_R–CVP is seen to be similar to $A_H F_H F'$; therefore, the measuring point M_R and the point of sight S_H are the same distance from CVP.

To make a perspective plan, assume the layout for M_R, M_L, S_H, and CVP. Select the line G at any desired elevation.

347. Problem 120. To make a parallel perspective drawing by the perspective plan method.

Analysis.—The perspective can be constructed on a perspective plan obtained as indicated in Problem 119. Heights and widths can be measured in the picture plane, and lines perpendicular to it vanish at CVP.

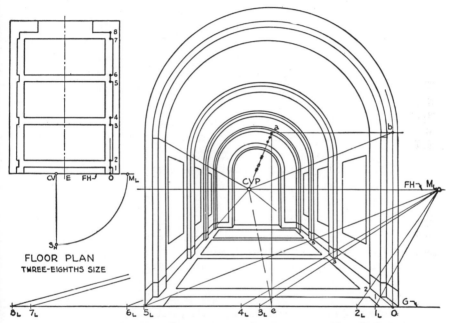

FLOOR PLAN
THREE-EIGHTHS SIZE

FIG. 221.—One-Point Perspective by the Perspective Plan Method.

Construction.—Fig. 221. *Given* the dimensions of an exhibition hall in a public building. *Required* to draw the interior perspective.

The small floor plan shows the location of the point of sight S_H, the center of vision CV, and the measuring point M_L. At the desired location of the perspective draw FH and locate CVP and M_L on it. The distance from CVP to M_L is the observer's distance from the picture plane. Locate the line G about five feet below FH. The line ae is the vertical center line of the hall, and a is the center of the arc for the section of the hall cut by the picture plane. Lay off ab equal to the radius of the arch of the ribs.

Draw $b0$ and from 0 lay off along G all the measurements for the length of the hall as 0–1_L, 0–2_L, etc. Draw the line CVP–0 and connect all the points 1_L, 2_L, etc., with the measuring point M_L. They intersect CVP–0 in the points 1, 2, etc., which are used to complete the perspective floor plan. The line CVP–a is the perspective of the center line of the arch, and CVP–b is the perspective of the springing line for each rib of the arch. By drawing vertical lines from points 1, 2, etc., on the floor and horizontals from their intersection with CVP–b to CVP–a, centers are found for all the circles of the arch and ribs.

The perspective plan method gives accurate intersections for the determination of the length of the hall along the line CVP–0.

348. Assignments.—See Chapter XIV, Group 13B.

349. *Problem 121.   To draw the perspective of a circle.*

Analysis.—The perspective of a circle may be drawn by finding the perspective of a circumscribing octagon or by finding a perspective of a number of points on a circle.

Construction.—Fig. 222. *Given* the blocks surmounted by short cylinders that have the centers of their circular tops at A and B. *Required* to draw the perspective of each.

The Circumscribing Octagon Method of drawing the perspective of the circle with center A.

First, circumscribe the circle by a square. Cut off corners of the square by lines tangent to the circle to obtain the octagon. Draw the perspective of the square. The right vanishing point and the point of sight are not shown. Locate the points 2, 3, 5, and 6 through which lines are drawn to complete the octagon. Note that two sides of the octagon vanish at each of the points L, R, and CVP; and that two are parallel to F. The inscribed ellipse is the perspective of the circle, and a is the perspective of the center of the circle, but is not the center of the ellipse, which is at c.

The Point Method of drawing the perspective of the circle with center B. In this case, eight points are selected, four of them being on the diagonals of the square and four at the points of tangency. Draw lines parallel to the sides of the square to find the points 2, 4, 6, and 8. Find the perspective of the square and locate on it points 1 to 9. Draw lines from these to L and R, whose intersections locate the perspectives of the selected points. The diagonals 1–9 and 5–CVP each pass through two of these points. Draw the ellipse through the points so located.

Since the point of sight which is in front of A is considerably to the right of B, the axis of this ellipse appears to be inclined, and the ellipse is not a satisfactory view of the circle.   If a person wishes to look at B, he would not use the picture plane F; but a picture plane perpendicular to his direction of sight.   Comparison of these two perspectives of identical objects illustrates the desirability of always selecting the center of vision near the center of width of the object.   Mechanically, the perspective of

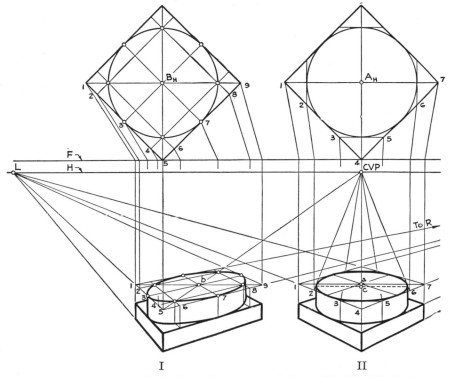

Fig. 222.—Horizontal Circles in Perspective.   Orthographic Plan Method.

the circle at B is correct.   Practically, it is impossible for the eye to see it in this manner.

350. Problem 122.   To draw the perspective of a circle by the use of measuring points.

Analysis.—A measuring point can be used for laying off the width dimensions for spacing points in the perspective.

Construction.—Fig. 223.   *Given* the dimensions of an arched doorway in a wall.   *Required* to draw the perspective of the circle of the arch and the perspective of the opening.

The drawing shows twelve points selected on the circle, and the perspective of these points is to be found.   Assume L, R, and the point S_F which is not shown on the drawing.   Locate M_L and M_R as in Problem 119. The center of the arch is located on FH.   Assume G at the bottom of the doorway, and lay off the measurements from 1_R to 7_R equal to those from 1 to 7.   Draw BR and intersect it by the lines from 1_R, 2_R, 3_R, etc., to M_R. The line BD is the vertical measuring line, and lines from points on it to R intersect the verticals drawn from the points just found to locate twelve points on the perspective of the circle.   The point a is the perspective of the center of the circle, but c is the center of the ellipse.   The drawing may be completed by the usual constructions.

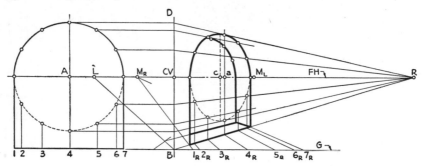

FIG. 223.—Vertical Circle in Perspective by Use of Measuring Points.

The major axis of this ellipse is vertical because the center of the circle is on the horizon line.   If the center had been above the horizon, the major axis would have been inclined with its top toward DB.   If it had been below the horizon, it would have been inclined with its top away from DB.

351. Assignments.—See Chapter XIV, Group 13C.

352. Problem 123.   To draw a shadow in perspective.

Analysis.—The direction of the sun's rays may be assumed, and the vanishing point found; but it is usually more satisfactory to assume the vanishing point so as to give a satisfactory shadow.   The shadow of a point of the object is found by assuming a vertical plane of light through the point and finding where the ray from this point intersects the line in which the plane of light cuts the plane which receives the shadow.

Construction.—Fig. 224.   *Given* the perspective of the object shown. *Required* to find its shadow on the ground and upon itself.

Assume Z to be the vanishing point of the parallel rays of sunlight. Then Y is the vanishing point for the lines in which vertical planes of light intersect the plane of the ground. The perspective plan of the cap is shown by $1_H2_H4_H6_H$. The vertical plane of light through 5 and 6 intersects the ground in the line 6_HY. The rays from 5 and 6 to Z cast their shadows at 5_S and 6_S. Other points on the cap cast shadows at 1_S, 2_S, 3_S, and 4_S, which are found in the same manner.

The vertical line at d_H casts a shadow which runs toward Y, and intersects 1_S2_S at point a_S, which is a point on the intersection of the shadow of the column and the shadow of the cap. Therefore, going back-

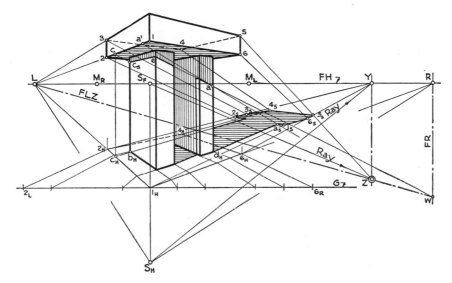

FIG. 224.—Shadows in Perspective.

ward on the ray from a_S, it is seen to be the shadow of point a on the column and a' on the cap. The shadow of the line 1–2 on the right faces of the two columns may be found as follows: FLZ is the vanishing line of the plane of light of the edge 1–2, and FR is the vanishing line of the plane of the right faces of the columns. The intersection w of FLZ and FR is a point on the line of intersection of these planes, and a is another point; therefore, the shadow ae is found by drawing wae. To find the shadow of edge 1–2 on the left face of the left column, draw the line b_Hc_H and locate c above c_H, which is the point on 1–2 that casts its shadow at c_S on the edge of the column. The lower edge of this shadow vanishes at L, and should pass through e, the point found by the previous construction.

353. Assignments.—See Chapter XIV, Group 13D.

CHAPTER XIV

PROBLEM ASSIGNMENTS

SUGGESTIONS AND INSTRUCTIONS FOR THE SOLUTION OF PROBLEMS

A working knowledge of descriptive geometry is attained only through the solution of a large number of problems with a minimum of assistance. Both the mental and the actual drawing-board solutions are essential for a complete understanding of this subject.

More than 50% of the problems of this edition have been illustrated. In some groups it seemed desirable to give layouts for nearly all the problems. These layouts are helpful to both the instructor and the student. They will expedite the work of the instructor in selecting problem assignments for the course; and they will be of invaluable aid to the student in visualizing the problem from the description. They will also serve as a check on the plotting of the data.

The coordinate system has been retained because it is believed to be the most accurate and rapid method of putting the data on the paper. Furthermore, and this is important, the data will be located on the paper so that space is available for the solution of the problem.

For efficient work in the solution of problems, the following procedure is recommended:

(1) Plot the data, examine it critically, then re-read the problem. (2) Note and visualize the given information. (3) Observe with care the requirements of the problem. (4) Analyze the problem and plan its solution in general terms according to fundamental principles. (5) Plan the most feasible drawing-board constructions. (6) Make the detailed constructions. (7) Show clearly the required information. (8) Check the work.

The character of the line work used in the solution of problems should be maintained at a high standard of excellence. Since usually only pencil work is desired, this should be neatly, accurately, and carefully executed. The notation of the points for principal views should be placed squarely on the sheet. For this, the lines on the descriptograph may be of assistance.

In many cases, the notation for points in other views may be placed in accordance with the orientation of the view.

The problems are numbered according to chapters and subjects. The first number represents the chapter; the following letter, the particular group; and the number following the dash, the specific number of each problem. For instance, 2A-1 immediately places the problem as being for Chapter II (Principal Views); Group A (Drawing Objects from Description); and Problem 1 of its group.

Standard practices are observed in the statement of problems: i.e., the size of a circle or a sphere is given by its diameter; the size of a regular hexagon is given by means of a diagonal which passes through its center, the length of this diagonal being the distance "across corners." The distance "across flats" is measured between parallel sides.

For the method of plotting points given by coordinates see pages 4, 5, and 6.

PROBLEMS FOR CHAPTER II

PRINCIPAL VIEWS

Group 2A. Drawing Objects from Description.

Draw three views of each of the following objects in accordance with the arrangement of views adopted by the American Standards Association. Use $\frac{1}{8}''$ capitals to letter the name of each view.

2A-1. $K(5\frac{1}{2}; \frac{1}{2}; 7)$ is one corner of a tetrahedron. The other corners are J, L, and M. J is $2\frac{1}{2}''$ above, $1''$ to the left of, and $2''$ in front of, K. L is $1\frac{1}{2}''$ to the right of, $3''$ above, and $\frac{1}{2}''$ in front of, K. M is $2''$ below, $2''$ to the right of, and $\frac{1}{2}''$ in front of, J. Draw the front, top, and left-side views of the tetrahedron.

2A-2. Draw three views of the tetrahedron $ABCD$. B is $\frac{1}{2}''$ to the right of, $1''$ in front of, and $2\frac{1}{2}''$ below, $A(7; 3; 6\frac{1}{2})$. C is $2''$ above, $2\frac{1}{2}''$ to the left of, and $1''$ in front of, B. D is $\frac{1}{2}''$ behind, $2''$ below, and $2\frac{1}{2}''$ to the left of, A.

2A-3. Draw front, top, and left-side views of the tetrahedron $A(5\frac{1}{2}; 3\frac{1}{2}; 6\frac{1}{2})$ BCD. C is $\frac{1}{2}''$ to the right of, $3''$ below, and $1''$ behind, A. B is $1''$ above, $2''$ to the left of, and $2''$ in front of, C. D is $2''$ in front of, $1''$ below, and $1\frac{1}{2}''$ to the right of, A.

2A-4. Draw front, top, and right-side views of the tetrahedron $RSTU$. S is $2''$ above, $1''$ to the right of, and $1\frac{1}{2}''$ behind, $R(\frac{1}{2}; 1\frac{1}{2}; 6)$. T is $3''$ to the right of, $1''$ below, and $\frac{1}{2}''$ behind, R. U is $1\frac{1}{2}''$ in front of, $1''$ above, and $2''$ to the right of, R.

2A-5. $A(\frac{1}{2}; 1; 5)$ is the lower, left, front corner of a block of wood $4''$ wide, $3''$ high, and $2''$ deep. A model is to be made from the block by discarding the following parts: the right three-fourths of the middle horizontal one-third; the right three-eighths of the upper one-third; and rounding the right end of the remaining upper portion to a radius of 1″. Draw the front, top, and right-side views of the model.

2A-6. $A(4; 1; 4\frac{1}{2})$ $D(7\frac{1}{2}; 1; 4\frac{1}{2})$ is the front side of a horizontal rectangle whose short sides are $2\frac{1}{2}″$ long. The rectangle is the base of a pyramid of 3″ altitude. A sliding support is to be made from the pyramid by discarding the upper one-half and cutting two centrally located slots through the top and bottom of the frustum. The bottom slot is 1″ wide and $\frac{1}{2}″$ high and extends parallel to the short sides of the base. The top slot is $\frac{1}{2}″$ by $\frac{1}{2}″$ and extends parallel to the long sides of the base. Draw front, top, and left-side views of the support.

Group 2B.   Typical Positions of a Plane.

In these problems divide the problem sheet into four equal rectangles by drawing a T-square line and an ortho-T-square line through the center of the sheet. Place each part of a problem in a separate space by arranging them in the following manner:

1	2
3	4

2B-1. Fig. 225-1. List the following planes and state their typical positions: $ABCD, CLKE, LMNJK, IJN, FHG$. Draw the front, top, and right-side views of each of the planes $FKJIH, DCE, CLKE$.

2B-2. Fig. 225-1. List the following planes and state their typical positions: $DCE, GHIO, GFH, FKJIH, INO$. Draw the front, top, and right-side views of each of the planes $ABCD, HIOG, IJN$.

2B-3. Fig. 225-2. List the following planes and state their typical positions: $GHKL, AEGF, LMF, FGL, DCIH$. Draw the front, top, and right-side views of each of the planes $ABCDE, AEGF, FGL$.

2B-4. Fig. 225-2. List the following planes and state their typical positions: $HIJK, FGL, EDHG, GHKL, ABCDE$. Draw the front, top, and right-side views of each of the planes $EDHG, HIJK, DCIH$.

2B-5. Fig. 225-3. List the following planes and state their typical positions: $GEH, GHQPO, KJI, FGOL, AFKI$. Draw the front, top, and right-side views of each of the planes $EDH, DCRQH, JKLMN$.

2B-6. Fig. 225-3. List the following planes and state their typical positions: $JKLMN, ABCDEF, LOPM, DCRQH, EDH$. Draw the front, top, and right-side views of each of the planes $GHQPO, LOPM, ABCDEF$.

2B-7. Fig. 225-4. List the following planes and state their typical positions: $LKNM, ABCDEF, LMQ, HGJI, HFG$. Draw the front, top, and right-side views of each of the planes $MNOP, GFEKJ, EDON$.

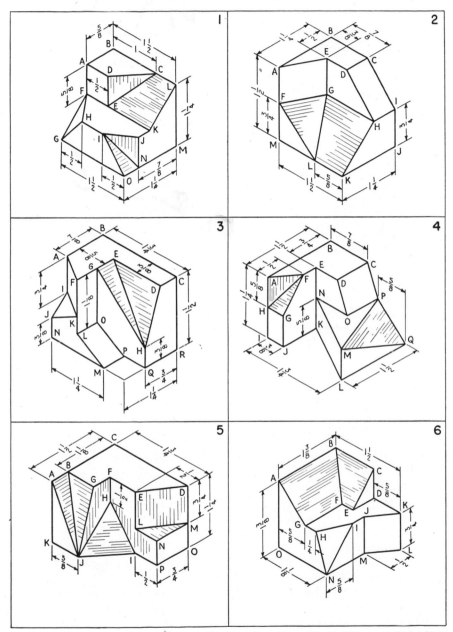

Fig. 225.—Objects for Groups 2B and 2C. Drawings Show Front, Top, and Right Side of the Blocks.

2B-8. Fig. 225-4. List the following planes and state their typical positions: *AFH, MNOP, GFEKJ, EDON, MPQ.* Draw the front, top, and right-side views of each of the planes *ABCDEF, MLKN, MPQ.*

2B-9. Fig. 225-5. List the following planes and state their typical positions: *GFHJ, AJK, HIJ, BCDEFG, BGJ.* Draw the front, top, and right-side views of each of the planes *EDML, FELNPIH, ABJ.*

2B-10. Fig. 225-5. List the following planes and state their typical positions: *ABJ, FELNPIH, EDML, HIJ, LMN.* Draw the front, top, and right-side views of each of the planes *GFIIJ, HIJ, BCDEFG.*

2B-11. Fig. 225-6. List the following planes and state their typical positions: *ABFG, AGHNO, CDE, JKLM, DKJIHGFE.* Draw the front, top, and right-side views of each of the planes *BCEF, IJMN, AGHNO.*

2B-12. Fig. 225-6. List the following planes and state their typical positions: *BCEF, IJMN, HIN, AGHNO, ABFG.* Draw the front, top, and right-side views of each of the planes *GFEDKJIH, HIN, ABFG.*

Group 2C.   Typical Directions of a Line.

In these problems divide the problem sheet into four equal rectangles and arrange the parts of a problem as in Group 2B. Draw the front, top, and right-side views of the specified lines. Name the lines; and, using subscripts, letter each end.

2C-1. Fig. 225-1. List the following lines and state their typical directions: *AB, DC, LK, CE, LM, HI, GH.* Draw the front, top, and right-side views of each of the lines *DC, IN, FG.*

2C-2. Fig. 225-1. List the following lines and state their typical directions: *IN, IJ, FK, GF, JN, OM, IO.* Draw the front, top, and right-side views of each of the lines *FH, EC, LK.*

2C-3. Fig. 225-2. List the following lines and state their typical directions: *FL, AE, EG, HK, GL, KJ, GH.* Draw the front, top, and right-side views of each of the lines *DH, GL, HK.*

2C-4. Fig. 225-2. List the following lines and state their typical directions: *DH, FG, IJ, HK, AB, GL, ML.* Draw the front, top, and right-side views of each of the lines *FL, AE, GL.*

2C-5. Fig. 225-3. List the following lines and state their typical directions: *GH, DH, IK, GO, FE, BC, EH.* Draw the front, top, and right-side views of each of the lines *DH, JK, EH.*

2C-6. Fig. 225-3. List the following lines and state their typical directions: *LM, JI, AF, EH, AB, ED, FL.* Draw the front, top, and right-side views of each of the lines *GH, IK, EG.*

2C-7. Fig. 225-4. List the following lines and state their typical directions: *EK, MP, DO, FG, AB, ED, HF.* Draw the front, top, and right-side views of each of the lines *MN, MQ, HF.*

2C-8. Fig. 225-4. List the following lines and state their typical directions:

$NM, HF, AI, MQ, JK, NO, PQ$. Draw the front, top, and right-side views of each of the lines MP, PQ, FG.

2C-9. Fig. 225-5. List the following lines and state their typical directions: $GJ, JI, EL, PO, AJ, FE, BJ$. Draw the front, top, and right-side views of each of the lines HJ, HI, ED.

2C-10. Fig. 225-5. List the following lines and state their typical directions: $HJ, LM, FH, BC, HI, BJ, CD$. Draw the front, top, and right-side views of each of the lines AJ, JI, BJ.

2C-11. Fig. 225-6. List the following lines and state their typical directions: $AG, NI, BF, JK, GF, BC, AO$. Draw the front, top, and right-side views of each of the lines BF, HI, HN.

2C-12. Fig. 225-6. List the following lines and state their typical directions: $CE, HN, HI, AB, BF, ON, JM$. Draw the front, top, and right-side views of each of the lines JK, AG, BF.

Group 2D. Visualization of a Line.

Draw three principal views of the plane figure given in each of the following problems. Read each line in the alphabetical order, and draw in the top view an arrow parallel to and in the direction of the line. Place a pencil in approximately the position the line occupies in space, as in Fig. 11. State the direction of each line by means of three letters as in Fig. 12.

2D-1. Fig. 226-1. The triangle $D(217)$ $E(3; 3\frac{1}{2}; 6)$ $F(1; 2\frac{1}{2}; 4)$.

2D-2. Fig. 226-2. The triangle $J(7; 3\frac{1}{2}; 6)$ $K(7; 1; 4\frac{1}{2})$ $L(537)$.

2D-3. Fig. 226-3. The triangle $A(1; 2; 6\frac{1}{2})$ $B(415)$ $C(234)$.

2D-4. Fig. 226-4. The triangle $A(247)$ $B(3\frac{1}{2}; 1; 5)$ $C(1; 2\frac{1}{2}; 5)$.

2D-5. Fig. 226-5. The parallelogram $C(4\frac{1}{2}; 2; 7)$ $D(7; 2\frac{1}{2}; 6)$ $E(7; 1\frac{1}{2}; 3\frac{1}{2})$ $F(4\frac{1}{2}; 1; 4\frac{1}{2})$.

2D-6. Fig. 226-6. The parallelogram $A(137)$ $B(3; 3\frac{1}{2}; 6)$ $C(3; 1\frac{1}{2}; 4\frac{1}{2})$ $D(1; 1; 5\frac{1}{2})$.

Group 2E. Points on a Line.

Draw three principal views of the given polygons and locate the required points in all three views. All distances are given as orthographic measurements.

2E-1. Fig. 226-1. Given the triangle $D(217)$ $E(3; 3\frac{1}{2}; 6)$ $F(1; 2\frac{1}{2}; 4)$. Locate the following points: point J on DF $\frac{3}{4}''$ to the left of D; point K on DE $1\frac{1}{4}''$ above D; point L on EF $1\frac{1}{4}''$ behind F.

2E-2. Fig. 226-2. Given the triangle $J(7; 3\frac{1}{2}; 6)$ $K(7; 1; 4\frac{1}{2})$ $L(537)$. Locate the following points: point X on JK $1''$ above K; point Y on KL $\frac{3}{4}''$ to the right of L; point Z on JL $\frac{1}{4}''$ behind J.

2E-3. Fig. 226-3. Given the triangle $A(1; 2; 6\frac{1}{2})$ $B(415)$ $C(234)$. Locate the following points: point R on AB $1''$ behind B; point S on AC $\frac{1}{2}''$ to the right of A; point T on BC $\frac{3}{4}''$ above B.

2E-4. Fig. 226-4. Given the triangle $A(247)$ $B(3\frac{1}{2}; 1; 5)$ $C(1; 2\frac{1}{2}; 5)$. Locate

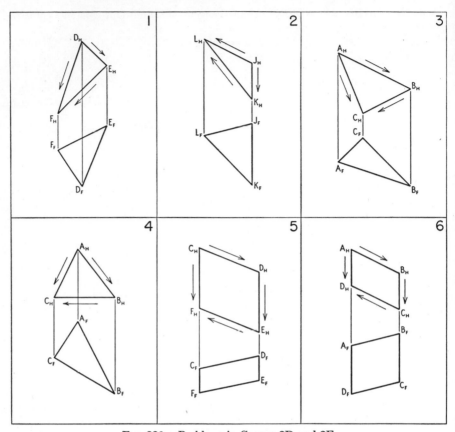

Fig. 226.—Problems in Groups 2D and 2E.

the following points: point X on AB $\frac{1}{2}''$ to the right of A; point Y on AC $\frac{1}{2}''$ in front of A; point Z on BC $\frac{3}{4}''$ below C.

2E-5. Fig. 226–5.   Given the parallelogram $C(4\frac{1}{2}; 2; 7)$ $D(7; 2\frac{1}{2}; 6)$ $E(7; 1\frac{1}{2}; 3\frac{1}{2})$ $F(4\frac{1}{2}; 1; 4\frac{1}{2})$.   Locate the following points: point W on CD $\frac{3}{4}''$ in front of C; point X on DE $1''$ in front of D; point Y on EF $\frac{1}{4}''$ below E; point Z on CF $1''$ behind F.

2E-6. Fig. 226-6.   Given the parallelogram $A(137)$ $B(3; 3\frac{1}{2}; 6)$ $C(3; 1\frac{1}{2}; 4\frac{1}{2})$ $D(1; 1; 5\frac{1}{2})$.   Locate the following points: point J on AB $\frac{1}{2}''$ to the right of A; point K on BC $1''$ in front of B; point L on CD $\frac{3}{4}''$ to the left of C; point M on AD $\frac{1}{2}''$ above D.

Group 2F.   Intersecting Lines.

Show the given and required lines in all views drawn.   Use notation with subscripts for the ends and the points of intersection of all lines.

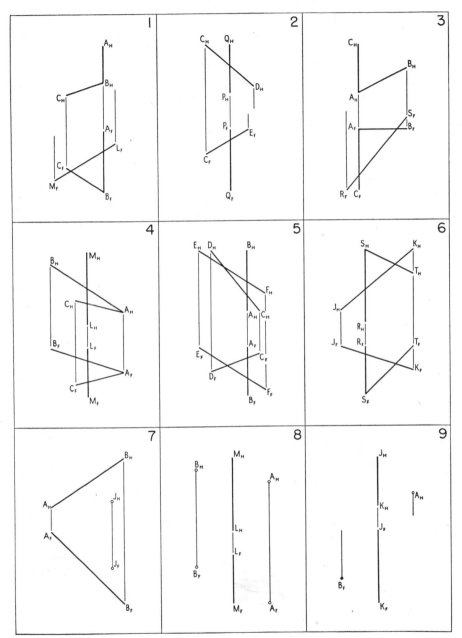

Fig. 227.—Intersecting Lines.   Group 2F.

2F-1. Fig. 227-1. Draw line $L(73X)$ $M(4\frac{1}{2}; 1\frac{1}{2}; X)$ intersecting $A(6\frac{1}{2}; 3\frac{1}{2}; 7)$ $B(6\frac{1}{2}; 1; 5\frac{1}{2})$ at point X, and $BC(525)$ at point Y. Draw three views of the lines.

2F-2. Fig. 227-2. Draw $C(1; 2\frac{1}{2}; 7)$ $D(3; X; 5\frac{1}{4})$ intersecting $P(2; 3\frac{1}{2}; 5)$ $Q(217)$ at point A, and $CE(2\frac{3}{4}; 3\frac{1}{2}; X)$ intersecting PQ at B. Draw three views of the lines.

2F-3. Fig. 227-3. Draw $R(1\frac{1}{2}; 1; X)$ $S(44X)$ intersecting $A(2; 3\frac{1}{2}; 5)$ $B(4; 3\frac{1}{2}; 6)$ at P and $AC(217)$ at Q. Draw three principal views of the lines.

2F-4. Fig. 227-4. Does $L(2\frac{1}{2}; 3; 4)$ $M(2\frac{1}{2}; 1; 7)$ intersect either of the lines $A(4; 2; 4\frac{1}{2})$ $B(1; 3; 6\frac{1}{2})$ or $AC(2; 1\frac{1}{2}; 5)$? Verify your answer.

2F-5. Fig. 227-5. Given the lines $A(3; 3; 4\frac{1}{2})$ $B(317)$, $C(3\frac{1}{2}; 2\frac{3}{4}; 4\frac{1}{2})$ $D(1\frac{1}{2}; 2; 7)$, and $E(137)$ $F(3\frac{3}{4}; 1\frac{1}{4}; 5\frac{1}{4})$. Do any of them intersect? Verify your answer.

2F-6. Fig. 227-6. Does $J(4; 3; 4\frac{1}{2})$ $K(727)$ intersect either of the lines $R(534)$ $S(517)$ or $ST(736)$? Verify your answer.

2F-7. Fig. 227-7. From point $J(3\frac{1}{2}; 2\frac{1}{2}; 5\frac{1}{4})$ draw a horizontal line JH, a frontal line JF, and a profile line JP, intersecting line $A(145)$ $B(417)$ at points H, F, and P, respectively. Draw three principal views of the lines.

2F-8. Fig. 227-8. Draw a horizontal line $B(1; 2\frac{1}{2}; 6\frac{1}{2})$ H intersecting $L(2\frac{1}{2}; 3; 4)$ $M(2\frac{1}{2}; 1; 7)$ at H, and a frontal line $A(416)F$ intersecting LM at F. Draw three principal views of the lines.

2F-9. Fig. 227-9. Draw a horizontal line $B(42X)H$, forward, $1\frac{3}{4}''$ long, intersecting $J(5\frac{1}{2}; 4; 7)$ $K(5\frac{1}{2}; 1; 5)$ at H. Draw a frontal line $A(7; X; 5\frac{1}{2})F$, downward, $2\frac{1}{2}''$ long, intersecting JK at F. Draw three views of the lines.

2F-10. Fig. 227-9. From $B(42X)$ draw a frontal line intersecting $J(5\frac{1}{2}; 4; 7)$ $K(5\frac{1}{2}; 1; 5)$ at F, $2''$ from B. Draw a horizontal line $A(7; X; 5\frac{1}{2})H$ intersecting JK at H, $1\frac{3}{4}''$ from A. Show three views of the lines.

Group 2G. Determination of Visibility.

Represent the object correctly in all views required by determining the visibility of each edge. If Rule 6 is necessary, use numbers as shown in Figs. 20 and 21.

2G-1. Fig. 228-1. Draw front, top, and right-side views of the tetrahedron $J(2\frac{1}{2}; 1\frac{1}{2}; 7)$ $K(3; 3\frac{1}{2}; 5\frac{1}{2})$ $L(1\frac{1}{2}; 3; 4\frac{1}{2})$ $M(1; 1; 5\frac{1}{2})$.

2G-2. Fig. 228-2. Draw front, top, and left-side views of the tetrahedron $A(6; 3; 4\frac{1}{2})$ $B(4\frac{1}{2}; 2\frac{1}{2}; 6\frac{1}{2})$ $C(617)$ $D(7; 1\frac{1}{2}; 5)$.

2G-3. Fig. 228-3. Draw front, top, and right-side views of the tetrahedron $A(217)$ $B(3\frac{1}{2}; 2\frac{1}{2}; 5\frac{1}{2})$ $C(2; 3; 4\frac{1}{2})$ $D(1; 1; 5\frac{1}{2})$.

2G-4. Fig. 228-4. $A(217)$ $B(3; 3; 4\frac{1}{2})$ $C(4; 2\frac{1}{2}; 6\frac{1}{2})$ $D(125)$ is a quadrilateral bent on BD. Draw front, top, and right-side views.

2G-5. Fig. 228-5. Draw the front, top, and right-side views of the bent quadrilateral $A(1; 2; 5\frac{1}{2})$ $B(217)$ $C(2; 3\frac{1}{2}; 4\frac{1}{2})$ $D(3\frac{1}{2}; 3\frac{1}{2}; 7)$ bent on BD.

2G-6. Fig. 228-6. $E(7; 3\frac{1}{2}; 7)$ $F(6; 3\frac{1}{2}; 4\frac{1}{2})$ $G(617)$ $H(5; 1\frac{1}{2}; 5\frac{1}{2})$ is a piece of sheet metal bent on HF. Draw the front, top, and left-side views.

2G-7. Fig. 228-7. $R(5; 3\frac{1}{4}; 7)$ $S(7; 2; 4\frac{3}{4})$ and $T(5\frac{1}{4}; 3\frac{3}{4}; 4\frac{3}{4})$ $U(6\frac{1}{2}; 1\frac{1}{4}; 6\frac{1}{4})$ are the center lines of two $\frac{1}{4}''$ diameter rods. Draw front, top, and left-side views of the rods. Draw the ends as freehand ellipses of the proper visibility.

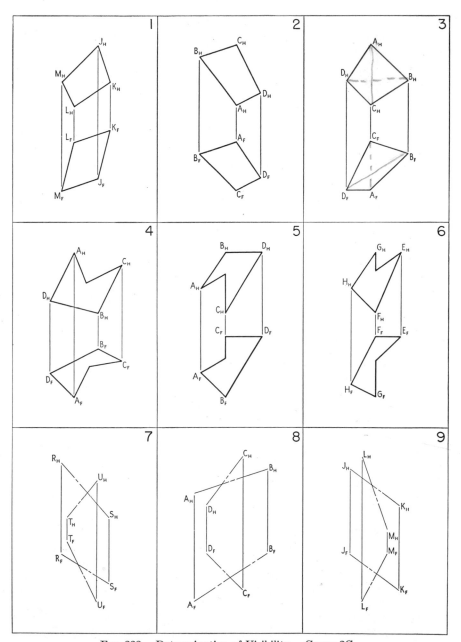

FIG. 228.—Determination of Visibility.   Group 2G.

2G-8. Fig. 228-8. $A(1; 1; 5\frac{1}{2})$ $B(4; 3; 6\frac{1}{2})$ and $C(3; 1\frac{1}{2}; 7)$ $D(1\frac{1}{2}; 3; 5)$ are the center lines of two $\frac{1}{4}''$ diameter rods. Draw front, top, and right-side views of the rods. Draw the ends as freehand ellipses of the proper visibility.

2G-9. Fig. 228-9. $J(5; 3; 6\frac{1}{2})$ $K(7; 1\frac{1}{2}; 5)$ and $L(5\frac{1}{2}; 1; 7)$ $M(6\frac{1}{2}; 3; 4)$ are the center lines of two $\frac{1}{4}''$ diameter rods. Draw front, top, and left-side views of the rods. Draw the ends as freehand ellipses of the proper visibility.

2G-10. Draw front, top, and right-side views of the tetrahedron $C(1; 2\frac{1}{2}; 6)$ $D(217)$ $E(3; 2\frac{1}{2}; 7)$ $F(2\frac{1}{2}; 3; 5)$.

2G-11. Draw front, top, and right-side views of the tetrahedron $R(1; 3; 5\frac{1}{2})$ $S(2\frac{1}{2}; 2\frac{1}{2}; 7)$ $T(3\frac{1}{2}; 1; 5\frac{1}{2})$ $U(2\frac{1}{2}; 1; 4\frac{1}{2})$.

2G-12. $A(5; 2\frac{1}{2}; 6)$ $C(7; 1\frac{1}{2}; 6\frac{1}{2})$ $B(6; 3\frac{1}{2}; 7)$ $D(615)$ is a piece of tin bent on AB. Draw front, top, and left-side views.

2G-13. Draw front, top, and right-side views of the tetrahedron $R(1; 2\frac{1}{2}; 4\frac{1}{2})$ $S(1\frac{1}{2}; 1; 6)$ $T(3; 2\frac{1}{2}; 7)$ $U(3; 3\frac{1}{2}; 6)$.

2G-14. Draw front, top, and right-side views of the tetrahedron $J(1; 2\frac{1}{2}; 7)$ $K(2; 3\frac{1}{2}; 7)$ $L(3\frac{1}{2}; 2\frac{1}{2}; 5)$ $M(2; 1; 5\frac{1}{2})$.

2G-15. Draw front, top, and right-side views of the tetrahedron $A(127)$ $B(217)$ $C(326)$ $D(2; 3; 5\frac{1}{2})$.

2G-16. Draw front, top, and right-side views of the bent quadrilateral $A(1; 2; 5\frac{1}{2})$ $C(3; 2; 6\frac{1}{2})$ $B(237)$ $D(2\frac{1}{2}; 1; 5\frac{3}{4})$ bent on CD.

2G-17. Draw front, top, and left-side views of the tetrahedron $J(4\frac{3}{4}; 1\frac{3}{4}; 6)$ $K(5\frac{3}{4}; 1\frac{1}{2}; 6\frac{1}{2})$ $L(736)$ $M(5\frac{3}{4}; 3; 5)$.

2G-18. Draw front, top, and left-side views of the tetrahedron $L(5; 1; 5\frac{1}{2})$ $M(617)$ $P(7; 2; 5\frac{1}{2})$ $Q(5\frac{1}{2}; 3; 5)$.

2G-19. $A(617)$ $B(7; 2\frac{1}{2}; 5)$ $D(526)$ $C(635)$ is a piece of sheet metal bent on AD. Draw front, top, and left-side views.

PROBLEMS FOR CHAPTER III

AUXILIARY VIEWS

Group 3A.   Auxiliary Elevations.

The direction of sight for an auxiliary view may be expressed concisely in such terms as these: "Draw an auxiliary elevation taken 30° in front of the right," meaning, "Draw an auxiliary elevation for which the direction of sight is 30° in front of that for a right-side view."

The front and top views are required in every problem in addition to the auxiliary view specified. Orientate and name the views.

3A-1. Fig. 229-1.   Given the tetrahedron $A(4\frac{1}{2}; 1; 7)$ $B(5\frac{1}{2}; 3; 4\frac{1}{2})$ $C(726)$ $D(715)$. Draw an auxiliary view 30° in front of the left.

3A-2. Fig. 229-2.   Given the tetrahedron $A(324)$ $B(3; \frac{1}{2}; 5\frac{1}{2})$ $C(4; 2\frac{3}{4}; 6)$ $D(5; 2; 4\frac{1}{2})$. Draw an auxiliary view 30° in front of the right, and an auxiliary view 45° to the rear of the left.

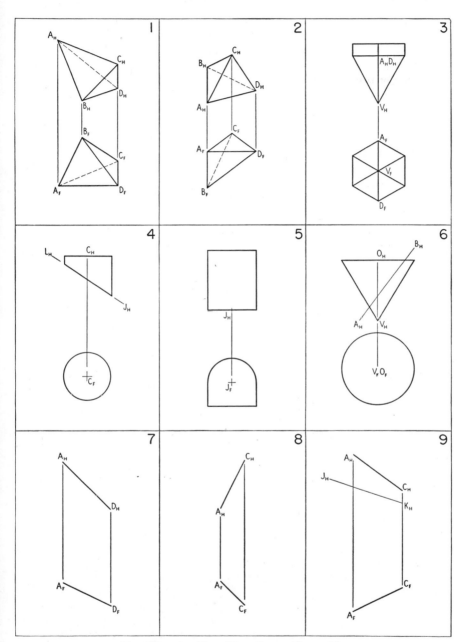

FIG. 229.—Auxiliary Elevations.   Group 3A.

3A-3. Fig. 229-3. $A(2; 3\frac{1}{2}; 7)$ $D(217)$ is a diagonal of a frontal regular hexagon which is the front base of a right prism of $\frac{1}{2}''$ altitude. The hexagon is also the base of a right pyramid with vertex $V(2; 2\frac{1}{4}; 5)$. Draw a view of the solid perpendicular to the right-hand triangular face of the pyramid.

3A-4. Fig. 229-4. $C(627)$ is the center of a $2''$ diameter frontal circle which is the rear base of a right cylinder that has been truncated by a vertical plane through $L(4\frac{1}{2}; X; 7)$ $J(7\frac{1}{2}; X; 5)$. Draw an auxiliary view of the truncated cylinder perpendicular to the cut surface.

3A-5. Fig. 229-5. $J(225)$ is the center of a frontal semicircle of 10 ft. radius, which is the front end of the cylindrical roof of a pump house. The house is 20' wide, 25' deep, and has walls 10' high. Scale: $1'' = 10$ ft. Draw an auxiliary view 30° in front of the right.

3A-6. Fig. 229-6. $O(2\frac{1}{2}; 2; 6\frac{1}{2})$ is the center of a $3''$ diameter frontal circle which is the base of a cone whose vertex is $V(2\frac{1}{2}; 2; 4)$. The cone is truncated by a vertical plane through $A(1\frac{3}{4}; X; 4)$ $B(4X7)$. Draw the front and top views of the cone and an auxiliary view perpendicular to the cut surface. Crosshatch the cut surface.

3A-7. Fig. 229-7. $A(5; 2\frac{1}{2}; 7)$ $D(7; 1\frac{1}{2}; 5)$ is a diagonal of a vertical regular hexagon. Draw the front and top views of the hexagon and the necessary auxiliary view.

3A-8. Fig. 229-8. $A(125)$ $C(217)$ is the lowest side of a vertical equilateral triangle which is the base of a right pyramid of $1\frac{1}{2}''$ altitude. The vertex is to the right of the base. Draw the necessary auxiliary view and the front and top views of the pyramid.

3A-9. Fig. 229-9. $A(5; 1; 7\frac{1}{2})$ $C(726)$ is a diagonal of a vertical square which is the base of a right pyramid of $2''$ altitude. The vertex is in front of the base. Draw the portion of the pyramid which is behind a vertical plane through $J(4; X; 6\frac{1}{2})$ $K(7; X; 5\frac{1}{2})$. Crosshatch the cut surface.

Group 3B. Right-Auxiliary and Left-Auxiliary Views.

The front and top views are required in every problem in addition to the auxiliary view specified. Orientate and name the views.

3B-1. Fig. 230-1. Given the tetrahedron $R(3; 1\frac{1}{2}; 7)$ $S(5; 1\frac{1}{2}; 6\frac{1}{2})$ $T(415)$ $U(436)$. Draw auxiliary views in the direction of the arrows $A(2\frac{1}{2}; 3; 6)$ $B(3\frac{1}{4}; 2\frac{1}{2}; 6)$ and $C(5\frac{1}{2}; 3; 6)$ $D(4\frac{3}{4}; 2\frac{1}{4}; 6)$.

3B-2. Fig. 230-2. $A(346)$ $C(547)$ is a diagonal of a horizontal square which is the upper base of a right prism of $1''$ altitude. Draw the front and top views of the prism and the following auxiliary views: (1) right-auxiliary view 30° above the horizontal; (2) left-auxiliary view 45° below the horizontal.

3B-3. Fig. 230-3. $V(5\frac{1}{2}; 3\frac{1}{2}; 6)$ is the vertex and $O(5\frac{1}{2}; 1; 6)$ is the midpoint of the pentagonal base of a right pyramid. $A(716)$ is one corner of the base. Draw an auxiliary view of the pyramid showing the true shape of the left lateral face.

3B-4. Fig. 230-4. $Q(2\frac{1}{2}; 2; 6)$ is the center of a $3''$ diameter horizontal circle which is the upper base of a right cylinder of $1''$ altitude. $A(1\frac{1}{2}; 2; 6)$ $C(3\frac{1}{2}; 2; 6)$ is a diagonal of a horizontal square which is the upper end of a hole cut through the cylinder. Draw a right-auxiliary view 30° above the horizontal.

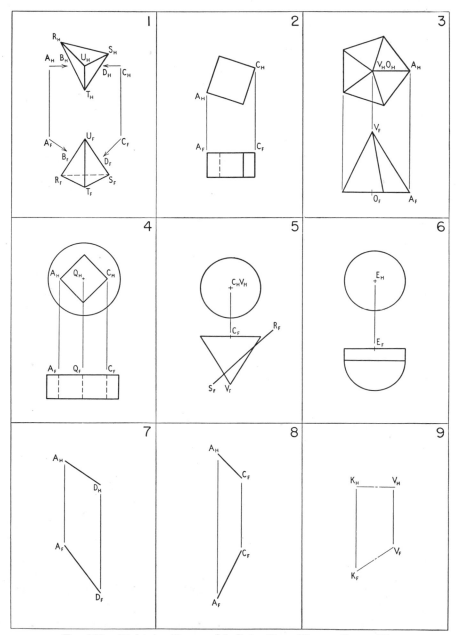

FIG. 230.—Right-Auxiliary and Left-Auxiliary Views.   Group 3B.

3B-5. Fig. 230-5. $V(2\frac{1}{4}; 2; 6)$ is the vertex and $C(2\frac{1}{4}; 4; 6)$ is the center of the $2\frac{1}{2}''$ diameter base of a right cone which is truncated by an ortho-frontal plane through $R(4; 4\frac{1}{4}; X)$ $S(1\frac{1}{2}; 2; X)$. Draw the front and top views of the truncated cone, and an auxiliary view perpendicular to the cut surface. Crosshatch the cut surface when visible.

3B-6. Fig. 230-6. $E(4; 2\frac{1}{2}; 6\frac{1}{4})$ is the center of a $2\frac{1}{2}''$ diameter horizontal circle which is the upper end of a vertical cylinder of $\frac{1}{2}''$ altitude. Joined to the bottom of the cylinder is a hemisphere of $1\frac{1}{4}''$ radius. Draw the following views: (1) right-auxiliary view 45° above the horizontal; (2) left-auxiliary view 30° above the horizontal.

3B-7. Fig. 230-7. $A(1; 3; 6\frac{1}{2})$ $D(2\frac{1}{2}; 1; 5\frac{1}{2})$ is a diagonal of an ortho-frontal hexagon which is the base of a right pyramid of $2''$ altitude. The vertex is to the right of the base. Draw front and top views, and the necessary auxiliary view.

3B-8. Fig. 230-8. $A(617)$ $C(736)$ is one diagonal of an ortho-frontal square which is the lower base of a right prism of $2''$ altitude. Draw the necessary auxiliary view and the front and top views.

3B-9. Fig. 230-9. $V(5; 4; 6\frac{1}{2})$ is the vertex of a right pyramid and $K(3\frac{1}{2}; 3; 6\frac{1}{2})$ is the center of its base, which is a regular hexagon $1\frac{1}{4}''$ across corners. Two sides of the base are horizontal. Draw the following views of the pyramid: (1) a right-auxiliary view showing the true shape of the base; (2) front view; (3) top view; (4) a right-auxiliary view showing true shape of one lateral face; (5) an auxiliary view 30° above the left; and (6) an auxiliary view 45° below the left.

Group 3C.   Front-Auxiliary and Rear-Auxiliary Views.

The front and top views are required in every problem in addition to the auxiliary view specified. Orientate and name the views.

3C-1. Fig. 231-1. Given the tetrahedron $R(217)$ $S(3\frac{1}{2}; 1\frac{1}{2}; 5)$ $T(2; 3\frac{1}{2}; 6)$ $U(1; 3; 5\frac{1}{2})$. Draw a view of the tetrahedron with the direction of sight parallel to TR.

3C-2. Fig. 231-2. $J(636)$ $K(637)$ is the axis of a right prism. The bases are squares, each having one $2\frac{1}{2}''$ diagonal vertical. JK is also the axis of a $1\frac{1}{2}''$ diameter hole drilled through the block. Draw a rear-auxiliary view 60° above the horizontal.

3C-3. Fig. 231-3. $A(4\frac{1}{2}; 1; 6)$ $C(717)$ is a diagonal of a horizontal square which is the base of a right pyramid of $2''$ altitude. Draw a front-auxiliary view of the pyramid 45° above the horizontal.

3C-4. Fig. 231-4. The side view is an edge view of the regular hexagon of which $A(116)$ $B(337)$ is a diagonal. Draw the front and top views of the hexagon and any other views that are necessary.

3C-5. Fig. 231-5. $V(247)$ is the vertex of a right pyramid and $O(2; 1\frac{1}{2}; 6)$ is the center of its base, which is a regular hexagon having two of its $1''$ sides horizontal. Draw a view showing the altitude of the pyramid, a view showing true shape of the base, and the front and top views.

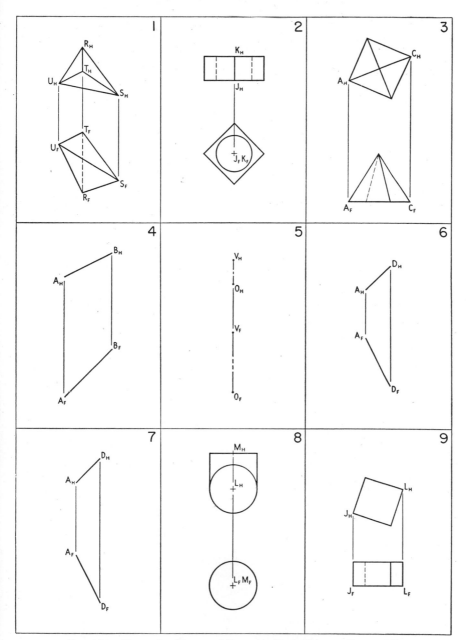

FIG. 231.—Front-Auxiliary and Rear-Auxiliary Views. Group 3C.

3C-6. Fig. 231-6. $A(135)$ $D(216)$ is a diagonal of a regular hexagon which is an edge view in the side view. This hexagon is the lower base of a right prism of $\frac{3}{4}''$ altitude. Draw the front and top views of the prism, and any other views that are necessary.

3C-7. Fig. 231-7. $A(636)$ $D(717)$ is a diagonal of an ortho-profile square. Draw the necessary auxiliary view and the front and top views of the square.

3C-8. Fig. 231-8. $L(626)$ $M(6;2;7\frac{1}{2})$ is the axis of a right cylinder of $2''$ diameter which has been truncated by an ortho-profile plane through L, sloping forward $45°$ with the horizontal. Draw an auxiliary view perpendicular to the cut surface.

3C-9. Fig. 231-9. $J(136)$ $L(337)$ is a diagonal of the lower horizontal square base of a right prism of $1''$ altitude. Draw a rear-auxiliary view of the prism $60°$ above the horizontal, and a rear-auxiliary view $30°$ below the horizontal.

3C-10. Fig. 231-9. Same layout as Problem 3C-9. Draw a front-auxiliary view $45°$ above the horizontal, and a front-auxiliary view $30°$ below the horizontal.

Group 3D. Miscellaneous Auxiliary Views.

3D-1. Fig. 232-1. $V(7;3;5\frac{1}{2})$ is the vertex of an isosceles triangle whose base is $1\frac{1}{2}''$ long. $O(5\frac{1}{2};1;5\frac{1}{2})$ is the midpoint of the base. This triangle is the front lateral face of a right hexagonal base pyramid with vertex V. Draw the front and top views of the pyramid, and the necessary auxiliary view.

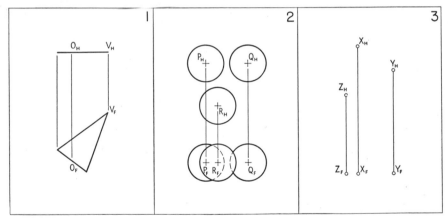

FIG. 232.—Miscellaneous Auxiliary Views. Group 3D.

3D-2. Fig. 232-2. $P(4\frac{1}{2};1\frac{1}{4};6\frac{1}{2})$, $Q(6\frac{1}{4};1\frac{1}{4};6\frac{1}{2})$, and $R(5;1\frac{1}{4};4\frac{3}{4})$ are the centers of $1\frac{1}{2}''$ diameter spheres. Find the center of another sphere of the same size resting on top of them. Draw front and top views of all four spheres.

3D-3. Fig. 232-3. Locate the center and draw a $3''$ diameter sphere which will have the points $X(5;1\frac{1}{4};6\frac{1}{2})$, $Y(6\frac{1}{2};1\frac{1}{4};5\frac{1}{2})$, and $Z(4\frac{1}{2};1\frac{1}{4};4\frac{1}{2})$ on its surface.

3D-4. $V(727)$ is the vertex of a right pyramid and $Q(4\frac{1}{2}; 2; 5\frac{1}{2})$ is the center of its square base. The square has $3''$ diagonals and one of its corners is $1''$ behind Q and below Q. Draw front and top views of the pyramid and the necessary auxiliary view.

3D-5. $J(536)$ $K(6\frac{1}{2}; 2; 6)$ is the axis of a right prism. The bases are equilateral triangles that may be inscribed in $2\frac{1}{2}''$ diameter circles. One corner of the triangle with base J is above J and $1''$ behind J. Draw the front and top views of the prism, and the necessary auxiliary view.

3D-6. $O(3\frac{1}{2}; 2; 5\frac{1}{2})$ is the center of a regular hexagon of $1\frac{1}{4}''$ sides which is the base of a right pyramid with vertex $V(127)$. One corner of the hexagon is in front of O and $\frac{3}{8}''$ below O. Draw front and top views of the pyramid and the necessary auxiliary view.

3D-7. $V(425)$ is the vertex and $K(227)$ is the center of the regular hexagonal base of a right pyramid. The sides of the base are $1\frac{1}{2}''$ long and one corner, A, is above K and $1''$ in front of K. Draw the front and top views of the pyramid and any other necessary view.

3D-8. $L(1\frac{1}{2}; 2; 6)$ $M(3; 3; 6)$ is the axis of a right prism. One corner of the regular pentagon which forms the upper base is in front of M and $\frac{3}{4}''$ above M. This pentagon can be inscribed in a $2\frac{1}{2}''$ diameter circle. Draw the front and top views of the prism, and the necessary auxiliary view.

3D-9. $V(647)$ is the vertex and $X(626)$ is the center of the base of a right pyramid. The base is a square having $1\frac{3}{4}''$ diagonals. One corner of the square is in front of X and $\frac{3}{4}''$ to the left of X. Draw the front and top views of the pyramid and any other views that are needed.

3D-10. $K(426)$ is the center of a regular pentagon which is the base of a right pyramid whose vertex is at $V(628)$. The pentagon may be inscribed in a $2\frac{1}{2}''$ diameter circle, and one corner, A, is to the right of K and $\frac{1}{2}''$ above it. Draw the front and top views of the pyramid. Show the locus plane for locating A.

3D-11. $A(117)$ $B(3\frac{1}{2}; 2; 7)$ is the base of an isosceles triangle of $1\frac{1}{2}''$ altitude. The vertex, C, is above AB and $\frac{3}{4}''$ in front of AB. This triangle is the rear base of a right prism of $1\frac{1}{2}''$ altitude. Draw the front and top views of the prism and the necessary auxiliary view.

3D-12. $R(1\frac{1}{2}; 1\frac{1}{2}; 6\frac{1}{2})$ $S(1\frac{1}{2}; 3; 5\frac{1}{2})$ is the axis of a right prism. Its bases are equilateral triangles that may be inscribed in $2\frac{1}{2}''$ diameter circles. One corner of the triangle with center S is to the right of S and $\frac{1}{2}''$ below S. Draw three principal views of the prism and the necessary auxiliary view.

3D-13. $K(216)$ is the center of the base of a right pyramid. The vertex is at $V(436)$. The base is a square which may be inscribed in a $3''$ diameter circle. One corner, A, of the base is in front of K and $1''$ below K. Draw the front and top views and any other necessary view of the pyramid. Show locus plane.

3D-14. $P(127)$ and $Q(3\frac{1}{2}; 2; 5\frac{1}{2})$ are the vertices of two equal right pyramids which have a common base. The base is a regular pentagon which may be inscribed in a $2\frac{1}{2}''$ diameter circle, and the lowest side is horizontal. Draw the front and top views of the pyramids, and the necessary auxiliary view.

3D-15. $C(4\frac{1}{2}; 3; 7)$ $D(7; 1\frac{1}{2}; 7)$ is the rear lateral edge of a right prism. The bases are equilateral triangles of $2''$ sides. The triangle of which C is one corner has another corner $1''$ below C. Draw the front and top views of the prism and the necessary auxiliary view.

3D-16. $B(146)$ $E(127)$ is one lateral edge of a right prism. The bases are squares having diagonals $2''$ long. One end of the diagonal which has B for the other end, is $1''$ in front of B and to the right of B. Draw three principal views of the prism and the necessary auxiliary view.

PROBLEMS FOR CHAPTER IV

OBLIQUE VIEWS

Group 4A. The Normal View of a Line and the Angle a Line Makes with a Principal Plane.

4A-1. Fig. 233-1. $M(3\frac{1}{2}; 2\frac{1}{2}; 5\frac{1}{2})$ $A(3; \frac{1}{2}; 7)$, $MB(2; \frac{1}{2}; 4\frac{1}{2})$, and $MC(5; \frac{1}{2}; 4\frac{3}{4})$ are legs of a tripod fastened to the floor of a garage at the points A, B, and C. Find the length of each leg and the angle it makes with the floor. Scale: $\frac{1}{2}'' = 1'\text{-}0''$.

4A-2. Fig. 233-2. $J(436)$ $A(2\frac{1}{2}; 3\frac{1}{2}; 7)$, $JB(4\frac{1}{2}; 1; 7)$, and $JC(5\frac{1}{2}; 4; 7)$ are three members of a structure fastened to a frontal wall at A, B, and C, respectively. Find the length of each member and the angle it makes with the wall. Scale: $\frac{1}{4}'' = 1'\text{-}0''$.

4A-3. Fig. 233-3. $A(446)$ is the top of a vertical flagpole $24'$ high. $K(436)$ $R(2\frac{3}{4}; X; 6\frac{1}{2})$, $KS(5X7)$, and $KT(4\frac{1}{4}; X; 5)$ are guy wires from the pole downward to the ground. KR is $15'$ long, KS is $18'$ long, and KT is $16'$ long. Draw the front view of the guy wires and measure the angle each makes with the pole. Scale: $\frac{1}{8}'' = 1'\text{-}0''$.

4A-4. Fig. 233-4. $L(2; 2\frac{1}{2}; 6)$ $A(1; 3\frac{1}{2}; 7)$, $LB(1; 1; 6\frac{1}{2})$, and $LC(1; 3; 4\frac{1}{2})$ are members of a support for a hoist. It is fastened to a profile wall at points A, B, and C. Find the lengths of the members and the angles they make with the wall. Scale: $\frac{1}{2}'' = 1'\text{-}0''$.

4A-5. Fig. 233-5. $J(4; 3\frac{1}{2}; 6)$ $A(3\frac{1}{2}; X; 7)$, $JB(2\frac{1}{2}; 1; X)$, and $JC(51X)$ are guy wires fastened to a pole at J. JA is $25'$ long and extends downward; JB is $35'$ long and extends forward; and JC extends forward and makes $15°$ with a frontal plane through J. Draw all three wires in the front and top views and find the length of JC. Scale: $1'' = 10$ ft.

4A-6. Fig. 233-6. $K(2\frac{1}{2}; 3; 5\frac{1}{2})$ $A(1\frac{1}{2}; 1; 6\frac{1}{4})$, $KB(2; 4; 6\frac{1}{2})$, and $KC(145)$ represent steel members of a structure which supports a chain hoist, and are fastened to the floor at A, to a frontal wall at B, and to a profile wall at C, respectively. Find the length of each member and the angle for the bracket needed to fasten it to the surface to which it is attached. Scale: $\frac{1}{4}'' = 1'\text{-}0''$.

4A-7. Fig. 233-7. Portions of an inaccessible vertical fir tree can be seen from $A(116)$ and $D(517)$, both at the edge of the water of a lake. A surveyor sets up his

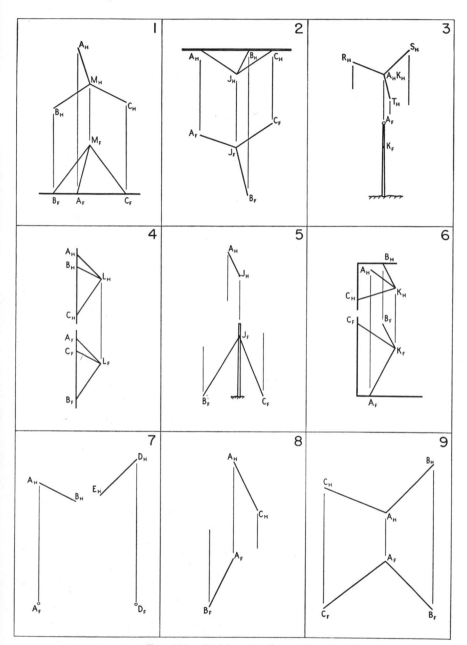

FIG. 233.—Problems in Group 4A.

transit at A and sights upward 20° in the direction $AB(2\frac{1}{2}; X; 5\frac{1}{4})$ to the base of the tree. At D he sights upward 47° in the direction $DE(3\frac{1}{2}; X; 5\frac{1}{2})$ to the top of the tree. Locate the tree in the front and top views and find its height. Scale: $1'' = 20$ ft.

4A-8. Fig. 233-8. $A(437)$ is the vertex of an isosceles triangle whose equal sides $AB(31X)$ and $AC(5X5)$ are each $2\frac{1}{2}''$ long. Draw front and top views of the triangle and find the length of the third side.

4A-9. Fig. 233-9. $A(435)$ $B(617)$ and $AC(1\frac{1}{2}; 1; 6)$ are members of a structure made of steel tubing. A third member is to be welded to AB at D, 9' from A, and to AC at E, 12' from A. Draw front and top views of the connecting piece and find its length. Scale: $\frac{1}{4}'' = 1'\text{-}0''$.

4A-10. Fig. 244-1. The front view is an edge view of the roof of a house and $P(4; 4\frac{1}{2}; 6)$ is the top of a vertical antenna pole fastened to the roof. The pole is guyed by three wires, $K(4; 3\frac{1}{2}; 6)$ $A(3X7)$, $KB(5; 1; 6\frac{1}{2})$, and $KC(3\frac{1}{2}; 2; 5)$, all fastened to the roof. Find the length of each wire and the angle it makes with the pole. What is the length of the pole? Scale: $1'' = 10$ ft.

4A-11. Fig. 244-2. Point $P(417)$ in a structure is to be connected to $A(4; 4; 5\frac{1}{2})$ $B(627)$ at a point 4' from A; and to $AC(216)$ at a point 6' from A, using steel tubing, and by welding. Find the length of the connecting pieces and draw them in the front and top views. Scale: $\frac{1}{2}'' = 1'\text{-}0''$.

4A-12. Fig. 245-1. $J(4; 2\frac{1}{2}; 5)$ $R(2\frac{1}{2}; 3\frac{1}{4}; 7)$, $JS(4\frac{1}{2}; 1; 7)$, and $JT(5\frac{1}{2}; 3\frac{1}{2}; 7)$ are members of a steel support fastened to a frontal wall at R, S, and T. Find the length of each member and the angle it makes with the wall. Scale: $\frac{1}{4}'' = 1'\text{-}0''$.

4A-13. Fig. 245-2. $K(425)$ $A(3\frac{1}{2}; 1; 7)$, $KB(5\frac{1}{2}; 1; 4\frac{1}{2})$, and $KC(2\frac{1}{2}; 1; 4)$ are the legs of a tripod resting on a level concrete slab. Find the length of the legs and the angle each makes with the slab. Scale: $\frac{1}{4}'' = 1'\text{-}0''$.

4A-14. Fig. 245-3. $M(6; 2; 5\frac{1}{2})$ $A(7; 1\frac{1}{2}; 7)$, $MB(7; 3\frac{1}{2}; 6)$, and $MC(7; 1; 4\frac{1}{2})$ are the members of a structure fastened to a profile wall at points A, B, and C. Find the length of each member and the angle it makes with the wall. Scale: $\frac{1}{4}'' = 1'\text{-}0''$.

4A-15. Fig. 245-4. $J(535)$ $R(5\frac{1}{2}; 4\frac{1}{2}; 7)$, $JS(616)$, and $JT(746)$ are members of a steel support fastened to a frontal wall at R, to the floor at S, and to a profile wall at T. Find the lengths of the members and the angle each makes with the surface to which it is attached. Scale: $\frac{1}{2}'' = 1'\text{-}0''$.

4A-16. Fig. 245-5. $A(436)$, $B(6; X; 4\frac{3}{4})$, and $C(1; X; 4\frac{1}{2})$ are points on the surface of the ground. A surveyor sets up his transit at A and looks downward at B and C. He reads vertical angles (angles with the horizontal) of 35° for AB and 18° for AC. Find the straight-line distances from A to B and from A to C. Find the difference in elevation between B and C, and the true length of BC. Scale: $1'' = 80$ ft.

4A-17. Fig. 245-6. $J(1; 2\frac{1}{2}; 5)$ $K(317)$ is the body diagonal of a rectangular prism whose mutually perpendicular sides are horizontal, frontal, and profile. Find the length of JK and the angles which it makes with the sides of the prism

4A-18. Fig. 244-3. Point $A(317)$ is to be connected to $J(3\frac{1}{2}; 3; 4\frac{1}{2})$ $K(616)$ at points B and C. B is $3'$ from K and C is $4'$ from J. These are steel rods fastened by welding. Find the length of each connecting piece and draw it in the front and top views. Scale: $\frac{1}{4}'' = 1'$-$0''$.

Group 4B.   Parallel Lines.

4B-1. Given the triangle $A(136)$ $B(217)$ $C(325)$. Draw the lines $R(5; 2\frac{1}{2}; 6)$ S, RT, and RU parallel and equal to the lines AB, AC, and BC, respectively. Show them in the front and top views.

4B-2. Given the lines $A(217)$ $B(1; 2\frac{1}{2}; 5)$ and $C(537)$ $D(7; 1; 5\frac{1}{2})$ and the points $J(235)$ and $L(4\frac{1}{2}; 3; 7)$. Draw JK $2''$ long, downward, and parallel to AB. Draw LM $2\frac{1}{2}''$ long, downward, and parallel to CD. Draw the lines in the front and top views.

4B-3. $A(246)$ $B(3; 3\frac{1}{2}; 5\frac{1}{2})$, $AD(1\frac{1}{2}; 3; 5\frac{1}{2})$, and $AE(1\frac{3}{4}; 2\frac{1}{2}; 7)$ are three adjacent edges of a parallelepiped. Draw three principal views of the solid.

4B-4. $R(225)$ $A(3\frac{1}{2}; 2\frac{1}{4}; 6)$, $RS(1; 2\frac{1}{2}; 5\frac{1}{2})$, and $RU(1\frac{1}{2}; 1; 5\frac{1}{2})$ are three adjacent edges of a parallelepiped. Draw three principal views of the parallelepiped.

4B-5. $A(736)$ $B(6\frac{1}{2}; 2\frac{1}{2}; 5\frac{1}{2})$, $AD(6\frac{1}{2}; 4; 7)$, and $AJ(6; 1; 5\frac{3}{4})$ are three adjacent edges of a parallelepiped. Draw the front, top, and left-side views of the parallelepiped.

4B-6. Are the lines $A(\frac{1}{2}; 3\frac{1}{2}; 5)$ $B(\frac{1}{2}; 1; 7)$ and $C(136)$ $D(117)$ parallel? Show why. Draw a line $J(6\frac{3}{4}; 1; 6\frac{1}{2})R$, $1\frac{1}{2}''$ long, backward, and parallel to the line $L(517)$ $M(725)$.

Group 4C.   Perpendicular Lines.

4C-1. Given the lines $A(136)$ $B(317)$ and $C(547)$ $D(716)$. Draw a horizontal line $J(3; 2\frac{1}{2}; 5\frac{1}{2})H$, $2''$ long and perpendicular to AB. Draw a frontal line $L(526)F$, $2''$ long and perpendicular to CD. Which, if any, of the lines intersect?

4C-2. Given the lines $A(1; 2; 5\frac{1}{2})$ $B(327)$ and $C(526)$ $D(736)$. Draw the line $R(335)$ $S(1\frac{1}{2}; X; X)$ perpendicular to and intersecting AB. Draw the line $T(5; 3\frac{1}{2}; 5)$ $K(6XX)$ perpendicular to and intersecting CD.

4C-3. Given the line $J(147)$ $K(2; 2; 5\frac{1}{2})$. Draw three principal views of the following lines, each perpendicular to JK and $1\frac{1}{2}''$ long: (1) a horizontal line KH extending forward; (2) a frontal line KF extending upward; and (3) a profile line KP extending backward.

4C-4. $A(217)$ $B(125)$ and $BC(3; X; 4\frac{1}{2})$ are the two perpendicular sides of a right triangle. Draw the front and top views of the triangle.

4C-5. $A(125)$ $B(337)$ is one side of a rectangle. The adjacent sides are $1\frac{1}{2}''$ long and one of them lies along the line $BK(5; X; 6\frac{1}{2})$. Draw the front and top views of the rectangle.

4C-6. Draw the front and top views of the lines $J(527)$ $K(4\frac{1}{2}; X; 6)$ and $L(615)$ $M(4; \frac{1}{2}; X)$ each perpendicular to the line JL.

4C-7. Fig. 234-1. Draw the front and top views of the lines $L(1; 2\frac{1}{2}; 7)$

$T(1\frac{1}{2}; 3\frac{1}{2}; X)$ and $M(2\frac{1}{2}; 1; 6\frac{1}{2})$ $U(3X7)$ both perpendicular to the line LM, and find their true lengths.

4C-8. Fig. 234-2. $A(1; 2\frac{1}{2}; 5)$ $C(2\frac{1}{2}; 1; 7)$ is one diagonal of a square, and $T(3\frac{1}{2}; 2\frac{1}{2}; X)$ is a point on the other diagonal, extended. Draw the square in the front and top views and in any other views needed.

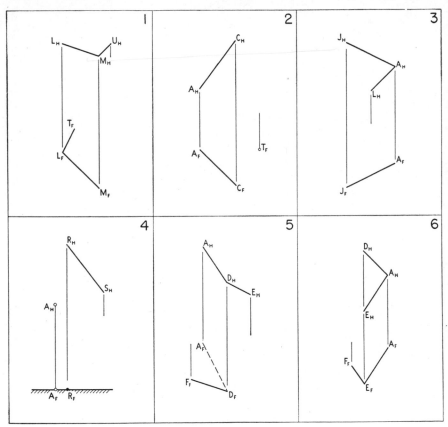

Fig. 234.—Perpendicular Lines. Group 4C.

4C-9. Fig. 234-3. Draw the front and top views of the rectangle $A(626)$ BCD. AB is $2''$ long and lies along $AJ(417)$. AD is $1\frac{1}{4}''$ long and lies along $AL(5X5)$.

4C-10. Fig. 234-4. $R(5\frac{1}{2}; 1; 7)$ $S(7X5)$ is a steel support fastened to the floor at R with a 45° bracket. Find the length of the support and the length of a brace perpendicular to it from a point $A(5; 1; 4\frac{1}{2})$ on the floor. Draw the front and top views of the two members. Scale: $\frac{1}{2}'' = 1'\text{-}0''$.

4C-11. Fig. 234-5. $A(237)$ $D(3; 1; 5\frac{1}{2})$ is one of the lateral edges of a right prism, the front base of which is $DE(4X5)$ $F(1\frac{1}{2}; 1\frac{1}{2}; X)$. Draw the front and top views of the prism.

4C-12. Fig. 234-6. $A(736)$ $BCD(6X7)$ is the upper base of a right prism, and $E(6; 1\frac{1}{2}; 4\frac{1}{2})$ $F(5\frac{1}{2}; 2\frac{1}{4}; X)$ GH is its lower base. AE is one of the lateral edges. Draw the front and top views of the prism.

Group 4D.   Oblique Views for Which the Direction of Sight Is Specified.

The front and top views are required in every problem in addition to oblique view specified.

4D-1. Fig. 235-1. $A(5\frac{1}{2}; 2; 7)$ $C(7\frac{1}{2}; 2; 7)$ is a diagonal of a frontal square which is the base of a right pyramid whose vertex is $V(6\frac{1}{2}; 2; 5\frac{1}{2})$. Draw a

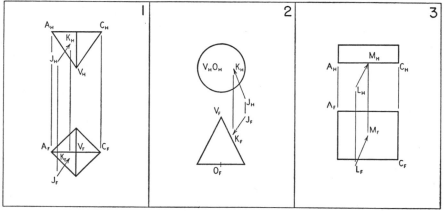

Fig. 235.—Oblique Views.—Specified Direction of Sight.   Group 4D.

view of the pyramid as seen when looking parallel to the arrow $J(5\frac{3}{4}; 1; 5\frac{3}{4})$ $K(6\frac{1}{4}; 1\frac{3}{4}; 6\frac{1}{2})$.

4D-2. Fig. 235-2. $V(235)$ is the vertex and $O(215)$ is the center of the 2″ diameter base of a right cone. Draw a view of the cone as seen when looking parallel to $J(3; 3; 3\frac{3}{4})$ $K(2\frac{1}{2}; 2\frac{1}{4}; 5)$.

4D-3. Fig. 235-3. $A(557)$ $C(7\frac{1}{2}; 3; 7)$ is a diagonal of a frontal rectangle which has two sides horizontal. The rectangle is the front base of a right prism of $\frac{3}{4}″$ altitude. Draw a view of the prism for a direction of sight parallel to $L(5\frac{3}{4}; 2\frac{3}{4}; 6)$ $M(6\frac{1}{4}; 4; 7)$.

4D-4. Fig. 229-3. $A(2; 3\frac{1}{4}; 7)$ $D(2; \frac{3}{4}; 7)$ is a diagonal of a frontal hexagon which is the front base of a right prism of $\frac{1}{2}″$ altitude, and also the base of a right pyramid with vertex $V(225)$. Draw a view of the solid as seen when looking parallel to the arrow $K(3; 1; 4\frac{1}{4})V$.

4D-5. Fig. 229-5. $J(2; 1\frac{1}{2}; 3\frac{1}{2})$ is the center of a frontal semicircle of 10′ radius, which is the front end of the cylindrical roof of a pump house. The house is 20′

wide, 25' deep, and has walls 10' high. Scale: $1'' = 10$ ft. Draw a view of the house as seen in the direction $A(1\frac{1}{4}; 3; 6\frac{1}{2})$ $B(2; 1\frac{1}{2}; 5)$.

4D-6. Fig. 230-1. Given the tetrahedron $R(1; 1; 6\frac{1}{2})$ $S(316)$ $T(2; \frac{1}{2}; 4\frac{1}{2})$ $U(2; 2\frac{1}{2}; 5\frac{1}{2})$. Draw a view of the tetrahedron as seen when looking parallel to $A(334)$ $B(2\frac{3}{4}; 2\frac{1}{4}; 5)$.

4D-7. Fig. 230-4. $Q(2\frac{1}{2}; 2; 6)$ is the center of a $3''$ diameter circle which is the upper end of a right cylinder of $1''$ altitude. $A(1\frac{1}{2}; 2; 6)$ $C(3\frac{1}{2}; 2; 6)$ is a diagonal of a horizontal square which is the upper end of a hole cut through the cylinder. Draw a view of the solid for a direction of sight parallel to the arrow $P(3\frac{1}{4}; 3\frac{1}{2}; 7)Q$.

4D-8. Fig. 231-1. Given the tetrahedron $R(2; \frac{1}{2}; 6\frac{1}{2})$ $S(3\frac{1}{2}; 1; 4\frac{1}{2})$ $T(2; 3; 5\frac{1}{2})$ $U(1; 2\frac{1}{2}; 5)$. Draw a view of the tetrahedron as seen when looking parallel to edge TS.

4D-9. Fig. 231-2. $J(636)$ $K(637)$ is the axis of a right prism. The bases are squares, each having one $2\frac{1}{2}''$ diagonal vertical. JK is also the axis of a $1\frac{1}{2}''$ diameter hole drilled through the block. Draw a view of the block as it would appear when looking parallel to the arrow $M(5; 1\frac{3}{4}; 4\frac{1}{4})J$.

4D-10. Fig. 231-3. $A(516)$ $C(7\frac{1}{2}; 1; 7)$ is a diagonal of a horizontal square which is the base of a right pyramid of $2''$ altitude. Draw a view of the pyramid as seen when looking parallel to the arrow $J(5; 3\frac{1}{2}; 7\frac{1}{2})$ $K(5\frac{3}{4}; 2; 6\frac{1}{2})$.

4D-11. Fig. 231-9. $J(114)$ $L(315)$ is a diagonal of the lower horizontal square base of a right prism of $1''$ altitude. Draw a view of the prism for a direction of sight parallel to the arrow $A(336)$ $B(2\frac{1}{4}; 2; 5)$.

4D-12. Fig. 230-1. Given the tetrahedron $R(1; 1; 6\frac{1}{2})$ $S(316)$ $T(2; \frac{1}{2}; 4\frac{1}{2})$ $U(2; 2\frac{1}{2}; 5\frac{1}{2})$. Draw a view showing the tetrahedron as it would appear when looking along the edge ST.

Group 4E.   Objects in an Oblique Position.

Draw complete views of each object. Orientate and name the views.

4E-1. $L(5\frac{1}{2}; 1\frac{3}{4}; 6)$ $M(6\frac{1}{2}; 1\frac{1}{4}; 5)$ is the axis of a right square base prism. $A(72X)$ is a corner of the square with center M. Draw the front and top views and any other views that are needed.

4E-2. One of the lateral edges of a right prism lies along $P(6; 1; 7\frac{1}{2})$ $Q(7\frac{1}{2}; 3; 6\frac{1}{2})$. P is one corner of the square which is the lower base of the prism, and $A(5\frac{1}{2}; 2\frac{1}{2}; 5)$ is one corner of the square which is the upper base. A and P are on diagonally opposite edges of the prism. Draw the front and top views of the prism and any other views needed.

4E-3. $V(2\frac{1}{2}; 2; 3\frac{1}{2})$ is the vertex and $O(1; 1; 4\frac{1}{4})$ is the center of the base of a right pyramid. The base is a regular pentagon that may be inscribed in a $2''$ diameter circle. It is turned so that the lowest side of the pentagon is horizontal. Draw the front and top views of the pyramid and any other views that are needed.

4E-4. $J(137)$ $K(2\frac{1}{4}; 1; 5\frac{3}{4})$ is the axis of a right square base prism. One of the $2''$ diagonals of each base is horizontal. Draw a view of the prism showing its altitude, one showing true shape of the bases, and the front and top views.

4E-5. Draw the front and top views, and any other necessary views of a right prism whose axis is $J(126)$ $K(2; 2\frac{1}{2}; 7)$. The bases are regular hexagons with $1\frac{1}{8}''$ sides. Two sides of each base are frontal.

4E-6. $V(2\frac{1}{2}; 1; 7)$ is the vertex and $O(1\frac{1}{2}; 2\frac{1}{2}; 6)$ is the center of the base of a right pyramid. The base is a $2'' \times 1''$ rectangle which has the long sides frontal. Draw a view of the pyramid showing the altitude, one showing true shape of the base, and the front and top views.

4E-7. $L(137)$ $M(2\frac{1}{2}; 1; 5)$ is the axis of a right prism whose bases are regular pentagons that may be inscribed in $2''$ diameter circles. The left side of each pentagon is profile. Draw front and top views of the prism and any other views that are necessary.

4E-8. $J(1; 2; 4\frac{1}{2})$ $K(2; 1; 6)$ is the axis of a right prism. The bases are regular hexagons of $\frac{3}{4}''$ sides. Two sides of each base are profile. Draw the front and top views of the prism and any other views that are needed.

4E-9. $A(3; 4\frac{1}{2}; 7)$ $B(135)$ is the center line of a chute for packages. It starts at a floor through A and ends at a frontal wall through B. A right section is $24''$ square, having two sides horizontal. Make a complete drawing of the chute using a right-auxiliary view. Show the true shape of the holes in the floor and the wall. Scale: $\frac{1}{2}'' = 1'\text{-}0''$.

4E-10. $V(1; 3\frac{1}{2}; 7\frac{1}{2})$ is the vertex and $K(2\frac{1}{2}; 1\frac{1}{2}; 6)$ is the center of the regular hexagonal base of a right pyramid. The sides of the base are $1''$ long, and one corner, A, is to the right of K and $\frac{5}{8}''$ in front of K. Draw the front and top views and any other necessary views of the pyramid.

4E-11. $O(5\frac{1}{2}; 1\frac{1}{4}; 7)$ is the center of the square base of a right pyramid and $V(7; 2; 5\frac{1}{2})$ is its vertex. Corner A of the base is $\frac{1}{2}''$ below O and to the left of O. The diagonal AC is $2''$ long. Draw the front, top, and all other necessary views.

4E-12. $R(746)$ $S(627)$ is the axis of a right prism which has square bases with $2''$ diagonals. Corner A of the square whose center is S is $\frac{1}{2}''$ in front of S and to the left of S. Draw the front and top views of the prism and any others that are necessary.

4E-13. $R(5\frac{1}{2}; 2\frac{1}{2}; 7)$ $S(6; 1\frac{3}{4}; 5\frac{1}{2})$ is the axis of a right prism whose bases are equilateral triangles of $2\frac{1}{2}''$ sides. One corner, A, of the lower base is $\frac{1}{4}''$ above S and to the right of S. Draw the necessary auxiliary and oblique views and the front and top views of the prism.

4E-14. $A(5\frac{1}{2}; \frac{3}{4}; 7)$ $B(7\frac{1}{2}; 3; 5\frac{1}{2})$ is the axis of a $4''$ shaft which has a pulley $16''$ in diameter by $8''$ wide mounted at its midpoint. Draw front and top views of the shaft and pulley. Omit hidden lines. Scale: $1\frac{1}{2}'' = 1'\text{-}0''$.

4E-15. $V(436)$ is the vertex and $K(616)$ is the center of the base of a right pyramid. The base is a $2''$ square, two sides of which make an angle of $35°$ with any horizontal plane. The lowest corner of the base is behind K. Draw the front and top views and any other necessary view of the pyramid.

4E-16. $V(125)$ is the vertex and $J(3; 1; 6\frac{1}{2})$ is the center of the base of a right pyramid. The base is a $2''$ square, two sides of which make an angle of $60°$ with any horizontal plane. The lowest corner of the base is in front of J. Draw the front and top views, and any other necessary views of the pyramid.

4E-17. $V(0; 2\frac{1}{2}; 5)$ is the vertex of a right pyramid, and $J(2; 1\frac{1}{2}; 6\frac{1}{2})$ is the center of its square base, two of whose $1\frac{1}{2}''$ sides make an angle of 60° with a horizontal plane. Draw the front and top views and any other necessary views of the pyramid.

PROBLEMS FOR CHAPTER V

LINE AND PLANE PROBLEMS

Group 5A. Visualization of a Plane.

When giving the bearing of a line, assume the top of the sheet is north unless otherwise specified.

5A-1. Visualize the plane of the point $R(1; 1\frac{1}{2}; 7)$ and the line $J(315)$ $L(437)$ by drawing the strike and dip lines and giving the bearing of the strike, angle of dip, and the direction of the dip line.

5A-2. Draw strike and dip lines of the plane $A(1; 1; 5\frac{1}{2})$ $B(237)$ $C(4; 1\frac{1}{2}; 5)$. Measure the dip of the plane and give the bearing of the strike. State the direction of the dip line as visualized.

5A-3. Given the intersecting lines $R(517)$ $S(7; 3; 5\frac{1}{2})$ and $T(6\frac{1}{2}; 1\frac{1}{2}; 7)$ $U(5\frac{1}{2}; 3; 5)$. Find the strike and dip of the plane of the lines. Draw the dip line from U and state its direction as visualized.

5A-4. Find the strike and dip of the plane of lines $C(237)$ $D(116)$ and $E(4; 3\frac{1}{2}; 6\frac{1}{2})$ $F(3; 1\frac{1}{2}; 5\frac{1}{2})$. Draw the dip line from C and give its direction as visualized.

5A-5. The strike of a plane through $A(636)$ is S 70° W. The plane has a dip of 35° southeasterly. Draw the front and top views of the plane as a triangle.

5A-6. $A(127)$ $B(2; 3\frac{1}{2}; 5)$ is a line of a plane which has a strike of S 65° E. Find the dip of the plane. Draw front and top views of the plane as a triangle.

Group 5B. Lines in a Plane.

5B-1. Fig. 236-1. Draw the lines $J(2\frac{1}{2}; X; 6\frac{1}{2})$ $K(5\frac{1}{2}; X; 5)$ and $L(31X)$ $M(53X)$ in the plane of the triangle $A(325)$ $B(437)$ $C(5; 1\frac{1}{2}; 6)$.

5B-2. Fig. 236-2. Draw the lines $J(236)$ $S(4\frac{1}{2}; 2\frac{1}{2}; X)$ and $L(524)$ $R(3X6)$ in the plane $JK(417)L$.

5B-3. Fig. 236-3. The strike of a plane through $A(6; 2\frac{1}{2}; 6)$ is S 40° W and the plane dips 55° northwesterly. Draw the lines $J(43X)$ $K(6\frac{1}{2}; 1\frac{1}{2}; X)$ and $L(5X7)$ $M(6X5)$ in the plane. Show front and top views of the lines.

5B-4. Locate the lines $A(2X5)$ $B(3X7)$ and $C(1; 2\frac{1}{2}; X)$ $D(3\frac{1}{2}; 1; X)$ in the plane which contains the point $M(326)$, strikes S 55° E, and dips 40° southwesterly. Draw the front and top views of the lines.

5B-5. In the triangle $R(234)$ $S(417)$ $T(545)$ draw the lines $TA(43X)$ and $SC(3\frac{1}{4}; X; 5)$.

5B-6. In three principal views of the triangle $A(\frac{1}{2}; 3; 7)$ $B(4\frac{1}{2}; 4; 6)$ $C(2\frac{1}{2}; 1; 4\frac{1}{2})$ draw a horizontal line AH, a frontal line BF, and a profile line CP.

5B-7. The triangle $C(425)$ $D(1X6)$ $E(3X7)$ strikes S 50° E and dips 35° southwesterly. Draw the front and top views of the triangle.

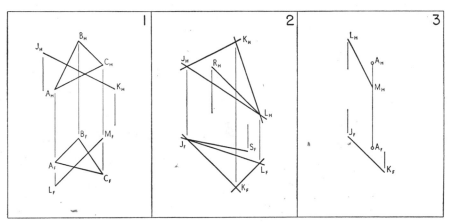

Fig. 236.—Lines in a Plane. Group 5B.

Group 5C.   Points in a Plane.

5C-1. Fig. 237-1.   Locate the points $A(4; X; 5\frac{1}{2})$, $B(22X)$, $C(52X)$, and $D(3; X; 4\frac{1}{2})$ in the plane $R(2; 3; 4\frac{1}{2})$ $S(417)$ $T(5; 4; 5\frac{1}{2})$.

5C-2. Fig. 237-2.   Determine which of the points $R(4; 2\frac{1}{2}; 5\frac{1}{2})$, $S(325)$, $T(3; 2\frac{1}{2}; 5\frac{3}{4})$, and $U(2; 3; 6\frac{1}{2})$ are in the plane of $J(3; 3\frac{1}{2}; 7)$ $K(5\frac{1}{2}; 2\frac{1}{2}; 5\frac{1}{2})$ $L(214)$. Tabulate the results.

5C-3. Fig. 237-3.   Draw the triangle $A(2\frac{1}{2}; 3; X)$ $B(42X)$ $C(5X5)$ in the plane $R(245)$ $S(317)$ $T(6; 3; 4\frac{1}{2})$.

5C-4. Fig. 237-4. $C(126)$ is one corner of a triangle which strikes S 75° E and dips 38° southwesterly. $D(3X7)$ and $E(2; X; 4\frac{1}{2})$ are the other corners.   Draw front and top views of the triangle.

5C-5. Fig. 237-5.   Locate the points $A(33X)$, $B(22X)$, $C(2\frac{1}{4}; X; 5\frac{1}{2})$ and $D(2\frac{1}{2}; X; 6\frac{1}{2})$ in the plane $J(126)$ $K(245)$ $L(436)$ $M(317)$.

5C-6. Fig. 237-6. $O(4; X; 5\frac{1}{4})$ is the center of a pentagon lying in the plane $R(215)$ $S(337)$ $T(6; 3; 5\frac{1}{2})$ $U(5; 1; 3\frac{1}{2})$, and $A(4; X; 6\frac{1}{4})$ is one of its corners.   The top view shows the pentagon as a regular polygon.   Draw the pentagon.

5C-7. $K(4; 2\frac{1}{2}; X)$ is the center of a hole in the triangle $A(237)$ $B(646)$ $C(4; 1; 4\frac{1}{2})$.   The front view of the hole appears as a regular hexagon having two of its $\frac{3}{4}''$ sides horizontal.   Draw the front and top views of the hole.

5C-8. $R(224)$, $S(4; 3\frac{1}{2}; 7)$, and $T(615)$ are points in the roof plane of a building. The axis of a vertical stack, 18″ in diameter, intersects the roof at $N(4; X; 5\frac{1}{2})$.

Show the front and top views of the hole in the roof occupied by the stack. Scale: $1'' = 1'\text{-}0''$.

5C-9. $A(626)$ is a point in a plane which has a strike of S 65° W and a dip of 25° northwesterly. Locate the points $B(4X7)$ and $C(5; X; 4\frac{1}{2})$ in the plane. Draw front and top views of the triangle ABC.

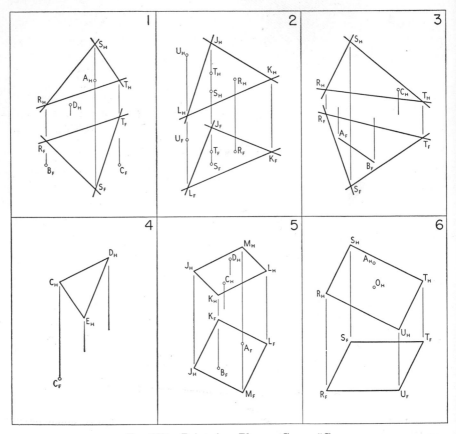

Fɪɢ. 237.—Points in a Plane. Group 5C.

Group 5D. Angle a Plane Makes with Principal Planes.

5D-1. Measure the angle which the triangle $A(3; 2\frac{1}{2}; 5)$ $B(417)$ $C(5; 3\frac{1}{2}; 6)$ makes with a horizontal plane, and the angle it makes with a frontal plane.

5D-2. Measure the angle which the triangle $C(337)$ $D(546)$ $E(4; 1\frac{1}{2}; 5)$ makes with a horizontal plane, and the angle which it makes with a frontal plane.

5D-3. Given the triangle $R(2; 2\frac{1}{2}; 7\frac{1}{2})$ $S(4; 1\frac{1}{2}; 6\frac{1}{2})$ $T(3; 4; 5\frac{1}{2})$. Measure the angles which it makes with horizontal, frontal, and profile planes.

5D-4. Find the strike (as a bearing) and the dip of the plane $Q(4; 3; 6\frac{1}{2})$ $R(548)$ $S(627)$. Also, measure the angles the plane makes with all frontal planes and all profile planes.

5D-5. Given the plane $A(124)$ $B(216)$ $C(2\frac{1}{2}; 3; 4\frac{1}{2})$. Find its strike and dip and the angle it makes with a profile plane.

5D-6. The plane $R(2\frac{1}{2}; 2; 6)$ $S(\frac{1}{2}; X; 7)$ $T(23X)$ strikes N 48° W and dips 58° southeasterly. Measure the angle the plane makes with a frontal plane, and the angle it makes with a profile plane.

5D-7. Fig. 237-4. $C(126)$ is one corner of a triangle which strikes S 75° E and dips 38° southwesterly. $D(3X7)$ and $E(2; X; 4\frac{1}{2})$ are the other corners. Measure the angle the triangle makes with a frontal plane.

5D-8. Fig. 237-5. Measure the angle which the plane $J(126)$ $K(245)$ $L(436)$ $M(317)$ makes with a horizontal plane, and the angle which it makes with a frontal plane.

5D-9. $J(535)$ $L(736)$ is the strike of a plane which dips 40° northeasterly. Measure the angle the plane makes with a frontal plane, and the angle it makes with a profile plane.

5D-10. Find the strike (as a bearing) and the dip of the plane $R(038)$ $S(2; 2\frac{1}{2}; 7)$ $T(146)$. Also, measure the angles the plane makes with all frontal planes and all profile planes.

Group 5E. Edge and Normal Views of a Plane.

5E-1. Fig. 238-1. $A(5; 1; 6\frac{1}{2})$ $C(7; 1; 5\frac{1}{2})$ is a diagonal of a horizontal square which is the base of a pyramid whose vertex is $V(636)$. Draw a view of the pyramid showing the true shape of the front triangular face. Measure the angle this face makes with the base.

5E-2. Fig. 238-2. $A(135)$, $B(236)$, $C(335)$, and $D(234)$ are the midpoints of the edges of the upper face of a cube. Cut off all eight corners by planes that pass through the midpoints of the edges. Then $ABCD$ is the upper face of the polyhedron of Archimedes used for the Dymaxion World Map. Draw a view of the polyhedron showing the true shape of the upper, right, front face, and any other necessary view.

5E-3. Fig. 238-3. $A(116)$ $C(317)$ is a diagonal of a horizontal rectangle having its long sides frontal. The rectangle is the lower base of a right prism of $1\frac{1}{2}''$ altitude which has one corner cut off by the plane $R(1; 2\frac{1}{2}; 7)$ $S(2\frac{1}{2}; 1\frac{1}{2}; 6)$ $T(1; 1\frac{1}{2}; 6)$. Draw a view of the truncated prism which shows the true shape of the cut surface.

5E-4. Fig. 238-4. Draw a line from K which represents the shortest distance between the lines $J(\frac{1}{2}; 2; 7)$ $K(1\frac{1}{2}; 1; 5)$ and $L(2; 2\frac{1}{2}; 6\frac{1}{2})$ $M(3; 1\frac{1}{2}; 4\frac{1}{2})$ and measure its length.

5E-5. Fig. 238-5. $A(7; 2; 5\frac{1}{2})$ $C(4\frac{3}{4}; 2\frac{1}{2}; 6)$ is a diagonal of a square lying in the plane $ACM(617)$. Draw the front and top views of the square.

5E-6. Fig. 238-6. $P(5\frac{1}{4}; X; 6\frac{1}{4})$ is one corner of a regular pentagon lying in the plane $A(425)$ $B(517)$ $C(726)$ $D(634)$. Its center is at the intersection of AC and BD. Draw the front and top views of the pentagon.

5E-7. Show in the front and top views the center of a $3''$ diameter pulley used to change the direction of a $\frac{1}{4}''$ diameter cable from $A(2; \frac{1}{2}; 5)$ $B(127)$ to $BC(336)$

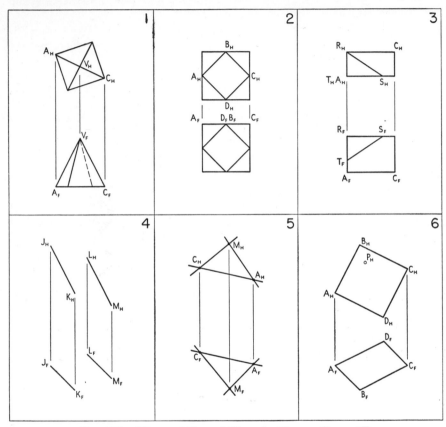

Fig. 238.—Edge and Normal View of a Plane.   Group 5E.

in an airplane.   Draw the pulley in the view where it appears as a circle.   Scale: $3'' = 1'\text{-}0''$.

5E-8. Draw the front and top views of a circle passing through the points $A(127)$ $B(2; 3\frac{1}{2}; 5\frac{1}{2})$ and $C(3; 2\frac{1}{2}; 6)$.

5E-9. Fig. 239-3.   Draw a line from $T(7\frac{1}{2}; 2; 6)$, $2\frac{1}{4}''$ long, intersecting $R(615)$ $S(537)$ at A.   Show front and top views of the lines.

5E-10. Fig. 239-6.   The steel rod $J(125)$ $K(337)$ is to be connected to point

$A(1; 3\frac{1}{2}; 6\frac{1}{4})$ by two rods, each $7'$ long. Draw the rods in the front and top views and measure the distance on JK between their ends. Scale: $\frac{1}{4}'' = 1'\text{-}0''$.

5E-11. Given the line $R(727)$ $S(5; 3; 5\frac{1}{2})$ and the point $T(417)$. Draw a regular hexagon of $1''$ sides lying in the plane RST. One end of one diagonal is $2''$ from R on RS and the other end is on RT.

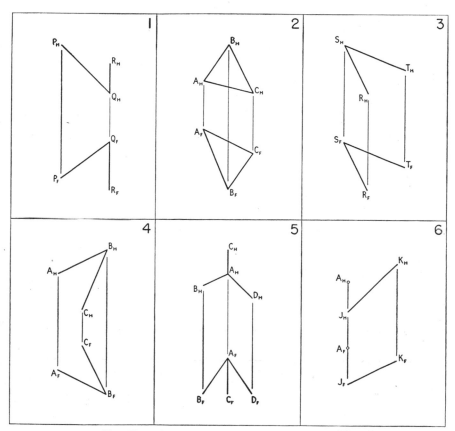

FIG. 239.—Angle between Two Lines. Group 5F.

5E-12. $K(2\frac{1}{2}; \frac{1}{2}; 7)$ is the midpoint of the $3''$ horizontal side of an equilateral triangle lying in the plane $J(\frac{1}{2}; 2; 6\frac{1}{2})$ $KL(4; 2\frac{1}{2}; 5)$. Draw the front and top views of the triangle.

5E-13. $A(\frac{1}{2}; 3\frac{1}{2}; 7\frac{1}{2})$ $B(3\frac{1}{2}; 3\frac{1}{2}; 6\frac{1}{2})$ is a portion of the ridge of a roof of one-half pitch ($45°$ slope). $O(1\frac{1}{2}; X; 6)$ is the center of a $16'$ diameter circle painted on the front portion of the roof. Draw the front and top views of the circle. Scale: $\frac{1}{8}'' = 1'\text{-}0''$.

5E-14. Find the strike as a bearing and the dip in degrees of the plane $Q(5; 1\frac{1}{2}; 6)$ $R(6; 2\frac{1}{2}; 8)$ $S(717)$. Also, find and measure the angle F, and show the true shape of QRS.

Group 5F.　The Angle between Two Lines.

5F-1. Fig. 239-1. Measure the angle between the lines $P(5; 1\frac{1}{2}; 7)$ $Q(735)$ and $QR(7; 1; 6\frac{1}{4})$.

5F-2. Fig. 239-2. Measure the angles of the triangle $A(5; 3\frac{1}{2}; 5\frac{1}{2})$ $B(617)$ $C(7; 2\frac{1}{2}; 5)$. Draw the bisector of the angle ABC.

5F-3. Fig. 239-3. $R(615)$ $S(537)$ and $ST(7\frac{1}{2}; 2; 6)$ are two steel members on a derrick. Find their true lengths and the angle between them. Scale: $\frac{1}{4}'' = 1'\text{-}0''$.

5F-4. Fig. 239-4. Measure the angle between the lines $A(526)$ $B(717)$ and $BC(6; 3; 4\frac{1}{2})$. Draw the bisector of the angle ABC and show it in all views drawn.

5F-5. Fig. 239-5. In a tripod the members $A(426)$ $B(3; \frac{1}{2}; 5\frac{1}{2})$, $AC(4; \frac{1}{2}; 7)$, and $AD(5; \frac{1}{2}; 5)$ are made of steel tubing and fastened by welding. Find the length of the legs and the angle between them. Scale: $\frac{1}{4}'' = 1'\text{-}0''$.

5F-6. Fig. 239-6. $J(125)$ $K(337)$ is a pipe to which point $A(1; 3\frac{1}{2}; 6\frac{1}{4})$ is to be connected, using a 45° fitting. Find the length of connecting pipe needed and show the pipe in the front and top views. Scale: $\frac{1}{8}'' = 1'\text{-}0''$.

5F-7. $C(1; 3\frac{1}{2}; 5)$ $D(217)$ and CE are of equal length and the angle between them is 50°. E is to the right of C. The strike of the plane of the lines is S 37° E. Draw front and top views of the lines.

5F-8. Draw a line backward from $K(1; \frac{1}{2}; 6)$ which will intersect $A(2; 2; 7\frac{1}{2})$ $B(3; \frac{1}{2}; 5)$ and make 53° with it.

5F-9. From the point $P(5; 1\frac{1}{2}; 5)$ draw a line intersecting line $L(637)$ $M(7\frac{1}{2}; 1; 5\frac{1}{2})$ at K and making 65° with LM. Find the length of PK.

5F-10. Draw a line $A(5; 2; 4\frac{1}{2})B$, downward from A, intersecting the line $J(5\frac{1}{2}; \frac{1}{2}; 7\frac{1}{2})$ $K(7\frac{1}{2}; 3; 5\frac{1}{2})$ at B and making 60° with it.

Group 5G.　The Intersection of a Line and a Plane.

5G-1. Fig. 240-1. Find the intersection of the line $L(2; 3\frac{1}{2}; 6\frac{1}{2})$ $M(6; 1\frac{1}{2}; 4\frac{1}{2})$ and the tetrahedron $A(225)$ $B(3; 3\frac{1}{2}; 7)$ $C(635)$ $D(514)$. Omit the part of LM inside the solid and indicate the visibility of the part outside.

5G-2. Fig. 240-2. Find the intersection of the line $A(1; 1\frac{1}{2}; 6\frac{1}{2})$ $B(4; 2\frac{1}{2}; 4\frac{1}{4})$ and the opaque quadrilateral $R(237)$ $S(425)$ $T(115)$ $U(2; 1; 5\frac{1}{2})$. Indicate correct visibility of the lines.

5G-3. Fig. 240-3. Find where the line $J(5\frac{1}{2}; 4\frac{1}{2}; 7)$ $K(2; 2; 4\frac{1}{2})$ intersects the pyramid $V(437)$ $A(245)$ $B(415)$ $C(645)$. Omit the part of JK which is inside the pyramid and indicate the visibility of the part outside.

5G-4. Fig. 240-4. Show the intersection of $L(2; 1\frac{1}{2}; 5)$ $M(636)$ with the tetrahedron $A(2\frac{1}{2}; 2\frac{1}{2}; 4\frac{1}{2})$ $B(3; 1\frac{1}{2}; 7)$ $C(5; 3\frac{1}{2}; 6\frac{1}{2})$ $D(5\frac{1}{2}; 1; 5)$. Omit the portion of LM inside the solid and show the visibility of the part outside.

5G-5. Fig. 240-5. $C(247)$ $D(4\frac{1}{2}; 4; 7)$ $E(4\frac{1}{2}; 1; 7)$ $F(217)$ is a galvanized iron gate in a fence. $R(1\frac{1}{2}; 4; 5\frac{1}{2})$ $S(5; 1; 7\frac{1}{2})$ is a guy wire from a pole to the ground.

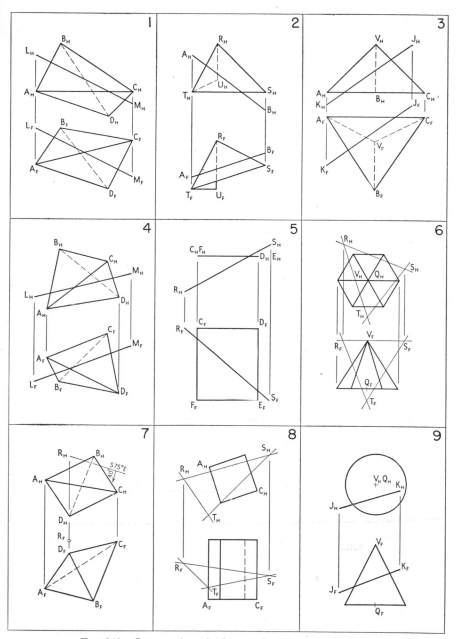

Fig. 240.—Intersection of a Line and a Plane.   Group 5G.

Find the shape of the slot that must be cut in the gate to allow it to be opened forward 90°.

5G-6. Fig. 240-6. $V(2; 3\frac{1}{2}; 6)$ is the vertex and $Q(2; 1\frac{1}{2}; 6)$ is the center of the base of a right pyramid. The base is a regular hexagon of $1\frac{1}{4}''$ sides with one diagonal frontal. Find the intersection of the edges of the pyramid with the plane $R(1; 3\frac{1}{2}; 7\frac{1}{2})$ $S(3\frac{1}{2}; 3\frac{1}{2}; 6\frac{1}{2})$ $T(2; 1; 4\frac{1}{2})$. Connect the points of intersection to obtain the cut surface on the pyramid.

5G-7. Fig. 240-7. Find the intersection of the edges of the tetrahedron $A(1; 1\frac{1}{2}; 6)$ $B(317)$ $C(4; 3\frac{1}{2}; 5\frac{1}{2})$ $D(2; 3; 4\frac{1}{2})$ with the plane through $R(2; 3\frac{1}{2}; 7)$ which strikes S 75° E and dips 40° southwesterly.

5G-8. Fig. 240-8. $A(5; 1; 6\frac{1}{2})$ $C(7; 1; 5\frac{1}{2})$ is a diagonal of a horizontal square which is the lower base of a right prism of $2\frac{1}{2}''$ altitude. Find where the edges of the prism intersect the plane of the points $R(4; 2\frac{1}{2}; 6)$, $S(7\frac{1}{2}; 2; 7)$, and $T(5; 1\frac{1}{2}; 4\frac{1}{2})$. Connect the points of intersection to obtain the line of intersection between the plane and the prism.

5G-9. Fig. 240-9. $V(4; 3\frac{1}{2}; 6)$ is the vertex of a right cone and $Q(416)$ is the center of its $2\frac{1}{2}''$ diameter base. Find where it is intersected by the line $J(2\frac{1}{2}; 1\frac{1}{2}; 5)$ $K(5; 2\frac{1}{2}; 5\frac{3}{4})$. Omit the portion of JK inside the cone.

5G-10. Find the intersection of the small rod $J(338)$ $K(615)$ with the tetrahedron $A(225)$ $B(418)$ $C(6\frac{1}{2}; 3; 6)$ $D(5; 4; 6\frac{1}{2})$. Omit the portion of the rod which is inside the tetrahedron and indicate the visibility of the portions which are outside.

5G-11. Find the intersection of the small rod $A(2; 2; 5\frac{1}{2})$ $B(718)$ with the tetrahedron $J(237)$ $K(407)$ $L(628)$ $M(525)$. Omit the portion of the rod which is inside the tetrahedron and indicate the visibility of the portions which are outside.

5G-12. Find the intersection of the small rod $C(2; 1\frac{1}{2}; 7)$ $D(6; 2\frac{1}{2}; 5)$ with the tetrahedron $P(216)$ $Q(448)$ $R(6; 1\frac{1}{2}; 6\frac{1}{2})$ $S(4\frac{1}{2}; 2; 5)$. Omit the portion of the rod which is inside the tetrahedron and indicate the visibility of the portions which are outside.

5G-13. Find the intersection of the small rod $J(235)$ $K(6; 2; 6\frac{1}{2})$ with the tetrahedron $C(2\frac{1}{2}; 3\frac{1}{2}; 5\frac{1}{2})$ $D(3; 1; 6\frac{1}{2})$ $E(5; 1\frac{1}{2}; 4\frac{1}{2})$ $F(5\frac{1}{2}; 3; 7)$. Omit the portion of the rod which is inside the tetrahedron and indicate the visibility of the portions which are outside.

5G-14. Find the points at which the small rod $J(127)$ $K(614)$ pierces the tetrahedron $A(1\frac{1}{2}; 2\frac{1}{2}; 5)$ $B(5; 3\frac{1}{2}; 6)$ $C(4; \frac{1}{2}; 4)$ $D(217)$. Omit the portion of the rod that lies within the tetrahedron.

5G-15. Find the points at which the line $A(2; 1\frac{1}{4}; 3\frac{1}{2})$ $B(6; \frac{1}{4}; 7\frac{1}{2})$ pierces the right cone whose vertex is $V(436)$ and whose base is a $3\frac{1}{2}''$ diameter circle having its center at $C(406)$. Omit the portion of the line inside the cone and indicate visibility.

5G-16. Given $K(325)$ $L(2; 3; 4\frac{3}{4})$, $KM(1\frac{1}{2}; \frac{1}{2}; 6)$ and $KN(1; 1\frac{1}{2}; 4)$ as the directions of the edges of a solid parallelepiped having $A(636)$ $G(5; 1; 6\frac{1}{4})$ for a body diagonal. Draw the front and top views of the solid.

5G-17. $A(236)$ $G(2\frac{1}{2}; 1; 6)$ is a body diagonal of a solid parallelepiped whose edges have the directions $J(525)$ $K(6\frac{1}{2}; 2\frac{1}{2}; 6)$ $JL(6; 3\frac{1}{2}; 5\frac{1}{4})$ and $JM(7; 1\frac{1}{2}; 4)$. Draw the front and top views of the parallelepiped.

5G-18. From the point $J(146)$ draw a line which intersects the lines $A(257)$ $B(515)$ and $C(417)$ $D(635)$.

5G-19. Draw a line which intersects the three skew lines: $A(116)$ $B(2; 3\frac{1}{2}; 4)$, $C(2\frac{1}{2}; 3\frac{1}{2}; 6\frac{1}{2})$ $D(4; \frac{1}{2}; 4)$, and $E(416)$ $F(634)$. An infinite number of lines satisfy this condition. Draw one which touches AB in the central one-third.

Group 5H.   A Line Perpendicular to a Plane.

5H-1. Fig. 241-1.   Find the distance from point $Q(3; 1\frac{1}{2}; 7)$ to the opaque triangle $A(1; 2; 6\frac{1}{2})$ $B(3\frac{1}{2}; 3\frac{1}{2}; 6)$ $C(2\frac{1}{2}; 1; 4\frac{1}{2})$.   Draw the line which represents this distance and indicate its visibility.

5H-2. Fig. 241-2.   Which of the points $R(2; 3\frac{3}{4}; 7)$ or $S(1\frac{1}{4}; 1\frac{1}{2}; 5)$ is nearer the plane $A(1; 2\frac{1}{2}; 6)$ $B(2; 3; 4\frac{1}{2})$ $C(4; 1\frac{1}{2}; 5\frac{1}{2})$ $D(317)$ and by how much?   Draw

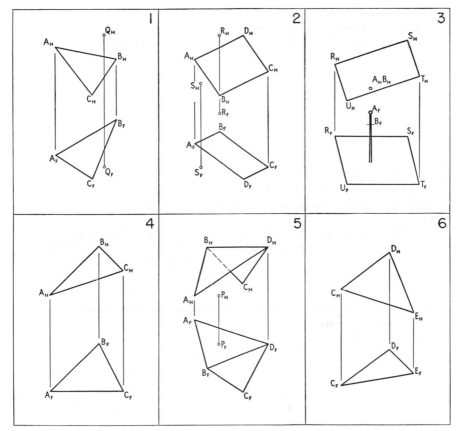

Fig. 241.—Line Perpendicular to a Plane.   Group 5H.

front and top views of the lines which represent the shortest distances and indicate their visibility.

5H-3. Fig. 241-3. $R(3\frac{1}{2}; 3; 6)$ $S(6\frac{1}{2}; 3; 7)$ $T(7; 1; 5\frac{1}{2})$ $U(4; 1; 4\frac{1}{2})$ is a portion of a roof. $A(545)$ is the top of a vertical antenna pole fastened to the roof. Find the length of the pole. Draw a guy wire from $B(5; 3\frac{1}{2}; 5)$ perpendicular to the roof and find its length. Scale: $\frac{1}{8}'' = 1'\text{-}0''$.

5H-4. Fig. 241-4. The triangle $A(415)$ $B(637)$ $C(716)$ is the lower base of a right prism of $1''$ altitude. Draw front and top views of the prism.

5H-5. Fig. 241-5. From point $P(335)$ draw the shortest lines that can be drawn to each of the planes $A(245)$ $B(2\frac{1}{2}; 2; 7)$ $D(537)$ and $BC(4; 1; 5\frac{1}{2})D$. Which plane is nearer P and by how much?

5H-6. Fig. 241-6. The triangle $C(2; 1\frac{1}{2}; 5\frac{1}{2})$ $D(437)$ $E(5; 2; 4\frac{1}{2})$ is the upper base of a right prism of $1\frac{1}{2}''$ altitude. Without drawing an edge view of the base, draw the front and top views of the prism.

5H-7. Draw a line $R(335)$ $S(4\frac{1}{2}; X; X)$ perpendicular to the opaque triangle $A(327)$ $B(5; 2\frac{1}{2}; 6)$ $C(415)$ and indicate its correct visibility.

5H-8. Draw the line $J(4\frac{1}{2}; 4; 7)$ $K(3XX)$ perpendicular to the plane $D(3; 1\frac{1}{2}; 7)$ $E(516)$ $F(4; 2\frac{1}{2}; 5)$.

5H-9. $L(117)$ $M(316)$ is the strike of a plane which dips 50° forward. Find the shortest distance from point $R(1\frac{1}{2}; 3; 5)$ to the plane. Draw front and top views of the line representing this distance.

5H-10. Draw the line $J(3; 4; 6\frac{1}{2})$ $K(4XX)$ perpendicular to the triangle $A(325)$ $B(417)$ $C(5; 2\frac{1}{2}; 6)$.

5H-11. Find the distance from point $P(4\frac{1}{2}; 3; 5)$ to the triangle $A(325)$ $B(4; 3\frac{1}{2}; 7)$ $C(516)$.

Group 5I.   Objects Having the Base in an Oblique Plane. (Geometrical Figures in an Oblique Plane.)

5I-1. Fig. 241-3. $O(5\frac{3}{4}; 2; 5\frac{3}{4})$ is the center of the regular pentagonal base of a right prism of $\frac{1}{2}''$ altitude resting on the plane $R(3\frac{1}{2}; 3; 6)$ $S(6\frac{1}{2}; 3; 7)$ $T(7; 1; 5\frac{1}{2})$ $U(4; 1; 4\frac{1}{2})$. The pentagons may be inscribed in $2''$ diameter circles and the low side of each is parallel to TU. Draw front and top views of the prism.

5I-2. $J(137)$ $K(2\frac{1}{2}; 3; 6\frac{1}{2})$ is the strike of a plane which dips 55° forward. Point $O(2; X; 5\frac{1}{2})$ in the plane is the center of the regular pentagonal base of a right prism of $\frac{3}{4}''$ altitude resting on the plane. The bases may be inscribed in $2''$ diameter circles. The low side of each base is frontal. Draw front and top views of the prism.

5I-3. The strike of a plane through $J(135)$ is N 35° E and the plane dips 50° southeasterly. $O(2\frac{1}{2}; X; 4\frac{1}{2})$ is the center of the $2''$ diameter base of a right cone of $1\frac{1}{2}''$ altitude resting on the plane. Draw front and top views of the cone.

5I-4. $J(6\frac{1}{2}; 1; 4\frac{1}{2})$, $K(7; 3; 6\frac{1}{2})$, and $L(537)$ are three points in a roof plane. $R(5; 3\frac{3}{4}; 5\frac{1}{2})$ is the center of a $24''$ diameter vertical stack passing through the roof at $O(5; X; 5\frac{1}{2})$. Find the true shape of the hole in the roof and draw the front and top views of the portion of the stack above the roof. Scale: $1'' = 1'\text{-}0''$.

5I-5. $O(22X)$ is the center of the base of a right prism of $\frac{3}{4}''$ altitude resting on the plane $R(\frac{1}{2}; 1; 5\frac{1}{2})$ $S(237)$ $T(3; 1\frac{1}{2}; 5)$. The bases of the prism are squares having $2''$ diagonals. One diagonal of each base is profile. Draw front and top views of the prism.

5I-6. $Q(5\frac{1}{2}; X; 6)$ is the center of a regular five-point star lying in the plane $J(4\frac{1}{2}; 3; 6\frac{1}{2})$ $K(7; 2\frac{1}{2}; 7)$ $L(5\frac{1}{2}; 1; 5)$. It may be inscribed in a $2''$ diameter circle and is turned so that its two lowest points lie on a horizontal line. Draw front and top views of the star.

5I-7. $O(2; 2\frac{1}{2}; X)$ is the center of a hole cut in the plane $P(\frac{1}{2}; 3; 5\frac{1}{2})$ $Q(217)$ $R(3\frac{1}{2}; 3\frac{1}{2}; 6)$. The hole is a regular hexagon of $\frac{3}{4}''$ sides and two of them are profile. Draw front and top views of the hexagon.

Group 5J. A Plane Perpendicular to a Line.

5J-1. Fig. 242-1. Draw the plane $J(3; 2\frac{3}{4}; 5\frac{1}{2})$ $K(1\frac{1}{2}; 1\frac{3}{4}; X)$ $L(\frac{1}{2}; 3\frac{1}{4}; X)$ perpendicular to the line $E(247)$ $F(215)$.

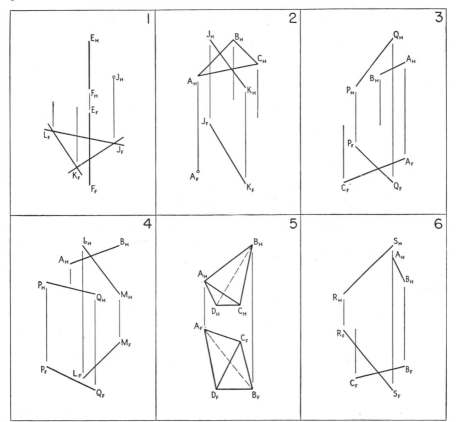

FIG. 242.—Plane Perpendicular to a Line. Group 5J.

5J-2. Fig. 242-2.   Draw the triangle $A(5; 1\frac{1}{2}; 5\frac{1}{2})$ $B(6\frac{1}{2}; X; 7)$ $C(7\frac{1}{2}; X; 6)$ perpendicular to the line $J(5\frac{1}{2}; 3\frac{1}{2}; 7)$ $K(715)$.

5J-3. Fig. 242-3.   Draw the triangle $A(326)$ $B(2; X; 5\frac{1}{2})$ $C(\frac{1}{2}; 1; X)$ perpendicular to the line $P(1; 2\frac{1}{2}; 5)$ $Q(2\frac{1}{2}; 1; 7)$.

5J-4. Fig. 242-4.   Through C, the midpoint of line $D(4; 2; 5\frac{1}{2})$ $Q(615)$, draw the triangle $A(5; X; 6\frac{1}{4})$ $B(7X7)$ C perpendicular to the line $L(5\frac{1}{2}; 1\frac{1}{2}; 7)$ $M(735)$ and find where LM pierces it.

5J-5. Fig. 242-5.   Given the tetrahedron $A(1; 3\frac{1}{2}; 5\frac{1}{2})$ $B(317)$ $C(2\frac{1}{2}; 3; 4\frac{1}{2})$ $D(1\frac{1}{2}; 1; 4\frac{1}{2})$.   Pass a plane through D perpendicular to the edge AB and show its intersection with the tetrahedron.

5J-6. Fig. 242-6.   Draw the triangle $A(3; X; 6\frac{1}{2})$ $B(3\frac{1}{2}; 2; 5\frac{1}{2})$ $C(1\frac{1}{2}; 1\frac{1}{2}; X)$ perpendicular to the line $R(1; 3\frac{1}{2}; 5)$ $S(317)$.   Show the intersection of RS with the triangle.

5J-7. Draw the plane $C(435)$ $D(3XX)$ $E(2XX)$ perpendicular to the line $A(1; 3\frac{1}{2}; 5\frac{1}{2})$ $B(317)$.

5J-8. Draw the plane $R(2\frac{1}{2}; 3; 5)$ $S(11X)$ $T(21X)$ perpendicular to the line $A(\frac{1}{2}; 2; 5\frac{1}{2})$ $B(327)$.   Draw the plane $J(6; 2\frac{1}{2}; 5)$ $K(5\frac{1}{2}; X; 7)$ $L(7X7)$ perpendicular to the line $C(516)$ $D(7\frac{1}{2}; 3; 6)$.

Group 5K.   A Plane Perpendicular to a Plane.

5K-1. Pass a plane $A(1\frac{1}{2}; 3; 7)$ $B(325)$ $C(X1X)$ perpendicular to a horizontal plane through B.   Pass a plane $E(535)$ $F(716)$ $G(XX5)$ perpendicular to a frontal plane through F.

5K-2. Pass a plane $C(716)$ $K(5\frac{1}{2}; 3; 6\frac{1}{2})$ $R(4\frac{1}{2}; X; X)$ through the line CK perpendicular to the triangle $A(436)$ $B(4\frac{1}{2}; 1; 7\frac{1}{2})$ C.

5K-3. Pass a plane $R(4\frac{1}{2}; 3\frac{1}{2}; 7)$ $S(626)$ $T(3XX)$ through the line RS perpendicular to the triangle $A(2\frac{1}{2}; 3; 6)$ $B(417)$ $C(525)$.

5K-4. Pass a plane $JKL(6XX)$ through the line $J(336)$ $K(5; 2; 4\frac{1}{2})$ perpendicular to the triangle $A(4; 4; 5\frac{1}{2})$ $B(517)$ $C(7; 2\frac{1}{2}; 5)$.

5K-5. Through $A(4; 4; 4\frac{1}{4})$ draw a plane $AB(3XX)$ $C(5XX)$ perpendicular to the planes $Q(125)$ $R(247)$ $S(316)$ and $T(527)$ $U(736)$ $V(6; 1; 4\frac{1}{2})$.

5K-6. Pass a plane $J(2\frac{1}{2}; X; X)$ $K(5XX)$ $L(4; 3\frac{1}{2}; 5\frac{1}{2})$ through point L, perpendicular to the planes $A(2; 3\frac{1}{2}; 4\frac{1}{2})$ $B(327)$ $D(515)$ and $BDC(6; 3\frac{1}{2}; 6)$.

5K-7. Pass a plane $J(4XX)$ $PQ(X; 1\frac{1}{2}; X)$ through point $P(5; 4\frac{1}{2}; 7)$ perpendicular to the plane $R(1; 3\frac{1}{2}; 5)$ $S(317)$ $T(4; 2\frac{1}{2}; 4)$ and to a horizontal plane through $K(626)$.

5K-8. Draw the plane $A(536)$ $B(4\frac{1}{2}; X; X)$ $C(4XX)$ perpendicular to the plane $R(3; 3\frac{1}{2}; 4\frac{1}{2})$ $S(226)$ $U(5; 1; 5\frac{1}{4})$ and $ST(627)$ U.

Group 5L.   A Line Parallel to a Plane.

5L-1. Draw the lines $J(4\frac{1}{2}; X; 5\frac{1}{2})$ $K(337)$ and $L(527)$ $M(6\frac{1}{2}; 2\frac{3}{4}; X)$ each parallel to the triangle $A(\frac{1}{2}; 3; 5\frac{1}{2})$ $B(217)$ $C(324)$.

5L-2. Draw the lines $R(646)$ $S(72X)$ and $T(\frac{1}{2}; 2; 4)$ $U(33X)$ each parallel to the triangle $D(3; 2\frac{1}{2}; 5)$ $E(4; 4; 7\frac{1}{2})$ $F(6; 2; 6\frac{1}{2})$.

5L-3. $A(137)$ $B(336)$ is the strike of a plane which dips 40° forward. Draw the line $L(3X7)$ $M(115)$ parallel to the plane. Is LM above or below the plane? Verify your answer.

5L-4. Draw the line $A(6\frac{1}{2}; 4; 7\frac{1}{2})$ $B(5\frac{1}{2}; 2; X)$ parallel to the plane through $K(737)$ having a strike of S 70° W and a dip of 30° southeasterly.

5L-5. Draw the line $C(1X6)$ $D(3; 3\frac{1}{2}; 4\frac{1}{2})$ parallel to the plane through $J(124)$ which has a strike of N 58° E and a dip of 48° northwesterly.

Group 5M.   A Plane Parallel to a Line.

5M-1. Fig. 243-1.   Pass a plane $C(2\frac{1}{2}; 2; 5)$ $D(434)$ $E(5\frac{1}{2}; X; X)$ through the line CD parallel to the line $A(3\frac{1}{2}; 1; 7)$ $B(2; 2; 5\frac{1}{2})$.

5M-2. Fig. 243-2.   Draw a plane parallel to the lines $J(517)$ $K(736)$ and $L(4\frac{1}{2}; 3\frac{1}{2}; 5)$ $M(6\frac{1}{2}; 2; 5\frac{1}{2})$ and measure its strike and dip.

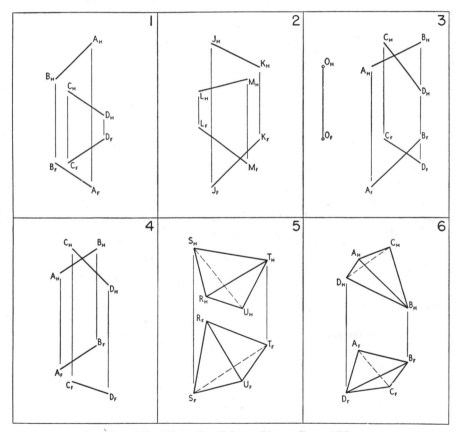

Fig. 243.—Plane Parallel to a Line.   Group 5M.

5M-3. Fig. 243-3. Through the point $O(336)$ draw a plane $OP(4XX)$ $Q(1XX)$ parallel to the lines $A(516)$ $B(737)$ and $C(5\frac{1}{2};3;7)$ $D(725)$.

5M-4. Fig. 243-4. Pass a plane CDE through the line $C(1\frac{1}{2};1\frac{1}{2};7)$ $D(3;1;5\frac{1}{2})$ parallel to the line $A(126)$ $B(2\frac{1}{2};3;7)$. Measure the strike and dip of the plane. Show AB in the view showing edge view of the plane.

5M-5. Fig. 243-5. $RSTU$ is a tetrahedron. Pass a plane parallel to the edges $R(4\frac{1}{2};4;5)$ $T(7;3;6\frac{1}{2})$ and $S(417)$ $U(6;1\frac{1}{2};4\frac{1}{2})$, $1\frac{1}{4}''$ from RT, and find its intersection with the tetrahedron. The intersection is a parallelogram.

5M-6. Fig. 243-6. Pass a plane parallel to the lines $A(5;2\frac{3}{4};6\frac{1}{2})$ $B(7;2\frac{1}{4};4\frac{1}{2})$ and $C(6\frac{1}{4};1\frac{1}{4};7)$ $D(4\frac{1}{2};1;5\frac{3}{4})$ which will intersect the tetrahedron $ABCD$ in a parallelogram having two sides twice as long as the other two. The long sides are parallel to AB. Find the lengths of the sides of the parallelogram and draw it in the front and top views.

Group 5N. A Plane Parallel to a Plane.

5N-1. Draw the triangle $A(315)$ $B(42X)$ $C(1X6)$ parallel to the plane $L(4\frac{1}{2};3;7)$ $M(7\frac{1}{2};2;6)$ $N(5\frac{1}{2};1;4)$.

5N-2. Draw the triangle $J(216)$ $K(3\frac{1}{2};2;X)$ $L(\frac{1}{2};X;5)$ parallel to the parallelogram $A(3\frac{1}{2};3;6)$ $B(5;1\frac{1}{2};7\frac{1}{2})$ $C(7\frac{1}{2};1;7)$ $D(6;2\frac{1}{2};5\frac{1}{2})$.

5N-3. Draw the triangle $R(115)$ $S(23X)$ $T(3X7)$ parallel to the triangle $A(5;3;4\frac{1}{2})$ $B(6\frac{1}{2};1;7\frac{1}{2})$ $C(746)$.

5N-4. Draw the triangle $A(1;X;6\frac{1}{2})$ $B(3X6)$ $C(245)$ parallel to the triangle $D(545)$ $E(617)$ $F(736)$.

5N-5. Draw the triangle $A(1\frac{1}{2};2\frac{1}{2};5\frac{1}{2})$ $B(3;1\frac{1}{2};X)$ $C(1X4)$ parallel to the plane whose strike is $J(137)$ $K(336)$ and which dips 50° forward.

5N-6. Pass three equally spaced parallel planes through the vertices of the tetrahedron $A(128)$ $B(246)$ $C(315)$ $D(4;2\frac{1}{2};7)$. The required sequence of the planes is B, A, D, C. Represent the planes by similar triangles, a vertex of each being at B, A, D, or C. How far apart are the planes?

5N-7. Pass four equally-spaced parallel planes through the points $A(1;1\frac{1}{2};6)$, $G(235)$, $L(3;2;5\frac{1}{2})$, and $E(4;1;6\frac{1}{2})$ in the order $AEGL$. Show the planes as equal opaque triangles lettered ABC, DEF, GHI, and JKL. How far apart are these planes?

Group 5O. The True Length of a Line by Revolution.

Solve these problems by the revolution method.

5O-1. Fig. 244-1. $P(4;4\frac{1}{2};6)$ is the top of a vertical antenna pole guyed to the roof of a house by the wires $K(4;3\frac{1}{2};6)$ $A(3X7)$, $KB(5;1;6\frac{1}{2})$, and $KC(3\frac{1}{2};2;5)$. The front view is an edge view of the roof. Find the length of the guy wires. Scale: $1'' = 10$ ft.

5O-2. Fig. 244-2. Point $P(417)$ in a structure is to be connected to $A(4;4;5\frac{1}{2})$ $B(627)$ at a point $4'$ from A; and to $AC(216)$ at a point $6'$ from A. Find the length of the connecting pieces and draw them in the front and top views. Scale: $\frac{1}{2}'' = 1'\text{-}0''$.

5O-3. Fig. 244-3. Point $A(317)$ is to be connected to $J(3\frac{1}{2}; 3; 4\frac{1}{2})$ $K(616)$ at points B and C. B is 3′ from K and C is 4′ from J. These are steel rods fastened by welding. Find the length of each connecting piece and draw it in the front and top views. Scale: $\frac{1}{4}'' = 1'\text{-}0''$.

5O-4. Fig. 233-1. $M(4; 3; 5\frac{1}{2})$ $A(3\frac{1}{2}; 1; 7)$, $MB(2\frac{1}{2}; 1; 4\frac{1}{2})$, and $MC(5\frac{1}{2}; 1; 4\frac{3}{4})$ are legs of a tripod fastened to the floor of a garage at the points A, B, and C. Find the length of each leg. Scale: $\frac{1}{2}'' = 1'\text{-}0''$.

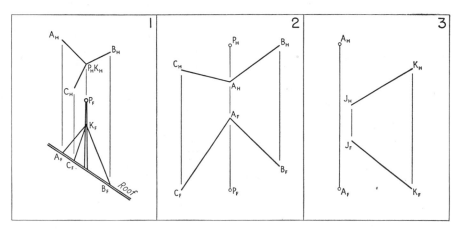

FIG. 244.—True Length of a Line by Revolution. Group 5O.

5O-5. Fig. 233-2. $J(436)$ $A(2\frac{1}{2}; 3\frac{1}{2}; 7)$, $JB(4\frac{1}{2}; 1; 7)$, and $JC(5\frac{1}{2}; 4; 7)$ are three members of a structure fastened to a frontal wall at A, B, and C. Find the length of the members. Scale: $\frac{1}{4}'' = 1'\text{-}0''$.

5O-6. Fig. 233-3. $A(446)$ is the top of a vertical flagpole 24′ high. $K(436)$ $R(2\frac{3}{4}; X; 6\frac{1}{2})$, $KS(5X7)$, and $KT(4\frac{1}{4}; X; 5)$ are guy wires from the pole downward to the ground. KR is 15′ long, KS is 18′ long, and KT is 16′ long. Draw the front view of the guy wires. Scale: $\frac{1}{8}'' = 1'\text{-}0''$.

5O-7. Fig. 233-4. $L(2; 2\frac{1}{2}; 6)$ $A(1; 3\frac{1}{2}; 7)$, $LB(1; 1; 6\frac{1}{2})$, and $LC(1; 3; 4\frac{1}{2})$ are members for a support for a hoist. It is fastened to a profile wall at points A, B, and C. Find the length of each of the members. Scale: $\frac{1}{2}'' = 1'\text{-}0''$.

5O-8. Fig. 233-8. $A(437)$ is the vertex of an isosceles triangle whose equal sides $AB(31X)$ and $AC(5X5)$ are each $2\frac{1}{2}''$ long. Draw the front and top views of the triangle and find the length of the third side.

5O-9. Fig. 233-9. $A(435)$ $B(617)$ and $AC(1\frac{1}{2}; 1; 6)$ are members of a structure made of steel tubing. A third member is to be welded to AB at D, 9′ from A; and to AC at E, 12′ from A. Draw front and top views of the connecting piece and find its length. Scale: $\frac{1}{4}'' = 1'\text{-}0''$.

Group 5P. The Angle a Line Makes with a Principal Plane. Revolution Method.

Solve these problems by the revolution method.

5P-1. Fig. 245-1. $J(4; 2\frac{1}{2}; 5)$ $R(2\frac{1}{2}; 3\frac{1}{4}; 7)$, $JS(4\frac{1}{2}; 1; 7)$, and $JT(5\frac{1}{2}; 3\frac{1}{2}; 7)$ are members of a steel support fastened to a frontal wall at R, S, and T. Find the length of each member and the angle it makes with the wall. Scale: $\frac{1}{4}'' = 1'\text{-}0''$.

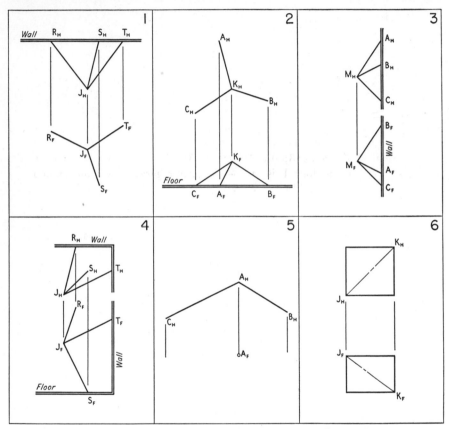

FIG. 245.—Angles H, F, and P by Revolution. Group 5P.

5P-2. Fig. 245-2. $K(425)$ $A(3\frac{1}{2}; 1; 7)$, $KB(5\frac{1}{2}; 1; 4\frac{1}{2})$, and $KC(2\frac{1}{2}; 1; 4)$ are the legs of a tripod resting on the floor. Find the length of each leg and the angle it makes with the floor. Scale: $\frac{1}{4}'' = 1'\text{-}0''$.

5P-3. Fig. 245-3. A steel structure having the members $M(6; 2; 5\frac{1}{2})$ $A(7; 1\frac{1}{2}; 7)$, $MB(7; 3\frac{1}{2}; 6)$, and $MC(7; 1; 4\frac{1}{2})$ is fastened to a profile wall at points A, B, and C. Find the length of each member and the angle it makes with the wall . Scale: $\frac{1}{4}''= 1'\text{-}0''$.

5P-4. Fig. 245-4. $J(535)$ $R(5\frac{1}{2}; 4\frac{1}{2}; 7)$, $JS(616)$, and $JT(746)$ are members of a steel support fastened to a frontal wall at R, to the floor at S, and to a profile wall at T. Find the length of each member and the angle it makes with the surface to which it is attached. Scale: $\frac{1}{2}'' = 1'\text{-}0''$.

5P-5. Fig. 245-5. $A(436)$, $B(6; X; 4\frac{3}{4})$, and $C(1; X; 4\frac{1}{2})$ are points on the surface of the ground. A surveyor finds that the line AB slopes downward 35°, and that AC slopes downward 18°. Find the straight-line distance from A to each of the points B and C. Find the difference in elevation between B and C; the true distance from B to C, and the slope of the line BC. Scale: $1'' = 80$ ft.

5P-6. Fig. 245-6. $J(1; 2\frac{1}{2}; 5)$ $K(317)$ is the body diagonal of a rectangular prism whose mutually perpendicular sides are horizontal, frontal, and profile. Find the angles which JK makes with the sides of the prism.

5P-7. Fig. 233-5. $J(4; 3\frac{1}{2}; 6)$ $A(3\frac{1}{2}; X; 7)$, $JB(2\frac{1}{2}; 1; X)$, and $JC(51X)$ are guy wires fastened to a telephone pole at J. JA is $25'$ long and extends downward; JB is $35'$ long and extends forward; and JC extends forward and makes 15° with a frontal plane through J. Draw all three wires in the front and top views and find the angle each makes with the horizontal. Scale: $1'' = 10$ ft.

5P-8. Fig. 233-6. $K(2\frac{1}{2}; 3; 6)$ $A(1\frac{1}{2}; 1; 6\frac{3}{4})$, $KB(247)$, and $KC(1; 4; 5\frac{1}{2})$ are the members of the support for a hoist in the corner of a garage. A is on the floor, B is on the rear wall, and C is on the side wall. Find the length of each member and the angle for the bracket needed to fasten it to the particular surface to which it is attached. Scale: $\frac{1}{4}'' = 1'\text{-}0''$.

5P-9. Fig. 233-7. Portions of an inaccessible vertical fir tree can be seen from $A(116)$ and $D(517)$, both at the water's edge of a lake. A surveyor sets up his transit at A and sights upward 20° in the direction $AB(2\frac{1}{2}; X; 5\frac{1}{4})$ to the base of the tree. At D he sights upward 47° in the direction $DE(3\frac{1}{2}; X; 5\frac{1}{2})$ to the top of the tree. Locate the tree in the front and top views and find its height. Scale: $1'' = 20$ ft.

Group 5Q. True Shape of a Plane by Revolution.

Solve these problems by the revolution method.

5Q-1. Find the true size of the triangle $D(5; 3\frac{1}{2}; 6)$ $E(7; 2\frac{1}{2}; 7)$ $F(645)$. Measure the length of its sides and the angles between them.

5Q-2. Find the true length of the lines $R(427)$ $S(7; 2\frac{1}{2}; 6)$ and $ST(515)$ and measure the angle between them.

5Q-3. $A(3; 1\frac{1}{2}; 7\frac{1}{2})$ $B(5; 2; 5\frac{1}{2})$ is a pipe in a laundry to which point $R(5; \frac{1}{2}; 6\frac{1}{2})$ is to be connected, using a 45° fitting. How much pipe is needed for the connection? How far from B will the pipe AB be cut for the fitting? Draw front and top views of the pipes. Scale: $\frac{1}{8}'' = 1'\text{-}0''$.

5Q-4. Find the true shape of the plane $A(\frac{1}{2}; 4; 7\frac{1}{2})$ $B(2\frac{1}{2}; 5\frac{1}{2}; 6\frac{1}{2})$ $C(4; 5; 6\frac{1}{2})$ $D(2; 3\frac{1}{2}; 7\frac{1}{2})$. $O(2\frac{1}{4}; 4\frac{1}{2}; X)$ is the center of a regular hexagonal hole cut through the plane. The sides of the hexagon are $\frac{5}{8}''$ long and two of them are horizontal. Draw the front and top views of the hole.

5Q-5. Draw the true shape of the triangle $A(4; 2; 6\frac{1}{2})$ $B(6; \frac{1}{2}; 7\frac{1}{2})$ $C(7; 2; 5\frac{1}{2})$. Draw the bisectors of its angles and at their intersection draw a regular pentagon lying in the triangle and having its lowest side frontal. The pentagon may be inscribed in a $1\frac{1}{2}''$ diameter circle.

5Q-6. Given the tetrahedron $A(2\frac{1}{2}; \frac{1}{2}; 6)$ $B(4\frac{1}{2}; \frac{1}{2}; 6)$ $C(4; \frac{1}{2}; 4\frac{1}{2})$ $V(3\frac{1}{2}; 2; 5\frac{1}{2})$. Find the true shape of all four faces, the true lengths of the edges, and the angles between the edges.

5Q-7. In a steel tower point $P(3; 1\frac{1}{2}; 7\frac{1}{2})$ is to be connected to $J(3; 2\frac{1}{2}; 6)$ $K(5; \frac{1}{2}; 6\frac{1}{2})$ with a piece $17'$ long. How far from J will the connection be made? Draw front and top views of the two members. Scale: $\frac{1}{8}'' = 1'\text{-}0''$.

5Q-8. In an airplane, $Q(\frac{1}{2}; 1\frac{1}{2}; 4\frac{1}{2})$ $S(2; \frac{1}{2}; 2)$ and $SR(4; 1; 3\frac{1}{2})$ are the center lines of a $\frac{3}{16}''$ rudder cable. Locate the center of a $4''$ diameter pulley tangent to the cable. Draw the pulley in the normal view and show its center in the front and top views. Scale: Half-size.

5Q-9. Draw the front and top views of a circle inscribed in the triangle $T(435)$ $U(547)$ $V(6; 2\frac{1}{2}; 6)$.

Group 5R.   The Distance from a Point to a Line.

5R-1. $A(5; 1; 7\frac{1}{2})$ $B(7; 2; 5\frac{1}{2})$ is an inclined working in a copper mine. Find the length of the shortest passage that can be driven from point $Q(536)$ on the ground to AB, and draw it in the front and top views. How far from A will it intersect AB? Scale: $1'' = 80$ ft.

5R-2. $J(116)$ $K(3; 2\frac{1}{2}; 6)$ and $R(237)$ $S(2; \frac{1}{2}; 4)$ are pipes that are to be connected to point $P(315)$ using $90°$ tee fittings. Find the length of the connecting pipes and draw the front and top views. Scale: $\frac{1}{8}'' = 1'\text{-}0''$.

5R-3. Find the length of a piece of steel tubing needed to make the shortest possible connection from $K(5; 3; 5\frac{1}{2})$ to $L(5\frac{1}{2}; 1; 7\frac{1}{2})$ $M(7\frac{1}{2}; 2; 6)$. Draw front and top views of the connecting piece. Scale: $\frac{1}{4}'' = 1'\text{-}0''$.

5R-4. Draw two steel braces from point $N(314)$ perpendicular to the rods $A(1\frac{1}{2}; 2; 5)$ $B(3\frac{1}{2}; 2\frac{1}{2}; 6)$ and $BC(515)$ and measure their lengths. Scale: $\frac{1}{4}'' = 1'\text{-}0''$.

5R-5. Which of the lines $A(1; \frac{1}{2}; 6)$ $B(3; 2; 7\frac{1}{2})$ or $C(3; \frac{1}{2}; 6)$ $D(5; 2; 7\frac{1}{2})$ is nearer point $J(3; 1; 6\frac{3}{4})$, and by how much? Draw front and top views of lines representing these distances.

5R-6. One corner of a square whose diagonals are $1\frac{1}{2}''$ long lies on the line $A(6\frac{1}{2}; 1\frac{1}{2}; 7)$ $B(7\frac{1}{2}; 2\frac{1}{2}; 5)$. The plane of the square is perpendicular to AB. The end of the diagonal opposite AB lies on the line $C(534)$ $D(616)$. Draw the front and top views of the square and any other necessary views.

Group 5S.   The Shortest Distance between Two Lines.

5S-1. Fig. 246-1. $L(4\frac{1}{2}; 5; 7)$ $M(7; 3; 6\frac{3}{4})$ and $R(5; 3; 6\frac{1}{2})$ $S(6\frac{1}{2}; 2\frac{1}{2}; 5\frac{1}{2})$ are the center lines of $1''$ diameter rods. Find the clearance between the rods. Draw front and top views of the shortest line connecting LM and RS.

5S-2. Fig. 246-2. Without using an oblique view draw and measure the common perpendicular between $A(717)$ $B(7; 3\frac{1}{2}; 5\frac{1}{2})$ and $C(5; 1\frac{1}{2}; 6)$ $D(7\frac{1}{2}; 3; 7)$. Show the perpendicular in all views.

5S-3. Fig. 246-3. $C(5; 2; 6\frac{1}{2})$ $D(735)$ is the center line of a $1''$ diameter rod in a structure. Find the diameter of the largest rod, having $E(615)$ $F(7; 2\frac{1}{2}; 7)$ as a center line, that can be used without interference. Show both rods in the oblique view. Show the point of contact in all views.

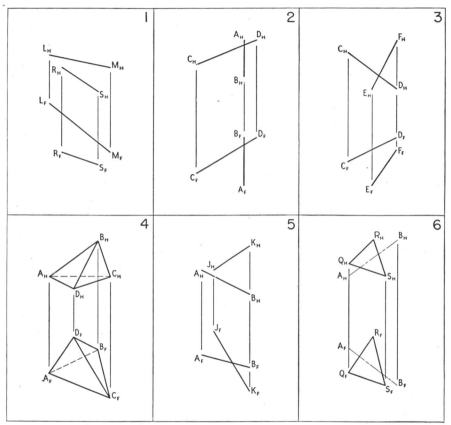

Fig. 246.—Shortest Distance between Skew Lines.   Group 5S.

5S-4. Fig. 246-4. Draw and measure the shortest line that can be drawn between AB and CD in the tetrahedron $A(126)$ $B(3; 3; 7\frac{1}{2})$ $C(3\frac{1}{2}; 1; 6)$ $D(2; 3\frac{1}{2}; 5\frac{1}{2})$. Show this line in all views.

5S-5. Fig. 246-5. $A(1; 2\frac{1}{2}; 6)$ $B(325)$ and $J(1\frac{1}{2}; 3\frac{1}{2}; 6)$ $K(317)$ are the center lines of two pipes. Using right angle tee fittings locate a connecting pipe. Draw the center line of this pipe in all views. Measure its length between AB and JK. Scale: $\frac{1}{4}'' = 1'\text{-}0''$.

5S-6. Fig. 246-6. $Q(1; 1\frac{1}{2}; 6)$ $R(237)$ $S(2\frac{1}{2}; 1; 5\frac{1}{2})$ is a hole in a thin plate. $A(1; 2\frac{1}{2}; 5\frac{1}{2})$ $B(317)$ is the center line for a pipe. What is the outside diameter of the largest pipe that can be used? Scale: $3'' = 1'\text{-}0''$. In the front and top views show the radius from AB to the point where the pipe touches the triangle QRS.

5S-7. $A(5; 1\frac{1}{2}; 7)$ $B(7\frac{1}{2}; 3; 8)$ is the center line of a control cable in an airplane, and $C(7; 3; 6\frac{1}{2})$ $D(718)$ is the center line of a rod. In all views draw the line which represents the clearance between the center lines. Measure its true length.

5S-8. $K(0; 2; 6\frac{1}{2})$ $L(3; \frac{1}{2}; 6)$ and $M(128)$ $N(1\frac{1}{2}; 0; 7)$ represent two small steel rods. Show in all views drawn the smallest square plate $ABCD$ which can be welded to KL along AB and have the midpoint of CD welded to MN. Indicate the hidden portion of MN. Measure the plate.

5S-9. In the tetrahedron $A(\frac{1}{2}; 2; 5\frac{1}{2})$ $B(1\frac{1}{2}; 4; 7\frac{1}{2})$ $C(2\frac{1}{2}; 1; 7)$ $D(3; 2; 5\frac{1}{2})$ draw the line which represents the shortest distance between edges AC and BD, and find its length.

5S-10. $R(137)$ $S(2\frac{1}{2}; 1; 6\frac{1}{4})$ and $T(4; 2\frac{1}{4}; 6)$ $U(235)$ are two members in a bridge. Find the clearance between them. Draw front and top views of the line that represents this distance. Scale: $1\frac{1}{2}'' = 1'\text{-}0''$.

5S-11. $A(5; 1\frac{1}{2}; 6)$ $B(6\frac{1}{2}; 2\frac{1}{2}; 5)$ and $C(5\frac{1}{2}; 3; 7\frac{1}{2})$ $D(7\frac{1}{2}; 1; 5)$ are two pipes to be connected using right angle fittings. Find length of the connecting pipe and draw it in the front and top views. Scale: $\frac{1}{4}'' = 1'\text{-}0''$.

5S-12. Draw a line perpendicular to both of the lines $J(5; 2; 6\frac{1}{2})$ $K(635)$ and $L(617)$ $M(736)$ and find its true length.

Group 5T. The Angle between a Line and a Plane.

5T-1. Fig. 247-1. Measure the angle between the line $A(5; 3; 5\frac{1}{2})$ $B(7; 2; 6\frac{1}{2})$ and the plane $R(546)$ $S(617)$ $T(735)$. Use the complementary angle method.

5T-2. Fig. 247-2. Using the complementary angle method, measure the angle between the line $R(3; 3\frac{1}{2}; 5)$ $S(227)$ and the triangle $A(1; 2\frac{1}{2}; 7)$ $B(436)$ $C(2; 1; 5\frac{1}{4})$.

5T-3. Fig. 247-3. $A(5; 2\frac{1}{2}; 6)$ $B(7; 2\frac{1}{2}; 7)$ $C(7\frac{1}{2}; 1; 6)$ $D(5\frac{1}{2}; 1; 5)$ is the upper surface of a truncated, vertical, right prism, the base of which is $\frac{1}{2}''$ below DC. $J(4\frac{3}{4}; 1\frac{1}{4}; 6\frac{3}{4})$ $K(7\frac{1}{4}; 3; 5)$ is the axis of a rod to be fastened to the inclined surface $ABCD$. Find the angle for the bracket needed. Show the intersection of JK and $ABCD$.

5T-4. Fig. 247-4. Measure the angle line $A(5\frac{1}{2}; 4\frac{1}{2}; 7\frac{1}{4})$ $B(6\frac{1}{2}; 3; 6\frac{1}{2})$ makes with the plane $Q(546)$ $R(628)$ $S(757)$. Use the direct method and check by revolution. Also show where AB pierces QRS considered as an opaque plane.

5T-5. Fig. 247-5. Find the angle between the line $A(236)$ $B(3\frac{1}{2}; 3\frac{1}{2}; 5\frac{1}{2})$ and the plane $S(135)$ $T(2; 4\frac{1}{2}; 7)$ $U(326)$. Use the direct method and check by revolution.

5T-6. Fig. 247-6. $A(2; \frac{1}{2}; 4)$ $B(016)$ $C(3\frac{1}{2}; 1\frac{3}{4}; 6\frac{1}{2})$ is the base of a pyramid whose vertex is $K(1\frac{3}{4}; 3; 5\frac{1}{2})$. By the revolution method find the lengths of KA, KB, and KC, and the angles they make with the plane ABC. Scale: $\frac{3}{4}'' = 1'\text{-}0''$.

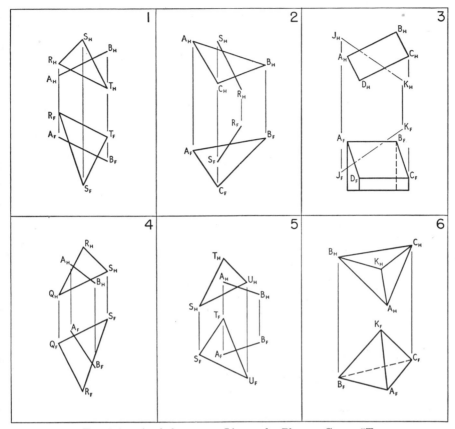

Fig. 247.—Angle between a Line and a Plane.   Group 5T.

5T-7. Find the angle the line $C(1; 1\frac{1}{2}; 7)$ $D(1; 3; 6\frac{1}{2})$ makes with the plane $R(0; 2; 7\frac{1}{2})$ $S(116)$ $T(237)$. Use the direct method and check by revolution. Include a normal view of *RST*.

5T-8. Measure the angle $C(\frac{1}{2}; 3; 7)$ $D(2; 2\frac{1}{2}; 6)$ makes with the plane $Q(046)$ $R(1; 1\frac{1}{2}; 5)$ $S(237)$. Use the direct method and check by revolution. Also show where *CD* pierces *QRS* considered an opaque plane.

5T-9. Fig. 244-1. $P(4; 4\frac{1}{2}; 6)$ is the top of a vertical antenna pole guyed to the roof of a house by the wires $K(4; 3\frac{1}{2}; 6)$ $A(3X7)$, $KB(5; 1; 6\frac{1}{2})$, and $KC(3\frac{1}{2}; 2; 5)$. The front view is an edge view of the roof. Find the angle each wire makes with the roof.

5T-10. Find the angle the line $A(536)$ $B(6\frac{1}{2}; 1; 5)$ makes with the plane $Q(525)$ $R(607)$ $S(736)$. Use the direct method and check by revolution. Also show where *AB* pierces *QRS* considered as an opaque plane.

5T-11. Using the complementary angle method, measure the angle between the line $J(1; 2\frac{1}{2}; 6)$ $K(3; 1; 6\frac{1}{2})$ and the triangle $A(237)$ $B(1; 1; 5\frac{1}{2})$ $C(325)$.

5T-12. Measure the angle the line $A(0; 2; 7\frac{1}{2})$ $B(1; \frac{1}{2}; 6\frac{1}{2})$ makes with the plane $Q(018)$ $R(\frac{1}{2}; 2; 6\frac{1}{2})$ $S(2; \frac{1}{2}; 7\frac{1}{2})$. Use the direct method and show a normal view of QRS. Find where AB pierces QRS. Check the angle by revolution.

5T-13. $A(118)$ $B(2; 0; 5\frac{1}{2})$ $C(327)$ is the base and $V(1; 2\frac{1}{4}; 6\frac{1}{4})$ is the vertex of a pyramid. Find the angle each lateral edge makes with the plane of the base. Use the revolution method.

5T-14. Find the angle the line $A(0; 3\frac{1}{2}; 5)$ $B(327)$ makes with the plane $Q(027)$ $R(336)$ $S(215)$. Use the complementary angle method but show QRS edgewise through R, and measure the distance from A to QRS.

Group 5U. The Intersection of Planes.

5U-1. Fig. 248-1. Find the intersection of the opaque triangles $A(2; 2; 6\frac{1}{2})$ $B(5; 1\frac{1}{4}; 6\frac{1}{2})$ $C(3; 3\frac{1}{2}; 4\frac{3}{4})$ and $D(447)$ $E(525)$ $F(2; 1; 5\frac{1}{2})$. Draw the edges with the proper visibility.

5U-2. Fig. 248-2. Find the intersection of the opaque triangles $R(2; 2\frac{1}{2}; 4\frac{1}{2})$ $S(3; 1; 6\frac{1}{2})$ $T(5; 3; 5\frac{1}{2})$ and $J(2; 3\frac{1}{2}; 6\frac{1}{2})$ $K(5; 2\frac{1}{2}; 7)$ $L(4; 1; 4\frac{1}{2})$, and draw the edges with the proper visibility.

5U-3. Fig. 248-3. Find the intersection of the two pieces of thin sheet metal $A(2\frac{1}{2}; 1; 7)$ $B(535)$ $C(1\frac{1}{2}; 2\frac{1}{2}; 4\frac{1}{2})$ and $J(1; 3; 5\frac{1}{2})$ $K(3; 3\frac{1}{2}; 7)$ $L(5\frac{1}{2}; 2; 6)$ $M(3\frac{1}{2}; 1\frac{1}{2}; 4\frac{1}{2})$ and draw them with the proper visibility.

5U-4. Fig. 248-4. Draw the intersecting opaque triangles $G(4; 1; 7\frac{1}{2})$ $H(5\frac{1}{2}; 3\frac{1}{2}; 5\frac{1}{2})$ $J(2; 2\frac{1}{2}; 4\frac{1}{2})$ and $L(2; 1; 6\frac{1}{4})$ $M(6; 2\frac{1}{4}; 7)$ $N(3\frac{1}{2}; 3\frac{1}{2}; 4\frac{1}{2})$.

5U-5. Fig. 248-5. Find the intersection of the two pieces of cardboard $A(2\frac{1}{2}; 3; 5)$ $B(4; 1; 7\frac{1}{2})$ $C(646)$ and $J(2\frac{1}{2}; 1\frac{1}{2}; 6\frac{3}{4})$ $K(5\frac{1}{2}; 2\frac{1}{2}; 7)$ $L(545)$.

5U-6. Fig. 248-6. Given the pyramid $V(436)$ $A(2\frac{3}{4}; 1; 7)$ $B(5\frac{1}{2}; 1; 6\frac{1}{2})$ $C(3\frac{1}{2}; 1; 4\frac{1}{2})$ and the plane $J(2\frac{1}{2}; 3\frac{1}{2}; 5\frac{3}{4})$ $K(4; 3\frac{1}{2}; 7\frac{1}{4})$ $L(5\frac{1}{2}; 1\frac{1}{2}; 5\frac{3}{4})$ $M(4; 1\frac{1}{2}; 4\frac{1}{4})$. Find the intersection. Draw the lines with the proper visibility.

5U-7. Fig. 248-7. Find the intersection of the planes of the points $J(\frac{1}{2}; 1; 6)$ $K(2\frac{1}{2}; 2; 7)$ $L(1\frac{1}{2}; 4; 5)$ and $R(536)$ $S(617)$ $T(745)$.

5U-8. Fig. 248-8. Find the intersection of the planes of the points $A(\frac{1}{2}; 3; 7)$ $B(2; 3\frac{1}{2}; 6)$ $C(1\frac{1}{2}; 1; 5)$ and $D(5; 3\frac{1}{2}; 6\frac{1}{2})$ $E(7; 2\frac{1}{2}; 7)$ $F(5\frac{1}{2}; 1; 5)$.

5U-9. Fig. 248-9. Find the intersection of the planes of the points $J(247)$ $K(\frac{1}{2}; 2; 5\frac{1}{2})$ $L(3\frac{1}{2}; 1; 5)$ and $R(5\frac{1}{2}; 4; 7)$ $S(7; 3\frac{1}{2}; 6)$ $T(615)$.

5U-10. Find the intersection of the planes $P(135)$ $Q(2; 1\frac{1}{2}; 7\frac{1}{2})$ $R(346)$ and $S(527)$ $T(7; 1; 6\frac{1}{2})$ $U(645)$.

5U-11. Find the intersection of the opaque triangles $A(1; \frac{1}{2}; 6)$ $B(517)$ $C(3; 3\frac{1}{2}; 4)$ and $D(1; 3; 4\frac{1}{2})$ $E(6; 2; 5\frac{1}{2})$ $F(3; 0; 7\frac{1}{2})$. Determine and show the visibility of all lines.

5U-12. Find the intersection of the thin metal plates $Q(1; 1\frac{1}{2}; 4)$ $R(407)$ $S(635)$ and $T(136)$ $U(627)$ $V(304)$. Determine the visibility of their edges.

5U-13. Find the intersection of the two pieces of sheet metal $A(\frac{1}{2}; 0; 5)$ $B(4; 3\frac{1}{2}; 4)$ $C(6; 1\frac{1}{2}; 7)$ and $Q(1; 2\frac{1}{2}; 4)$ $R(3; 0; 6\frac{1}{2})$ $S(6\frac{1}{2}; 3; 5)$. Indicate the visibility of their edges.

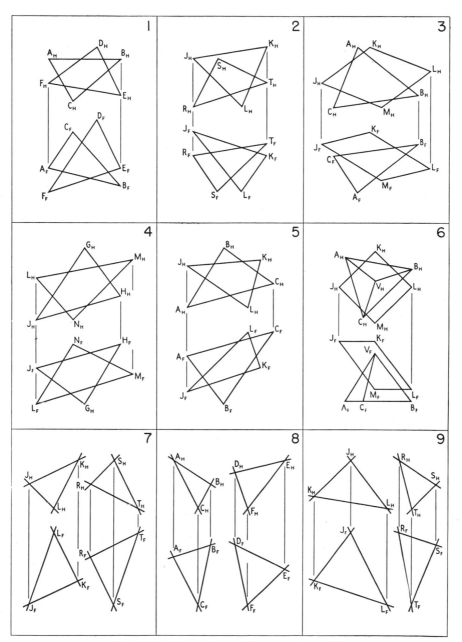

Fɪɢ. 248.—Intersection of Planes.   Group 5U.

Group 5V.   The Angle between Two Planes.   Dihedral Angle.

5V-1. Fig. 249-1. Measure the angle between the planes $A(1; 3\frac{1}{4}; 7)$ $B(317)$ $D(1\frac{1}{2}; 2; 5)$ and $C(117)BD$.

5V-2. Fig. 249-2. Measure the angle between the planes $D(6; 3\frac{1}{2}; 5)$ $E(527)$ $G(7; 1\frac{1}{2}; 5\frac{1}{2})$ and $EGF(617)$.

5V-3. Fig. 249-3. Measure the angle between the planes $J(1; 2\frac{1}{2}; 6)$ $K(2; 3\frac{1}{2}; 7\frac{1}{2})$ $L(3; 1\frac{1}{2}; 7)$ and $KLM(3\frac{1}{2}; 3; 5\frac{1}{2})$.

5V-4. Fig. 249-4. $A(6; 3; 4\frac{1}{2})$ $B(524)$ $D(734)$ $C(716)$ is a piece of steel bent on BC to be used for a bracket. Measure the angle between ABC and BCD.

5V-5. Fig. 249-5. $V(2; 3\frac{1}{2}; 6)$ is the apex and $R(126)$ $S(2; 1\frac{1}{2}; 7)$ $T(316)$ $U(2; 1\frac{1}{2}; 5)$ is the base of a pyramidal spire on a roof. Measure the angle between the sides VRS and VST.

5V-6. Fig. 249-6. $A(1\frac{1}{2}; 2\frac{1}{2}; 7)$ $B(2\frac{1}{2}; 3; 4\frac{3}{4})$ $C(3; 1\frac{1}{2}; 5\frac{1}{4})$ is a steel plate to be fastened to the surface $J(1; 2\frac{1}{2}; 6\frac{1}{2})$ $K(2\frac{1}{2}; 1; 6\frac{1}{2})$ $L(2\frac{1}{2}; 1; 4\frac{1}{4})$ $M(1; 2\frac{1}{2}; 4\frac{1}{4})$ with a bracket. Find the angle for the bracket whose faces lie in these planes.

5V-7. Fig. 249-7. $A(145)$ $B(148)$ $C(3\frac{3}{4}; 3\frac{1}{2}; 7\frac{3}{4})$ $D(3\frac{3}{4}; 3\frac{1}{2}; 5\frac{1}{4})$ is the upper end of a hopper and $E(226)$ $F(227)$ $G(327)$ $H(326)$ is its lower end. Measure the angle between the sides $BCGF$ and $HGCD$.

5V-8. Fig. 249-8. In an airplane, $Q(1\frac{1}{2}; 2; 4)$ $R(2\frac{1}{4}; 3\frac{1}{4}; 5\frac{1}{2})$ $S(3; 1\frac{1}{4}; 4\frac{3}{4})$ is a mounting surface for a bracket to support a pulley for changing the direction of a cable from $A(1; 1\frac{3}{4}; 4\frac{1}{4})$ $C(2\frac{1}{2}; 1; 4\frac{3}{4})$ to $CB(1\frac{3}{4}; 2\frac{1}{4}; 6)$. Find the angle for the bracket, i.e., the angle between the planes ABC and QRS. This angle may be found without finding the intersection of the planes by using the following suggestion: after obtaining a view showing the true shape of QRS, a true-length line parallel to QRS may be drawn in ABC in order that the next view may be an edge view of both planes.

5V-9. Fig. 249-9. Measure the angle between the planes $A(\frac{1}{2}; 2\frac{1}{4}; 6\frac{3}{4})$ $B(236)$ $C(1; 1\frac{1}{2}; 5)$ and $Q(\frac{3}{4}; 3\frac{1}{4}; 6)$ $R(1\frac{1}{2}; 2\frac{1}{2}; 5)$ $S(2\frac{1}{4}; 3\frac{3}{4}; 5\frac{3}{4})$.

5V-10. Find the dihedral angle between the planes $A(\frac{1}{2}; 2\frac{1}{4}; 6\frac{3}{4})$ $B(236)$ $C(1; 1\frac{1}{2}; 5)$ and $Q(1; 3; 5\frac{3}{4})$ $R(1\frac{1}{2}; 2\frac{1}{2}; 5)$ $S(2; 3\frac{1}{2}; 5\frac{1}{2})$. Use the edge view method.

Group 5W.   A Line Making Given Angles with Two Planes.

5W-1. From $A(326)$ draw a line AB, $2''$ long, downward, forward, and to the right, making $28°$ with a horizontal plane and $50°$ with a frontal plane.

5W-2. A brace extends from point $P(1; 3\frac{1}{2}; 5)$ on a profile wall backward and downward to a point K on a frontal wall. It makes an angle of $40°$ with the profile wall and $30°$ with the frontal wall. Draw front and top views of the brace and find its length. Scale: $\frac{1}{2}'' = 1'\text{-}0''$.

5W-3. A brace extends from $J(537)$ in a frontal wall forward and to a point $H(X1X)$ in the floor. It makes $25°$ with the floor and $35°$ with the wall. Draw the front and top views of the brace and find its length. Scale: $\frac{1}{2}'' = 1'\text{-}0''$.

5W-4. Draw four lines from $A(3\frac{1}{2}; 2; 6)$, $1\frac{1}{4}''$ long, which make $20°$ with a frontal plane, $15°$ with plane $Q(116)$ $R(327)$ $S(2; 3\frac{1}{2}; 5)$, and would intersect plane QRS if extended.

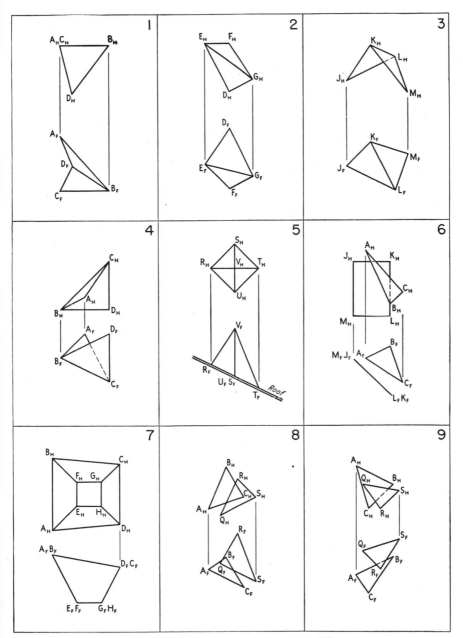

Fig. 249.—Dihedral Angles. Group 5V.

5W-5. Fig. 250-1. $Q(534)$ $R(735)$ is the strike of a plane QRS which dips 75° northwesterly. Draw the front and top views of all the lines from $V(6; 1\frac{1}{2}; 6\frac{1}{2})$ to the plane QRS which make 45° with it, and 30° with a horizontal plane. Measure the distance along these lines to QRS. Scale: $1'' = 1'\text{-}0''$.

5W-6. Fig. 250-2. From $A(2\frac{1}{2}; 4; 7)$ draw the front and top views of all the lines that make 40° with a horizontal plane and 45° with $Q(137)$ $R(245)$ $S(3; 2; 6\frac{1}{2})$. Measure the distance on these lines from A to the plane of QRS. Scale: $1'' = 1'\text{-}0''$.

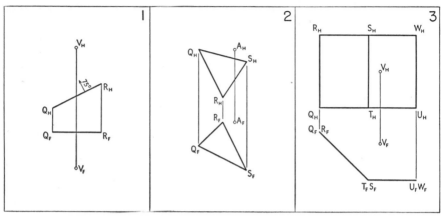

Fig. 250.—Line Making Given Angles with Two Planes. Group 5W.

5W-7. Fig. 250-3. Draw all the lines from $V(3\frac{1}{2}; 2\frac{1}{2}; 5\frac{1}{2})$ that make 50° with the plane $Q(134)$ $R(137)$ $S(317)$ $T(314)$ and 40° with the plane $STU(514)$ $W(517)$. Measure the length of the lines from V to the first plane and the segment between the planes produced. Scale: $1'' = 1'\text{-}0''$. Make your solution show that there are no other lines.

5W-8. $A(045)$ $B(0; 4\frac{1}{2}; 7)$ $C(4; 4\frac{1}{2}; 7)$ $D(445)$ represents a roof attached to a frontal wall along BC. The roof is to be supported by two pipes, each having a 45° ell and flange at each end, and connected to the wall. From $J(1\frac{1}{2}; 3; 7)$ draw the center line of a support running to K near A; and from $M(2\frac{1}{2}; 3; 7)$ draw the center line of another support to N near D. Neglect dimensions of the fittings.

5W-9. $A(2; 1\frac{3}{4}; 4\frac{1}{2})$ $B(2; 1\frac{1}{4}; 5\frac{1}{2})$ $C(3\frac{1}{2}; 1\frac{1}{4}; 5\frac{1}{2})$ $D(3\frac{1}{2}; 1\frac{3}{4}; 4\frac{1}{2})$ is the top of a mixing bin which is to be connected to a tank at $J(1\frac{1}{4}; 2\frac{3}{4}; 7)$ using a piece of $2''$ pipe with a 45° ell and flange at each end. Draw the center line for the connecting pipe and find its length. Scale: $\frac{1}{4}'' = 1'\text{-}0''$. Neglect dimensions of the fittings.

Group 5X. A Plane Making Given Angles with Two Planes.

5X-1. Draw the plane $R(436)$ $S(5\frac{1}{2}; X; X)$ $T(5XX)$ sloping downward, backward, to the right, making 48° with a horizontal plane and 67° with a frontal plane. Draw cones with vertices at $A(226)$.

5X-2. Plane $A(1; 3\frac{1}{2}; 7)$ $H(3XX)$ $F(3XX)$ slopes downward, backward, to the right; and plane $B(5; 3\frac{1}{2}; 7)HF$ slopes downward, backward, to the left. Both make 58° with a horizontal plane and 40° with a frontal plane. Draw front and top views of the planes. Construction cones have vertices at $V(626)$.

5X-3. Draw a plane $J(736)$ $K(6XX)$ $L(5XX)$ which slopes downward, backward, to the left, and makes 55° with a horizontal plane and 60° with a frontal plane. Use $A(336)$ for vertex of construction cones.

5X-4. Draw the plane $Q(1XX)$ $R(235)$ $S(4XX)$ which slopes downward, forward, to the right, and makes 35° with a horizontal plane and 65° with a frontal plane. Use $V(636)$ as vertex of construction cones.

5X-5. Through point Q, pass a plane $P(1\frac{1}{2}; X; X)$ $Q(235)$ $R(3XX)$ which slopes downward, backward, to the right, and makes 51° with a horizontal plane and 65° with the plane which has the strike $J(737)$ $K(536)$ and a dip of 60° southeasterly. Use $A(5\frac{1}{2}; 2; 7)$ as vertex of construction cones.

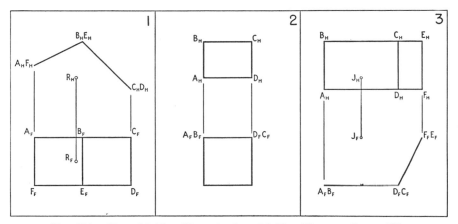

Fig. 251.—Plane Making Given Angles with Two Planes. Group 5X.

5X-6. Fig. 251-1. Through point $R(3\frac{3}{4}; 2; 5\frac{1}{2})$ pass a plane $RS(1XX)$ $T(7XX)$ which slopes downward, forward, to the right, and makes 40° with plane $A(236)$ $B(437)$ $E(417)$ $F(216)$ and 60° with plane $BC(535)$ $D(615)E$. Construct cones with vertex at R.

5X-7. Fig. 251-2. $A(1; 3; 5\frac{1}{2})$ $B(137)$ $C(337)$ $D(3; 3; 5\frac{1}{2})$ is the upper base of a right prism of 2″ altitude. Pass a plane through A which slopes downward, backward, to the left, and makes 45° with the left side of the prism and 65° with the rear side. Find the intersection of the plane and prism and draw three principal views of the truncated prism.

5X-8. Fig. 251-3. Through $J(2\frac{1}{2}; 3; 5\frac{1}{2})$ pass a plane $K(1XX)$ $JL(4XX)$ which slopes downward, forward, to the left, and makes 70° with plane $A(115)$ $B(117)$ $C(417)$ $D(415)$, and 65° with plane $CE(537)$ $F(535)$ D.

Group 5Y. A Plane through a Line and Making a Given Angle with Another Plane.

5Y-1. Pass a plane $ABC(4XX)$ through the line $A(536)$ $B(715)$ which has a dip of 50° southeasterly. Measure the bearing of the strike of the plane.

5Y-2. Pass planes $J(117)$ $K(3; 2\frac{1}{2}; 5\frac{1}{2})$ $L(4XX)$ and $JKM(3XX)$ through the line JK, each making 70° with the horizontal. Measure the bearing of the strike of each plane.

5Y-3. Measure the strike and dip of a plane $L(135)$ $M(416)$ $N(2XX)$ through the line LM, sloping forward, and making 30° with a frontal plane. Draw front and top views of the plane.

5Y-4. Pass a plane through the line $A(4; 3\frac{1}{2}; 7)$ $B(425)$ which will slope forward and make 70° with an ortho-frontal plane through $J(23X)$ $K(51X)$. Find the strike and dip of the plane.

5Y-5. Pass two planes through the line $J(3; 1; 5\frac{1}{2})$ $K(125)$ which will slope backward from JK and make 40° with a vertical plane through $KL(3X7)$.

5Y-6. Pass a plane through the line $L(1; 1\frac{1}{2}; 7)$ $M(2\frac{1}{2}; 3; 5)$ which slopes backward and makes 55° with a profile plane. Measure the strike and dip of the plane.

Group 5Z. Planes Tangent to Cones and Cylinders.

5Z-1. $V(336)$ is the vertex and $O(316)$ is the center of the $2\frac{1}{2}''$ diameter base of a right cone. Draw a plane through $K(3\frac{1}{2}; X; 5\frac{1}{2})$, on the surface of the cone, tangent to the cone and find its strike and dip.

5Z-2. $V(336)$ is the vertex of a right cone and $O(316)$ is the center of its $2\frac{1}{2}''$ diameter base. Pass two planes through the point $J(4\frac{1}{2}; 2; 5)$ tangent to the cone and measure the bearing of their strikes.

5Z-3. $O(515)$ is the center of the $2''$ diameter horizontal base of an oblique cone whose vertex is $V(336)$. Pass a plane through $R(2; 2; 5\frac{1}{2})$ tangent to the cone. The plane dips forward. Measure the dip.

5Z-4. $V(315)$ is the vertex of an oblique cone and $Q(536)$ is the center of its $2''$ diameter horizontal base. Draw two planes, each tangent to the cone and parallel to the line $J(215)$ $K(136)$.

5Z-5. $J(236)$ $L(415)$ is the axis of an oblique cylinder which has $1\frac{1}{2}''$ diameter horizontal bases. $K(3\frac{1}{4}; 2; X)$ is a point on the front side of the cylinder. Draw a plane through K tangent to the cylinder.

5Z-6. $L(4; 4; 5\frac{1}{2})$ $M(627)$ is the axis of an oblique cylinder which has $2''$ diameter frontal bases. Pass a plane through $J(236)$ tangent to the cylinder on the upper side.

5Z-7. $P(215)$ $Q(536)$ is the axis of an oblique cylinder which has $1\frac{1}{2}''$ diameter horizontal bases. Pass a plane through the line $A(5; 2; 4\frac{1}{2})$ tangent to the front side of the cylinder.

5Z-8. $O(346)$ is the center of a $2''$ diameter horizontal circle which is the common base of two oblique cones with vertices $V(116)$ and $A(535)$. Draw two planes through line VA and tangent to both cones.

5Z-9. $C(4; 4; 5\frac{3}{4})$ and $D(747)$ are the vertices of two cones whose common base is the $2\frac{1}{2}''$ diameter frontal circle with center $Q(5\frac{1}{2}; 2; 4\frac{1}{2})$. Draw two planes through CD tangent to the cones.

5Z-10. $V(7; 1\frac{1}{2}; 7)$ is the vertex of an oblique cone and $O(5; 3; 5\frac{1}{2})$ is the center of its $1\frac{1}{2}''$ diameter profile base. Pass two planes through the point $P(6; 1; 5\frac{1}{2})$ tangent to the cone.

Group 5AA. Miscellaneous Problems.

5AA-1. Fig. 252-1. Through $J(625)$ draw a line which is parallel to the plane $Q(1; 4; 4\frac{1}{2})$ $R(2; 2\frac{1}{2}; 6)$ $S(335)$ and intersects the line $A(3\frac{1}{2}; 1; 4)$ $B(5; 4; 6\frac{1}{2})$.

5AA-2. Fig. 252-2. Find the top view of the line $B(\frac{1}{2}; 3; 5)$ $C(2\frac{1}{4}; 2\frac{1}{4}; X)$ which makes an angle of $30°$ with $BA(2; 1\frac{1}{2}; 6)$. Show two positions of BC.

5AA-3. Fig. 252-3. Through the line $A(125)$ $B(316)$ pass two planes, each equidistant from the points $C(\frac{1}{2}; \frac{1}{2}; 5\frac{1}{2})$ and $D(217)$. Prove your solution is correct in an edge-view of both planes. How far are the points from each plane?

5AA-4. Fig. 252-4. Through the point $J(3; \frac{1}{2}; 7)$ pass four planes, each equidistant from the points $A(0; 1\frac{1}{2}; 6)$, $B(217)$ and $C(3; 2\frac{1}{2}; 5)$. The solution for two of the planes may be checked in a view which is an edge view of two of them.

5AA-5. Fig. 252-5. $B(525)$ $C(637)$ $D(7; 1\frac{1}{2}; 6)$ is the base of a pyramid. Locate its vertex A, above its base so that AB, AC, AD are mutually perpendicular.

5AA-6. Fig. 252-6. Given the points $A(\frac{1}{2}; 2\frac{1}{4}; 6)$ and $C(2\frac{1}{2}; 3; 6\frac{1}{2})$, and the plane $Q(127)$ $R(3; 2\frac{1}{2}; 6\frac{1}{2})$ $S(2; 1; 4\frac{1}{2})$. Obstructions prevent using a straight pipe between A and C. Make a drawing showing a connection for which AB is $16''$ long, CD is $12''$, and the pipe BD lies in the plane QRS, and has a maximum grade. The fittings at B and D are $90°$ ells. Measure BD. Scale: $\frac{3}{4}'' = 1'\text{-}0''$.

5AA-7. Fig. 252-7. Given the pyramid $A(1; 1; 6\frac{1}{2})$ $B(3\frac{1}{2}; 1; 6)$ $C(1\frac{1}{2}; 1; 5)$ $D(1\frac{3}{4}; 2\frac{1}{2}; 5\frac{3}{4})$. Draw a view in which $ABCD$ appears as a parallelogram. Through the point $J(4; 1; 7\frac{1}{2})$ draw the arrow JK to establish the direction of sight for this view.

5AA-8. Fig. 252-8. Through $A(147)$ $B(328)$ pass an opaque plane that will cut a $1\frac{1}{2}''$ diameter circle from the $2''$ diameter sphere whose center is $K(1\frac{1}{2}; 2; 6\frac{1}{2})$. Cut the sphere above its center. Show the plane as ABC with AC and BC tangent to the required circle. Complete all views. The ellipses in the principal views may be drawn by using conjugate axes.

5AA-9. Fig. 252-9. $A(3; 3\frac{1}{2}; 6\frac{1}{2})$ $B(3; \frac{1}{2}; 6\frac{1}{2})$ and $C(2\frac{1}{2}; 2; 8)$ $D(\frac{1}{2}; \frac{1}{2}; 6)$ are the center lines of two pipes which are to be connected by a piece $J(3; 2\frac{1}{4}; 6\frac{1}{2})$ K using $45°$ ell fittings. Draw the center line of the connecting pipe and find the lengths AJ, JK, and KD. Scale: $\frac{1}{4}'' = 1'\text{-}0''$.

5AA-10. $A(\frac{1}{4}; 3\frac{1}{4}; 8)$ $B(1; 3\frac{5}{8}; 5\frac{1}{4})$ and $C(1\frac{1}{4}; 2; 6)$ $D(1\frac{5}{8}; 4; 7\frac{1}{2})$ are two skew lines. Draw the common perpendicular and two lines which intersect AB at an angle of $45°$ and intersect CD at $60°$. Hint: start with an auxiliary elevation which shows a normal view of CD.

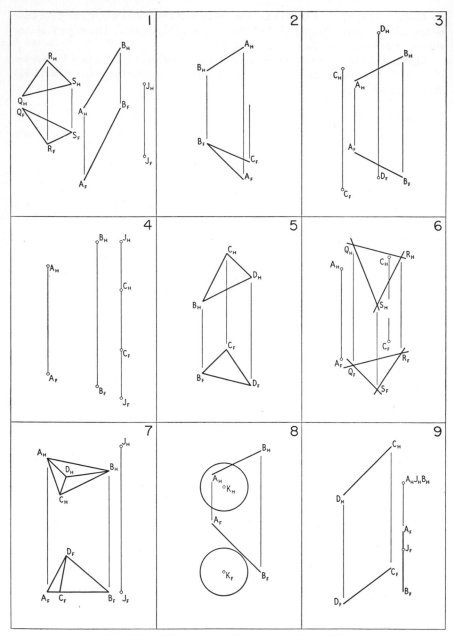

FIG. 252.—Miscellaneous Problems.   Group 5AA.

5AA-11. $V(2\frac{1}{2}; 3; 6)$ is the vertex and $A(2\frac{1}{2}; 0; 6)$ is the center of the $2''$ diameter base of a right circular cone. Show six equal spheres tangent to the cones externally, tangent to the plane of its base, and tangent to each other.

5AA-12. The line $A(4; 4; 6\frac{1}{2})$ $B(6; 2\frac{1}{2}; 5\frac{1}{2})$ is the bisector of the angle B between a horizontal line and a frontal line of a plane. Find the front and top views of the plane by drawing these lines at B so as to represent the plane as an isosceles triangle.

5AA-13. Draw a line EF which is normal to the surfaces of the right circular cones whose axes are $A(3; 4; 5\frac{1}{2})$ $B(3; 1; 5\frac{1}{2})$ and $C(527)$ $D(137)$. The base at B has a diameter of $2\frac{1}{2}''$, and that at D $2''$. Measure the shortest distance between the cones.

PROBLEMS FOR CHAPTER VI

SURFACES AND DEVELOPMENTS

Group 6A. Development of Right Prisms.

6A-1. Fig. 253-1. $A(\frac{1}{2}; 4; 6)$ $D(2\frac{1}{2}; 4; 6)$ is a diagonal of a horizontal regular hexagon which is the upper base of a right prism which has been truncated by an ortho-frontal plane through $J(\frac{1}{2}; 2; X)$ $K(2\frac{1}{2}; 3\frac{1}{2}; X)$. Make a development of the truncated prism, including the base and cut surface.

6A-2. Fig. 253-2. $A(\frac{1}{2}; 5; 6)$ $B(\frac{1}{2}; 5; 7)$ $C(2\frac{1}{2}; 5; 7)$ $D(2\frac{1}{2}; 5; 6)$ is the upper end of a two-piece elbow for a $90°$ bend in the rectangular duct of an air conditioning system. The lower end of this piece of the elbow is an ortho-frontal plane through $K(1\frac{1}{2}; 3\frac{1}{2}; 6\frac{1}{2})$. Develop the piece.

6A-3. Fig. 253-3. $J(7; 4; 6\frac{1}{2})$ $K(7; 2; 6\frac{1}{2})$ is the axis of a truncated right prism. The upper base is an ortho-frontal plane sloping $45°$ down to the left through J, and the lower base is an ortho-frontal plane sloping $30°$ down to the right through K. The top view is a regular pentagon with one corner at $A(6; X; 6\frac{1}{2})$. Find true shapes of the bases and make a development for the entire prism.

6A-4. Fig. 253-4. $J(\frac{1}{2}; 1\frac{1}{4}; 5)$ $K(3; 1\frac{1}{4}; 8)$ is the axis of a $4'' \times 6''$ sheet metal tube in a quick freezing machine. The $6''$ faces are vertical. Develop the tube. Scale: $3'' = 1'\text{-}0''$.

6A-5. Fig. 253-5. $R(5; 1; 6\frac{1}{2})$ $S(714)$ is the axis of the $6'' \times 8''$ discharge pipe from a mixing vat. The $8''$ faces are vertical. The end at S is cut off perpendicular to RS and the end at R is cut to fit the frontal and profile sides of the vat. Develop the pipe. Scale: $1\frac{1}{2}'' = 1'\text{-}0''$.

6A-6. Fig. 253-6. $L(7\frac{1}{2}; 4; 7)$ $M(617)$ is the axis of a $4' \times 3'$ rectangular chute intersecting a profile wall at L and the floor at M. The $4'$ sides are vertical. Develop the portion of the chute between the floor and the wall. Scale: $\frac{1}{4}'' = 1'\text{-}0''$.

6A-7. Fig. 253-7. $A(\frac{1}{2}; 2; 7)$ $B(1; 2\frac{1}{2}; 7)$ $C(2; 3\frac{1}{2}; 6\frac{1}{2})$ $D(1\frac{1}{2}; 3; 6)$ $E(1; 2\frac{1}{2}; 6)$ $F(1; 2\frac{1}{2}; 6\frac{1}{2})$ is the lower end of a vertical prism. The upper end is ortho-frontal and slopes downward to the right $30°$ through point $X(1; 4\frac{1}{2}; 6)$. Develop the prism, including the ends.

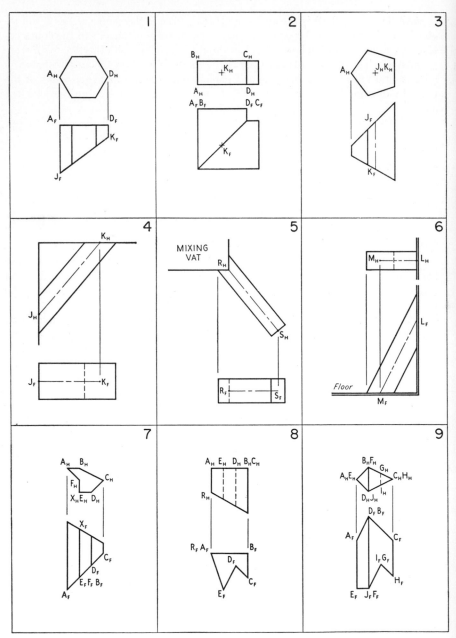

FIG. 253.—Development of Right Prisms. Group 6A

6A-8. Fig. 253-8. Make a development for the truncated right prism which has $A(6; 2\frac{1}{2}; 7)$ $B(7\frac{1}{2}; 2\frac{1}{2}; 7)$ $C(7\frac{1}{2}; 1\frac{1}{2}; 7)$ $D(727)$ $E(6\frac{1}{2}; 1; 7)$ for its rear base, and the vertical surface, inclined 30° forward through $R(6; 2\frac{1}{2}; 6)$, for its front base. Include the bases in the development.

6A-9. Fig. 253-9. Make a development of the lateral surface only of the prism which has $A(\frac{1}{2}; 4; 6\frac{1}{2})$ $B(157)$ $C(2; 4; 6\frac{1}{2})$ $D(156)$ for its upper end, and $E(\frac{1}{2}; 2; 6\frac{1}{2})$ $F(127)$ $G(1\frac{1}{2}; 3; 6\frac{3}{4})$ $H(2; 2\frac{1}{2}; 6\frac{1}{2})$ $I(1\frac{1}{2}; 3; 6\frac{1}{4})$ $J(126)$ for its lower end.

Group 6B. Development of Oblique Prisms.

6B-1. Fig. 254-1. $P(6; 1\frac{1}{2}; 6)$ $Q(7; 2\frac{1}{2}; 7\frac{1}{2})$ is the axis of an oblique prism whose bases are frontal regular hexagons that may be inscribed in $1\frac{1}{2}''$ diameter circles. One diagonal of each base is horizontal. Develop the lateral surface of the prism.

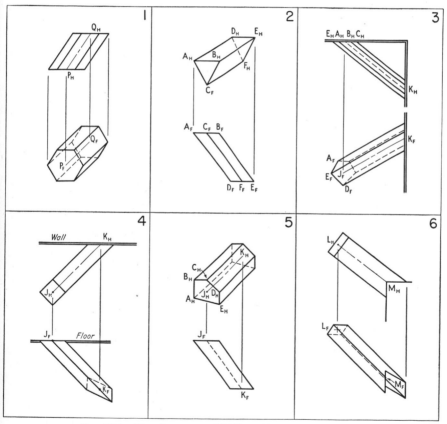

FIG. 254.—Development of Oblique Prisms. Group 6B.

6B-2. Fig. 254-2. Make a development of the sheet metal chute whose ends are the triangles $A(\frac{1}{2}; 3; 6)$ $B(1\frac{1}{2}; 3; 6)$ $C(135)$ and $D(217)$ $E(317)$ $F(2\frac{1}{2}; 1; 6)$.

6B-3. Fig. 254-3. $J(5; 1; 7\frac{1}{2})$ $K(7\frac{1}{2}; 2\frac{1}{2}; 5\frac{1}{2})$ is the axis of an oblique sheet metal chute connecting openings in a frontal wall and in a profile wall. The opening in the frontal wall is $A(4\frac{3}{4}; 1\frac{1}{2}; 7\frac{1}{2})$ $B(5\frac{1}{4}; 1\frac{1}{2}; 7\frac{1}{2})$ $C(5\frac{1}{2}; 1; 7\frac{1}{2})$ $D(5; \frac{1}{2}; 7\frac{1}{2})$ $E(4\frac{1}{2}; 1; 7\frac{1}{2})$. Develop the chute.

6B-4. Fig. 254-4. $J(1; 2\frac{1}{2}; 6)$ $K(3; \frac{1}{2}; 8)$ is the center line of a metal chute. Point J, in a floor, is the center of the horizontal 24″ square end of the chute; two sides of the square are perpendicular to JK. The chute terminates at a frontal wall through K. Find the shape of the end at K, and the size of the right section of the chute. Draw the pattern for making the chute. Scale: $\frac{3}{8}'' = 1'\text{-}0''$.

6B-5. Fig. 254-5. $J(1; 2\frac{1}{2}; 5\frac{1}{2})$ $K(2\frac{1}{2}; \frac{1}{2}; 7)$ is the axis of an oblique prism having horizontal bases. The upper base is $A(\frac{1}{2}; 2\frac{1}{2}; 5\frac{1}{2})$ $B(\frac{1}{2}; 2\frac{1}{2}; 6)$ $C(1; 2\frac{1}{2}; 6)$ $D(1\frac{1}{2}; 2\frac{1}{2}; 5\frac{1}{2})$ $E(1\frac{1}{2}; 2\frac{1}{2}; 5)$. Develop the lateral surface of the prism.

6B-6. Fig. 254-6. $L(5; 2\frac{3}{4}; 7\frac{1}{2})$ $M(7; \frac{3}{4}; 6)$ is the axis of a 2″ × 4″ rectangular mail chute cut to fit the corner of a bin at M. The 2″ sides are vertical. The long sides of the rectangular opening at L are horizontal and the opening is perpendicular to LM. Draw front and top views of the chute and make a development for it. Scale: $3'' = 1'\text{-}0''$.

6B-7. $J(2\frac{1}{2}; 5; 6\frac{1}{2})$ $K(1; 2\frac{1}{2}; 8)$ is the center line of a package chute entering a frontal wall at K. The end at J is a 12″ square perpendicular to JK, and two sides of the square are horizontal. Draw the chute in the front and top views, and show the true shape of the hole in the wall. Scale: $1'' = 1'\text{-}0''$. Develop the chute on a separate sheet of paper.

Group 6C.   Development of Right Pyramids.

6C-1. Fig. 255-1. $V(1\frac{1}{2}; 3; 6)$ is the vertex of a right pyramid and $O(1\frac{1}{2}; 1; 6)$ is the center of its base. The base is a regular hexagon that may be inscribed in a 2″ diameter circle and has one diagonal frontal. Develop the portion of the pyramid between its base and an ortho-frontal plane through $E(\frac{1}{2}; 3; X)$ $F(31X)$. Include the base and cut surface in the development.

6C-2. Fig. 255-2. $Q(6; 1; 6\frac{3}{4})$ is the center of the hexagonal base of a right pyramid and $V(6; 3; 6\frac{3}{4})$ is its vertex. One of the $2\frac{1}{2}''$ diagonals of the base is frontal. The pyramid is truncated by an ortho-frontal plane through $L(73X)$ $M(4\frac{1}{2}; \frac{1}{2}; X)$. Draw front and top views. Develop portion of pyramid below the plane, including base and cut surface.

6C-3. Fig. 255-3. $A(4\frac{1}{2}; 2\frac{1}{2}; 7\frac{1}{2})$ $C(7\frac{1}{2}; 1\frac{1}{2}; 7\frac{1}{2})$ is a diagonal of a frontal square which is the base of a pyramid whose vertex is $V(6; 2; 5\frac{1}{2})$. The pyramid is truncated by a vertical plane through $P(4; X; 7\frac{1}{2})$ $Q(7\frac{1}{2}; X; 6)$. Draw front and top views. Find true shape of cut surface. Develop the truncated pyramid.

6C-4. Fig. 255-4. $V(237)$ is the vertex of a right pyramid and $A(2; 1; 5\frac{1}{2})$ is one corner of its horizontal equilateral triangular base. Truncate the pyramid with an ortho-frontal plane through $E(\frac{1}{2}; 2\frac{1}{2}; X)$ $F(4; 1\frac{1}{2}; X)$. Find true shape of cut surface, and develop the truncated pyramid.

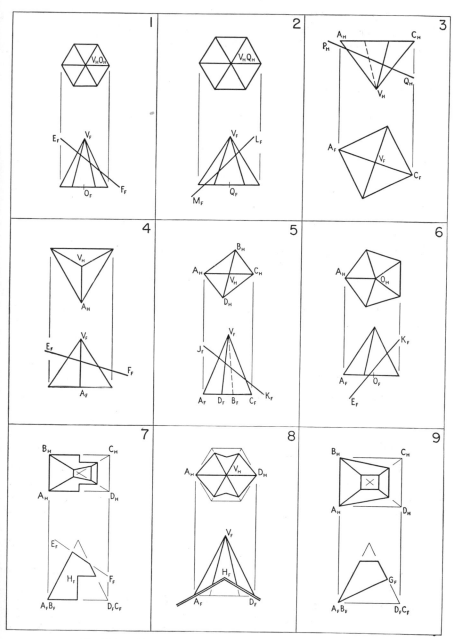

Fig. 255.—Development of Right Pyramids.   Group 6C.

6C-5. Fig. 255-5. $A(\frac{1}{2};1;7)$ $B(1\frac{3}{4};1;8)$ $C(2\frac{1}{2};1;7)$ $D(1\frac{1}{4};1;6)$ is the base of a pyramid whose vertex is $V(1\frac{1}{2};3\frac{1}{2};7)$. Develop the portion of the pyramid which lies below an ortho-frontal plane through $J(\frac{1}{2};3;X)$ $K(31X)$. Include base and cut surface in the development.

6C-6. Fig. 255-6. $O(1\frac{1}{2};2;6\frac{1}{2})$ is the center of a horizontal regular pentagon and $A(\frac{1}{4};2;6\frac{1}{2})$ is one of its corners. The pentagon is the base of a right pyramid of $2''$ altitude. Truncate the pyramid by an ortho-frontal plane through $E(\frac{1}{2};1;X)$ $K(2\frac{1}{2};3\frac{1}{2};X)$ and develop the portion above the plane. Show base and cut surface in the development.

6C-7. Fig. 255-7. $A(\frac{1}{2};1;6)$ $B(\frac{1}{2};1;7\frac{1}{2})$ $C(3;1;7\frac{1}{2})$ $D(316)$ is the base of a right pyramid of $2\frac{1}{2}''$ altitude which has been truncated by an ortho-frontal plane through $E(\frac{3}{4};3\frac{1}{2};X)$ $F(32X)$ and cut to fit a horizontal surface and a profile surface through $H(1\frac{3}{4};2;X)$. Develop the lateral surface of the remaining portion of the pyramid.

6C-8. Fig. 255-7. $A(5\frac{1}{4};1;7)$ $D(7\frac{3}{4};1;7)$ is a diagonal of a horizontal hexagon which is the base of a right pyramid whose vertex is $V(6\frac{1}{2};3\frac{1}{2};7)$. The pyramid is truncated to form a sheet metal spire to fit a roof, shown in edge view in the front view through points $AH(6\frac{1}{2};1\frac{3}{4};X)$ and DH. Develop the spire.

6C-9. Fig. 255-9. $A(\frac{1}{2};1;6)$ $B(\frac{1}{2};1;8)$ $C(318)$ $D(316)$ is the base of a right pyramid of $2\frac{1}{2}''$ altitude, which has been truncated by a horizontal plane $\frac{3}{4}''$ below the vertex and by an ortho-frontal plane through $AG(2\frac{1}{2};2;X)$. Develop the portion between the planes as a sheet metal transition piece.

Group 6D.   Development of Oblique Pyramids.

6D-1. Fig. 256-1. $A(\frac{1}{2};2;8)$ $B(1;2\frac{3}{4};8)$ $C(238)$ $D(328)$ $E(2\frac{1}{2};1;8)$ $F(1\frac{1}{2};1;8)$ is the base of a pyramid and $V(2\frac{1}{2};2\frac{1}{4};6)$ is its vertex. Make a development for the pyramid, including the base.

6D-2. Fig. 256-2. $V(4\frac{1}{2};3;7\frac{1}{4})$ is the vertex and $A(5\frac{1}{2};1;8)$ $B(7\frac{1}{2};1;8)$ $C(7\frac{1}{2};1;6\frac{1}{2})$ $D(5\frac{1}{2};1;6\frac{1}{2})$ is the base of an oblique pyramid truncated by a horizontal plane $1''$ below the vertex. Develop the truncated portion as a sheet metal coupling.

6D-3. Fig. 256-3. $O(1\frac{1}{2};2\frac{1}{2};6\frac{1}{2})$ is the center of a horizontal regular pentagon and $A(\frac{1}{4};2\frac{1}{2};6\frac{1}{2})$ is one of its corners. $V(2;\frac{1}{2};6)$ is the vertex of a pyramid having the pentagon for its base. Develop the lateral surface of the pyramid.

6D-4. Fig. 256-4. $O(6\frac{1}{2};1\frac{1}{2};8)$ is the center of a frontal square. One of its $2\frac{1}{2}''$ diagonals is vertical. The square is the base of a pyramid whose vertex is $V(5;2\frac{1}{2};6)$. Develop the portion of the pyramid between its base and a vertical plane through $L(4\frac{3}{4};X;8)$ $M(7;X;6\frac{1}{2})$. Show true shape of cut surface.

6D-5. Fig. 256-5. $V(3\frac{1}{2};2\frac{1}{2};7)$ is the vertex of a pyramid whose base is $A(\frac{1}{4};\frac{1}{2};7)$ $B(1;1\frac{1}{2};8)$ $C(2\frac{1}{4};\frac{1}{2};8)$ $D(2\frac{1}{2};\frac{1}{2};7\frac{1}{4})$ $E(1;\frac{1}{2};6\frac{1}{2})$. Develop the portion of the pyramid between its base and an ortho-frontal plane through $J(2;2\frac{1}{2};X)$ $K(3;\frac{1}{2};X)$. Include the base and cut surface in the development.

6D-6. Fig. 256-6. $O(2;1\frac{1}{2};6)$ is the center of a frontal regular hexagon that is $2''$ across flats and has one diagonal vertical. The hexagon is the common base

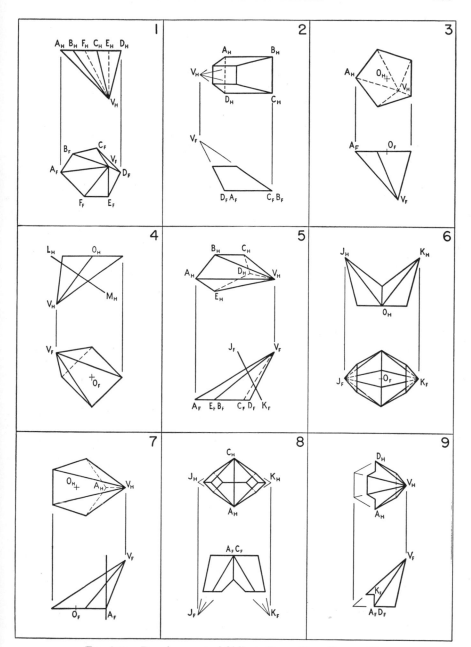

FIG. 256.—Development of Oblique Pyramids. Group 6D.

of two sheet metal pyramids having vertices $J(\frac{1}{2}; 1\frac{1}{2}; 8)$ and $K(3\frac{1}{2}; 1\frac{1}{2}; 8)$. The hexagonal end is open. Draw the intersecting pyramids and develop the right half of the piece.

6D-7. Fig. 256-7. $V(3\frac{1}{2}; 2\frac{1}{2}; 6\frac{1}{2})$ is the vertex of a pyramid whose base is a horizontal regular pentagon with center $O(1\frac{1}{2}; \frac{1}{2}; 6\frac{1}{2})$ and one corner at $A(2\frac{3}{4}; \frac{1}{2}; 6\frac{1}{2})$. Truncate the pyramid with a profile plane through A and develop the lateral surface of the truncated portion.

6D-8. Fig. 256-8. $A(6; 2\frac{1}{2}; 6)$ $C(6; 2\frac{1}{2}; 8)$ is a diagonal of a horizontal square which is the open end of a sheet metal connection. The square is the common base of two pyramids with vertices $J(4\frac{1}{2}; 0; 7)$ and $K(7\frac{1}{2}; 0; 7)$, which have been truncated by a horizontal plane $1\frac{1}{2}''$ below AC. Draw the connection and develop the left half.

6D-9. Fig. 256-9. $A(1\frac{1}{4}; \frac{1}{2}; 6)$ $D(1\frac{1}{4}; \frac{1}{2}; 8)$ is a diagonal of a horizontal hexagon which is the base of a pyramid with vertex $V(2\frac{1}{2}; 2\frac{1}{2}; 7)$. The lower left portion is cut away by a horizontal plane and a profile plane through $K(1\frac{1}{4}; 1\frac{1}{2}; X)$.

Group 6E. Development of Right Cylinders.

6E-1. Fig. 257-1. $A(128)$ $B(3\frac{1}{4}; 2; 7\frac{1}{4})$ $C(2\frac{1}{2}; 0; 5)$ $D(\frac{1}{4}; 0; 5\frac{3}{4})$ is the base of a sheet metal flue for a $12''$ vertical pipe. $E(1\frac{3}{4}; 2\frac{1}{2}; 6\frac{1}{2})$ is the center of the horizontal circular end of the cylindrical part of the flue. Draw the front and top views and develop the flue. Scale: $1\frac{1}{2}'' = 1'\text{-}0''$.

6E-2. Fig. 257-2. $J(2; 2; 4\frac{1}{2})$ is the center of a $6''$ diameter frontal circle which is the front end of a horizontal pipe with axis $JK(2; 2; 5\frac{1}{2})$, cut to fit the vertical planes through $C(\frac{1}{2}; X; 6\frac{1}{2})$ $A(2; 3\frac{1}{2}; 5\frac{1}{2})$ and $D(3X7)$ A, which intersect on the line $AB(2; \frac{1}{2}; 5\frac{1}{2})$. Scale: $1\frac{1}{2}'' = 1'\text{-}0''$. Develop the pipe.

6E-3. Fig. 257-3. $A(1\frac{1}{2}; 4; 6\frac{1}{2})$ $B(1\frac{1}{2}; 2\frac{1}{2}; 6\frac{1}{2})$ and $BC(3; 1\frac{3}{4}; 6\frac{1}{2})$ are the center lines for a pipe connection for an $8''$ diameter pipe. The two pieces of the connection are truncated right cylinders and the ends at A and C are right sections. Scale: $3'' = 1'\text{-}0''$. Draw the front view of the connection and develop the vertical piece.

6E-4. Fig. 257-4. $A(2; 4\frac{1}{2}; X)$, $B(\frac{3}{4}; 1\frac{3}{4}; X)$ and $C(3\frac{1}{4}; 1\frac{3}{4}; X)$ are the ends of a "Y" pipe connection having the frontal axes $AD(23X)$, BD, and CD. The connection is made of $18''$ diameter pipe. Develop the portion having the axis CD. Scale: $1'' = 1'\text{-}0''$.

6E-5. Fig. 257-5. $C(126)$ $D(1; 2; 4\frac{1}{2})$ is the axis of a $6''$ diameter sheet metal pipe whose ends are vertical planes. The front end is inclined $30°$ through D, backward to the right, and the rear end is inclined $45°$ through C, forward to the left. Scale: $3'' = 1'\text{-}0''$. Develop the pipe.

6E-6. Fig. 257-6. $J(146)$ $K(126)$ is the axis of a $1\frac{1}{2}''$ diameter cylinder truncated at the top by ortho-frontal planes through $A(\frac{1}{4}; 3\frac{1}{2}; X)$ J and $JB(1\frac{3}{4}; 3; X)$ and at the bottom by ortho-frontal planes sloping downward from K through $KD(\frac{1}{4}; 1; X)$ and $KC(1\frac{3}{4}; 1\frac{1}{2}; X)$. Develop the cylinder.

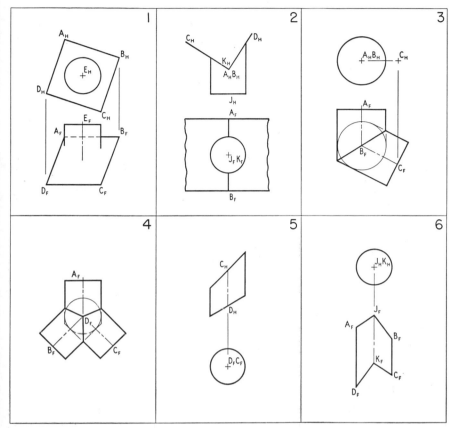

Fig. 257.—Development of Right Cylinders.   Group 6E.

Group 6F.   Development of Oblique Cylinders.

6F-1. Fig. 258-1. $C(5\frac{1}{2}; 1; 6\frac{1}{2})$ is the center of a 6'' frontal circle and $D(7\frac{1}{2}; 1; 4\frac{1}{2})$ is the center of a 6'' profile circle.   The circles are the ends of a sheet metal pipe. Develop the pipe.   Scale: 3'' = 1'-0''.

6F-2. Fig. 258-2. $A(7; 2\frac{1}{2}; 8)$ $B(5\frac{1}{2}; 1; 6)$ is the axis of an oblique cylinder which has $1\frac{1}{4}''$ diameter frontal circular ends.   Make a development for the lateral surface of the cylinder.

6F-3. Fig. 258-3. $J(1\frac{1}{4}; 1; 6)$ $K(308)$ is the axis of an oblique cylinder which has 2'' diameter horizontal circular ends.   Develop the lateral surface of the cylinder.

6F-4. Fig. 258-4. $A(757)$ and $B(5\frac{1}{2}; 3; 7)$ are the centers of the 6'' diameter horizontal ends of two vertical pipes to be connected with an oblique cylinder whose ends are the circular ends of the pipes.   A branch pipe of the same size has the axis $AC(7\frac{3}{4}; 4; 7)$. Make a development for the left branch of the required connection, having axis AB. Scale: $3'' = 1'\text{-}0''$.

6F-5. Fig. 258-5. $E(\frac{1}{2}; 1\frac{1}{2}; 5\frac{3}{4})$ $F(2\frac{1}{2}; 0; 7\frac{1}{4})$ is the axis of an oblique cylinder. The lower end is a $1\frac{1}{2}''$ diameter horizontal circle with center F and the upper end lies in a profile plane through E. Develop the lateral surface of the cylinder.

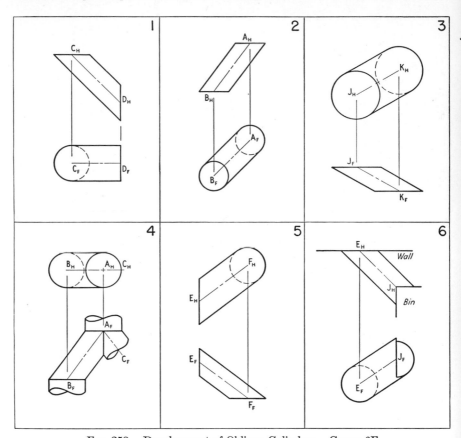

FIG. 258.—Development of Oblique Cylinders.　Group 6F.

6F-6. Fig. 258-6. $E(5\frac{1}{2}; \frac{1}{2}; 8)$ $J(7; 1\frac{1}{2}; 6\frac{1}{2})$ is the axis of a cylindrical pipe whose intersection with a frontal wall at E is a $6''$ diameter circle. It intersects the rear corner of a bin having frontal and profile sides at J. Scale: $3'' = 1'\text{-}0''$.

Group 6G.　Development of Right Cones.

6G-1. Fig. 259-1. $V(6; 1\frac{1}{2}; 5\frac{1}{2})$ is the vertex of a right cone and $O(6; 1\frac{1}{2}; 8)$ is the center of its $3''$ diameter base. Develop the portion of the cone which lies between the vertex and a vertical plane through $E(4\text{X}8)$ $J(7\frac{1}{2}; \text{X}; 6\frac{1}{2})$.

6G-2. Fig. 259-2. $V(6; 2; 6\frac{1}{2})$ is the vertex and $C(6; 0; 6\frac{1}{2})$ is the center of the 3" diameter base of a right cone. Develop the portion of the cone lying below the ortho-frontal plane through $L(51X)$ and $M(7\frac{1}{2}; \frac{1}{2}; X)$.

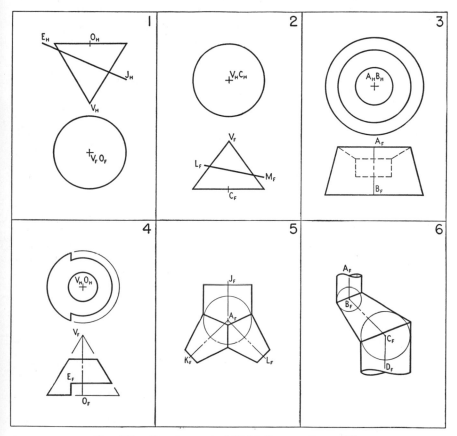

Fig. 259.—Development of Right Cones.   Group 6G.

6G-3. Fig. 259-3. $A(226)$ is the center of a 3" diameter horizontal circle and $B(206)$ is the center of a 4" diameter horizontal circle. The circles are the ends of the outside conical surface of a piece used in an ice making machine. By triangulation make a development for the rear one-half of the surface.

6G-4. Fig. 259-4. A sheet metal connection is made from the right cone whose vertex is $V(2; 2\frac{1}{2}; 6\frac{1}{2})$ and whose base is a 3" diameter circle with center $O(2; 0; 6\frac{1}{2})$, by discarding the following: (1) the portion above a horizontal plane 1" below the vertex, and (2) the portion below a horizontal plane through $E(1\frac{1}{2}; \frac{1}{2}; X)$ and to the right of a profile plane through E. Develop the connection.

6G-5. Fig. 259-5. $J(2; 4\frac{1}{2}; X)$ $A(23X)$, $L(3\frac{1}{2}; 1\frac{1}{2}; X)A$, and $K(\frac{1}{2}; 1\frac{1}{2}; X)A$ are the frontal axes of three pipes to be connected. Pipe with axis JA is 8″ in diameter and the others are of 3″ diameter. Design the connecting piece to consist of a cylinder and two cones, all circumscribing an 8″ diameter sphere with the center A. Develop the right-hand branch of the connection. Scale: 3″ = 1′-0″.

6G-6. Fig. 259-6. $A(248)$ $B(238)$ $C(3\frac{1}{2}; 1\frac{1}{2}; 8)$ $D(3\frac{1}{2}; 0; 8)$ is the center line for an off-set pipe. The pipe at AB has a diameter of 12″ and that at CD 24″. On the center line BC design a conical connecting piece as a portion of a right circular cone. Draw the complete front view. Develop the connecting piece. Scale: 1″ = 1′-0″.

Group 6H.   Development of Oblique Cones.

6H-1. Fig. 260-1. $O(1\frac{1}{2}; 0; 7)$ is the center of a 2″ diameter horizontal circle which is the base of an oblique cone whose vertex is $V(326)$. Develop the portion of the cone which lies below an ortho-frontal plane through $E(1\frac{1}{2}; 2; X)$ $F(3\frac{1}{2}; \frac{1}{2}; X)$.

6H-2. Fig. 260-2. $A(3\frac{1}{2}; 2; 6\frac{1}{2})$ is the vertex of an oblique cone whose $2\frac{1}{2}″$ diameter horizontal base has its center at $Q(1\frac{1}{2}; 0; 6\frac{1}{2})$. Develop the portion of the cone which is to the left of a profile plane through $E(32X)$.

6H-3. Fig. 260-3. $E(137)$ and $F(2\frac{1}{4}; 1; 7)$ are the centers of the horizontal circular ends of an off-set pipe connection between two vertical pipes. The pipe at E is of 6″ diameter and the one at F is of 8″ diameter. Draw, and develop by triangulation, the connecting piece. Scale: 3″ = 1′-0″.

6H-4. Fig. 260-4. $Q(6\frac{1}{2}; 3; 6\frac{1}{2})$ is the center of a 6″ diameter horizontal circle which is the top of an off-set funnel. $O(7\frac{1}{4}; 1\frac{1}{2}; 6\frac{1}{2})$ is the center of the top of the spout, which is a horizontal circle $1\frac{1}{2}″$ in diameter. The spout is 3″ long and the diameter at the small end is $\frac{1}{2}″$. Make a development for the funnel and one for the spout. Scale: Half-size.

6H-5. Fig. 260-5. The center line for a portion of a 24″ diameter right cylindrical pipe is $A(2; 3\frac{1}{2}; 5)$ $B(235)$; the center line for a $13\frac{1}{2}″$ diameter pipe is $C(3; 1\frac{3}{4}; 5)$ $D(4; 1\frac{1}{4}; 5)$. The connection joining the circular ends at B and C is a frustum of an oblique cone having its vertex at $V(405)$. Draw the complete front view and develop the connection. Scale: 1″ = 1′-0″.

6H-6. Fig. 260-6. $J(118)$ is the center of an 8″ diameter frontal circle. $L(2\frac{1}{2}; 2; 6\frac{1}{2})$ is the center of a 12″ diameter frontal circle. These circles are the ends of a conical sheet metal pipe connection. By triangulation, develop the half lying above an ortho-frontal plane through JL. Scale: 3″ = 1′-0″.

6H-7. Fig. 260-7. $V(5; 2\frac{1}{2}; 6\frac{3}{4})$ is the vertex of an oblique cone and $O(6\frac{3}{4}; 0; 6\frac{3}{4})$ is the center of its $2\frac{1}{2}″$ diameter horizontal base. Truncate the cone by removing the portion above a horizontal plane through $H(61X)$ and to the left of a profile plane through H. Develop the lateral surface of the truncated cone.

6H-8. Fig. 260-8. $Q(6\frac{1}{2}; 1\frac{1}{2}; 8)$ is the center of a $2\frac{1}{2}″$ diameter frontal circle which is the base of a cone whose vertex is $A(536)$. Develop the portion of the cone between the vertex and a vertical plane through $J(4\frac{3}{4}; X; 7)$ $K(7X8)$. Show the intersection of the plane in the front view.

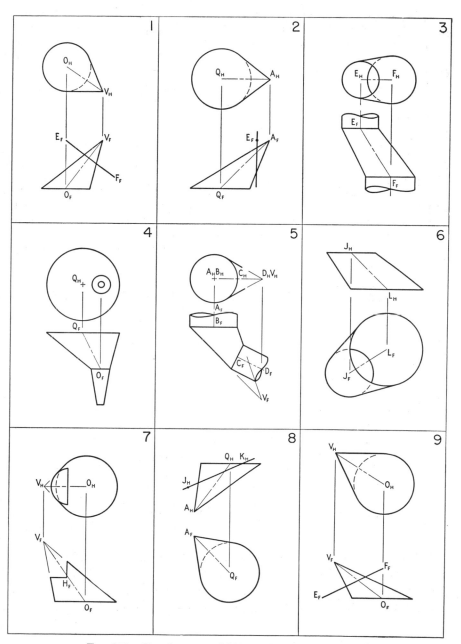

FIG. 260.—Development of Oblique Cones. Group 6H.

6H-9. Fig. 260-9. $V(4\frac{1}{2}; 1\frac{1}{2}; 8)$ is the vertex of a cone and $O(6\frac{1}{2}; 0; 6\frac{3}{4})$ is the center of its $2\frac{1}{2}''$ diameter horizontal base. Develop the portion of the cone below the ortho-frontal plane through $E(40X)$ $F(6\frac{1}{2}; 1\frac{1}{4}; X)$.

Group 6I. Development of Hoppers and Transition Pieces.

In each of the problems of this group, draw complete front and top views.

6I-1. Fig. 261-1. $A(\frac{1}{2}; 2; 7)$ $C(2\frac{1}{2}; 2; 5)$ and $E(1; \frac{1}{2}; 6)$ $G(2; \frac{1}{2}; 6)$ are the diagonals of two horizontal squares which are the ends of a hopper. Develop the hopper.

6I-2. Fig. 261-2. A sheet metal hopper has a feeder opening $A(728)$ $B(828)$ $C(826)$ $D(726)$ and a discharge opening $E(6\frac{1}{4}; 0; 7\frac{3}{4})$ $F(6\frac{3}{4}; 0; 7\frac{3}{4})$ $G(6\frac{3}{4}; 0; 7)$ $H(6\frac{1}{4}; 0; 7)$. Develop the hopper.

6I-3. Fig. 261-3. $A(107)$ $C(1\frac{3}{4}; 0; 5)$ is a diagonal of a horizontal rectangle with its short sides frontal. $E(1; 2; 6\frac{1}{4})$ $G(2\frac{3}{4}; 2; 5\frac{3}{4})$ is a diagonal of a horizontal rectangle with its long sides frontal. These rectangles are the ends of a transition piece. Make its development.

6I-4. Fig. 261-4. $A(518)$ $B(7\frac{1}{2}; 2; 8)$ $C(7\frac{1}{2}; 2; 6\frac{1}{2})$ $D(5; 1; 6\frac{1}{2})$ is the feeder opening of a hopper and $E(608)$ $F(708)$ $G(7; 0; 7\frac{1}{2})$ $H(6; 0; 7\frac{1}{2})$ is the discharge opening. Develop the hopper.

6I-5. Fig. 261-5. $K(217)$ is the center of an ortho-frontal square which slopes downward 45° to the left and has two of its $18''$ sides frontal. $J(1; 2\frac{1}{2}; 7)$ is the center of an $18''$ diameter circle. Design a transition piece to connect the two openings and develop its rear one-half. Scale: $1'' = 1'-0''$.

6I-6. Fig. 261-6. Make a development for the upper one-half of the transition piece which has the rectangle $A(\frac{1}{2}; 1\frac{1}{4}; 8)$ $B(2; 1\frac{1}{4}; 8)$ $C(2; \frac{3}{4}; 8)$ $D(\frac{1}{2}; \frac{3}{4}; 8)$ and the $12''$ diameter frontal circle with center $Q(2\frac{1}{2}; 1; 6\frac{1}{2})$, for its ends. Scale: $1\frac{1}{2}'' = 1'-0''$.

6I-7. Fig. 261-7. The $6''$ diameter frontal circle with center $O(7; 1\frac{1}{2}; 6\frac{1}{2})$ and the rectangle $A(6; 3; 7\frac{1}{2})$ $B(6\frac{1}{2}; 3; 8)$ $C(6\frac{1}{2}; 0; 8)$ $D(6; 0; 7\frac{1}{2})$ are the ends of a transition piece. Develop the upper one-half. Scale: $3'' = 1'-0''$.

6I-8. Fig. 261-8. The rectangle $A(008)$ $B(2\frac{1}{2}; 1\frac{1}{2}; 8)$ $C(2\frac{1}{2}; 1\frac{1}{2}; 6)$ $D(006)$ and the $12''$ diameter horizontal circle with center $Q(1\frac{1}{2}; 2; 7)$ are the ends of a transition piece. Make a development for the rear one-half. Scale: $1\frac{1}{2}'' = 1'-0''$.

6I-9. Fig. 261-9. $O(1\frac{1}{2}; 1\frac{1}{2}; 5)$ is the center of a $1''$ diameter horizontal circle. $J(1\frac{1}{2}; 0; 5)$ is the center of a horizontal equilateral triangle and $A(1\frac{1}{2}; 0; 3\frac{3}{4})$ is one of its corners. These are the open ends of a transition piece. Make its development.

6I-10. In an air conditioning system the $24''$ diameter pipe ending at the frontal circle with center $O(2\frac{1}{2}; 1\frac{1}{2}; 3\frac{1}{2})$, and the rectangular pipe beginning at $A(3\frac{1}{4}; 3; 5\frac{1}{4})$ $B(434)$ $C(404)$ $D(3\frac{1}{4}; 0; 5\frac{1}{4})$, are connected by a transition piece. Develop the upper one-half of the piece. Scale: $1'' = 1'-0''$.

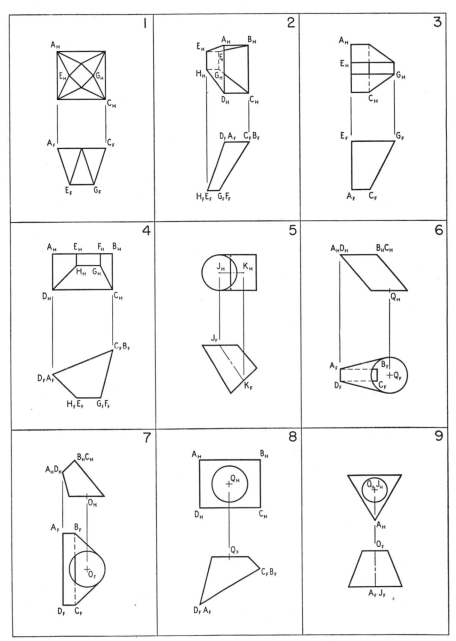

FIG. 261.—Development of Hoppers and Transition Pieces. Group 6I.

Group 6J.   Development of Elbows and Pipe Connections.

6J-1. Fig. 262-1. $A(224)$ is the center of the lower end of a 36″ diameter vertical pipe and $B(2\frac{1}{2}; 0; 4)$ is the center of the upper end of a 24″ diameter vertical pipe. The pipes are connected by a piece having horizontal circular ends at A and B. Develop the front half of the piece by triangulation using 16 elements for the cone. Scale: $1″ = 1'\text{-}0″$.

6J-2. Fig. 262-2. $A(3\frac{1}{2}; 0; 8)$ $B(3\frac{1}{2}; 0; 6\frac{1}{2})$ $C(205)$ $D(105)$ is the center line for a reducing elbow. The portion at AB is a 24″ diameter cylinder, that at CD is a 12″ diameter cylinder. On the center line BC design the reducing piece as a portion of a right circular cone. Draw the complete top view. Develop the reducing piece. Scale: $1″ = 1'\text{-}0″$.

6J-3. Fig. 262-3. $A(33X)$ and $B(11X)$ are the centers of the ends of a 90° elbow for a 6″ diameter pipe. The front view is a normal view of the center lines of the pipes. Design a three-piece elbow with a minimum radius of bend of 4″, and make its development. Scale: $3″ = 1'\text{-}0″$.

6J-4. Fig. 262-4. $C(1; 4; 5\frac{1}{2})$ $D(1; 2; 5\frac{1}{2})$ and $DE(2\frac{3}{4}; 1; 5\frac{1}{2})$ are the center lines of two 6″ diameter pipes to be connected by a four-piece elbow. C and E are in the ends of the elbow. Design the elbow with a minimum radius of bend of 9″ and develop one of the end pieces and the adjacent piece. Scale: $3″ = 1'\text{-}0″$.

6J-5. Fig. 262-5. $A(50X)$ is the center of an 8″ diameter horizontal circle and $B(7\frac{1}{2}; 2\frac{1}{2}; X)$ is the center of a 4″ diameter profile circle. These are the ends of pipes to be connected by a three-piece reducing elbow. The radius of bend of the center line is 10″. Design the elbow as the frustum of a cone and make its development. Scale: $3″ = 1'\text{-}0″$.

6J-6. Fig. 262-6. $C(4; 2\frac{1}{2}; X)$ is the center of a 2″ diameter profile circle and $D(1\frac{1}{2}; 0; X)$ is the center of a 10″ diameter horizontal circle. Design a four-piece reducing elbow connecting these circles. The radius of bend for the center line is 10″. The pieces of the elbow should all be parts of the same cone. Make its development. Scale: $3″ = 1'\text{-}0″$.

6J-7. Fig. 262-7. $A(124)$ $B(126)$ and $BC(2\frac{3}{4}; 2; 7)$ are the center lines of two 6″ diameter pipes to be joined by a five-piece elbow. The vertical circles at A and C are the ends of the elbow, which has a minimum radius of bend of 9″. Draw complete top view. Develop one end piece and the adjacent piece. Scale: $3″ = 1'\text{-}0″$.

6J-8. Fig. 262-8. $A(024)$ $B(1\frac{1}{2}; 2; 4)$ $C(1\frac{1}{2}; 1\frac{1}{4}; 4)$ $D(0; 1\frac{1}{4}; 4)$ and $R(3\frac{1}{4}; 2; 7\frac{1}{4})$ $S(3\frac{1}{4}; 1\frac{1}{4}; 7\frac{1}{4})$ $T(3\frac{1}{4}; 1\frac{1}{4}; 7\frac{1}{4})$ $U(3\frac{1}{4}; 2; 7\frac{1}{4})$ are the ends of two horizontal rectangular pipes to be connected by a four-piece elbow. The minimum radius of bend is 18″. Draw front and top views of the elbow. Develop one end piece and the adjacent piece. Scale: $1″ = 1'\text{-}0″$.

6J-9. Fig. 262-9. Two vertical 8″ diameter pipes with center lines $A(\frac{1}{2}; 3\frac{1}{2}; 8)$ $B(\frac{1}{2}; 3; 8)$ and $F(3\frac{1}{2}; 3\frac{1}{2}; 8)$ $E(3\frac{1}{2}; 2\frac{3}{4}; 8)$ are to be connected to another pipe of 18″ diameter, having the center line $C(2; 1\frac{1}{2}; 8)$ $D(2; \frac{1}{2}; 8)$. A, F, and D are in the ends of the pipes. Design a "Y" connection using inscribed spheres, so that the branches are truncated right cones. Develop the right-hand branch. Scale: $1″ = 1'\text{-}0″$.

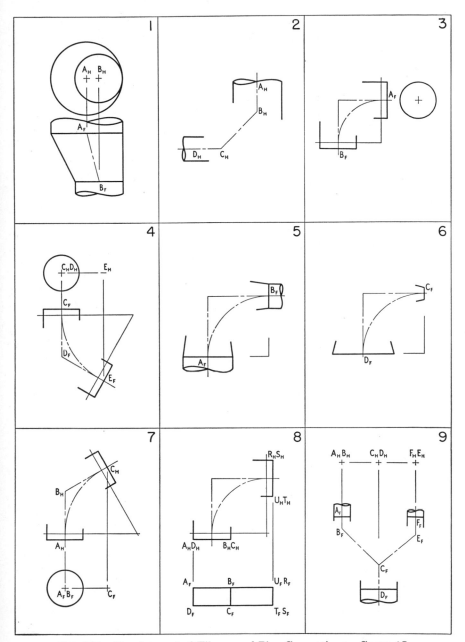

Fig. 262.—Development of Elbows and Pipe Connections. Group 6J.

Group 6K.   The Helix.

6K-1. $A(446)$ is the center of the upper end of a vertical opaque right cylinder, 2″ diameter and $3\frac{1}{2}$″ tall. Starting at $B(546)$ draw on its surface a right-hand helix of 3″ lead, and starting at $C(346)$ draw a left-hand helix of $1\frac{1}{2}$″ lead.

6K-2. $A(224)$ $B(227)$ and $C(524)$ $D(527)$ are the axes of two $1\frac{1}{2}$″ diameter right cylinders in a simple transformer which has a $\frac{1}{2}$″ plate at each end. The cylinder AB is wound with two turns of fine wire as a right-hand helix, and the cylinder CD, with four turns as a left-hand helix. Draw the transformer with the windings.

6K-3. $M(126)$ $N(426)$ is the axis of an opaque right circular cylinder. Show in the front and top views two turns of a right-hand helix having a lead of $1\frac{1}{2}$″ and beginning at $A(416)$.

6K-4. $A(557)$ $B(227)$ is the axis of an open, right-hand, coil spring made of small wire. The lead of the helix of its coils is $1\frac{1}{2}$″. Neglecting the size of the wire and beginning at $C(5\frac{1}{2}; 4\frac{1}{2}; 7)$ draw the front, top, and auxiliary views of $3\frac{1}{2}$ turns of the spring.

6K-5. $C(416)$ is the center of a 2″ diameter horizontal circle that is the base of an opaque right cone of 3″ altitude. Draw on the cone in the front and top views four turns of a right-hand helix having a lead of $\frac{3}{4}$″ and ending at $A(316)$. This helix is similar to the crest of the thread on the point of a wood boring bit. Name the curve of the helix as shown in the top view.

Group 6L.   Construction and Development of Convolutes.

6L-1. $C(5\frac{1}{2}; 4; 7)$ $D(5\frac{1}{2}; 0; 7)$ is the axis of a $1\frac{1}{4}$″ diameter left-hand helix that has a lead of 4″ and begins directly behind C. This helix is the directrix of a convolute that terminates in a horizontal plane through D. In the front and top views draw 16 elements of the lower nappe of the convolute as an opaque surface. Show a horizontal section 2″ below C. Develop the portion above the section.

6L-2. $A(\frac{1}{4}; 6; 8)$ $B(4\frac{1}{2}; 6; 8)$ is the axis of a steam-heated pipe having a 6″ outside diameter to which a steel, right-hand, helical convolute of $1\frac{1}{2}$″ lead is welded for making the screw of a drying conveyer. The outside diameter of the screw is $11\frac{1}{4}$″. In the front and side views show two turns of the convolute by drawing 12 elements per turn on the right side of the screw. Start at a point on the pipe directly in front of B, and use the left nappe of the convolute. Develop one turn. Scale: $3″ = 1'\text{-}0''$.

6L-3. Fig. 263-1. $A(4; 1; 3\frac{1}{2})$ is the center of a 3″ diameter frontal circle and $B(4; 1\frac{1}{4}; 6\frac{1}{2})$ is the center of a frontal ellipse whose horizontal major axis is 4″ and whose minor axis is $2\frac{3}{4}$″. The upper halves of these are to be connected by a sheet metal piece designed as a convolute by the tangent plane method. Draw 13 elements, and show the form of a supporting rib midway between the ends.

6L-4. Make a development of the convolute surface of Problem 6L-3.

6L-5. Fig. 263-2. A convolute, sheet metal, transition piece connects the end of a flume at $L(234)$ with an opening in a tank at $M(4\frac{1}{2}; 2\frac{1}{2}; 7)$. The end of the flume is the lower half of a $2\frac{1}{4}$″ by 4″ frontal ellipse having a horizontal minor axis with center L. The opening in the tank is the lower half of a $2\frac{1}{2}''$ diameter frontal circle with center M. Draw the front and top views of the convolute by using eleven other elements drawn with proper visibility on both sides of the metal.

6L-6. Make a development of the transition piece of Problem 6L-5.

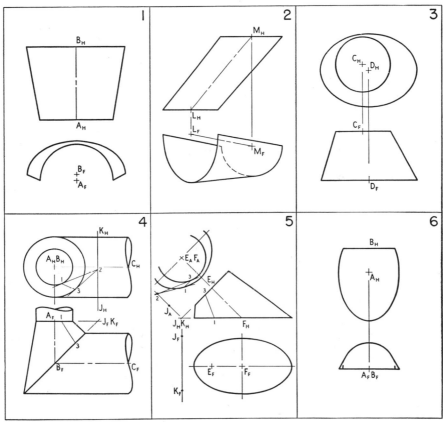

FIG. 263.—Construction and Development of Convolutes. Group 6L.

6L-7. Fig. 263-3. In the front and top views draw 24 elements of a convolute transition piece to connect the $2\frac{1}{4}''$ diameter horizontal circle whose center is $C(3\frac{3}{4}; 3; 5\frac{3}{4})$ with the horizontal ellipse whose center is $D(4; 1; 5\frac{1}{2})$. The ellipse has a $4''$ frontal major axis and a $3''$ minor axis. Show the form of a reinforcing rib midway between the ends.

6L-8. Fig. 263-4. The $1\frac{1}{2}''$ diameter horizontal circle at $A(3; 3\frac{3}{4}; 6)$ is the lower end of a vertical pipe, and $B(326)$ $C(626)$ is the center line of a $2\frac{1}{2}''$ diameter pipe which has been cut off at an ortho-frontal plane through $BJ(4\frac{1}{4}; 3\frac{3}{4}; 4\frac{1}{4})$. In the front and top views draw 16 elements of a convolute reducing piece connecting the ends of the pipe. One tangent plane, 1–2–3, for finding the element 1–3 is shown.

6L-9. Fig. 263-5. The $2''$ diameter circle at $E(3\frac{3}{4}; 2; 5\frac{1}{4})$ and the $2\frac{1}{4}''$ by $4''$ ellipse at $F(524)$ are the ends of a convolute transition piece. The plane of the circle is normal to EF and the ellipse is frontal with a horizontal major axis. Draw 16 elements of the surface in the top view and the auxiliary elevation. One tangent plane, 1–2–3, for finding the element 1–3 is shown.

6L-10. Fig. 263-6. $A(215)$ is the center of a $2\frac{1}{2}''$ by $4''$ horizontal ellipse whose minor axis is frontal. The rear portion of this ellipse is cut off at a frontal plane through $B(216)$. B is the center for the upper half of a frontal circle connected to the ellipse at each side. Show in three principal views a convolute surface covering these curves by drawing eleven well spaced elements.

Group 6M. Approximate Development of Double Curved Surfaces. Development of Domes.

6M-1. $A(1\frac{1}{2}; 2; 6)$ is the center of a $3''$ diameter sphere. Make an approximate development of one-eighth of its surface by the gore method.

6M-2. $A(5\frac{1}{2}; 1\frac{1}{2}; 6)$ is the center of a $4''$ diameter hemisphere resting on a $4''$ vertical cylinder $1\frac{1}{2}''$ high. Circumscribe the cylinder with an octagonal prism and the hemisphere with an octagonal dome to represent a building. Develop one piece of the dome giving dimensions at six places.

6M-3. Develop one gore of a hexagonal dome inscribed in a $4''$ diameter hemisphere whose center is $C(216)$.

6M-4. $C(2; 2\frac{1}{2}; 6)$ is the center of a prolate spheroid generated by revolving a $2\frac{1}{4}''$ by $3''$ ellipse about its vertical major axis. Show the approximate development of one-eighth of its surface by the gore method.

6M-5. $B(226)$ is the center of a $2\frac{3}{4}''$ diameter sphere. Make an approximate development of the sphere by the zone method using eight zones.

6M-6. $E(626)$ is the center of an oblate spheroid generated by revolving a $2\frac{1}{4}''$ by $3''$ ellipse about its minor axis. Make an approximate development of the spheroid by the zone method. Use eight zones having equal chords around the ellipse.

6M-7. $A(4\frac{1}{2}; 1; 8)$ $C(8; 1; 4\frac{1}{2})$ is a diagonal of a horizontal square which has its corners cut off by $45°$ lines $2''$ from its center. The resulting octagon is the base of a dome, the outline of which is a semicircle in the front view. Develop one gore of each type found in the dome.

PROBLEMS FOR CHAPTER VII

SURFACES AND INTERSECTIONS

General Instructions. In all problems for Chapter VII draw the objects by using light lines, find the intersection, and finish the drawing by using standard-weight lines for the intersection and for all edges and outlines which are not inside of either object. The objects should appear as a solid casting, or "as a unit." Leave as light construction lines those portions of edges or outlines which are inside of the other object. Show all construction, mark cutting planes, and give full notation for all points. Unless otherwise specified, complete front and top views are required.

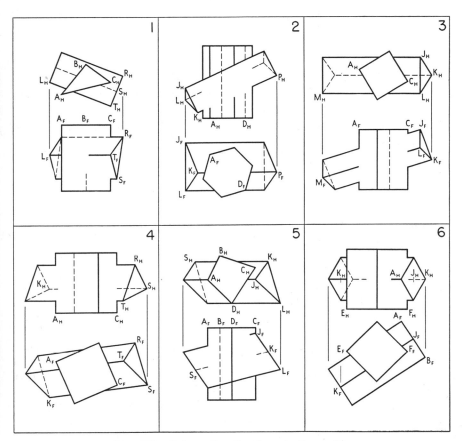

FIG. 264.—Intersection Problems in Group 7A.

Group 7A.   Intersection Problems for the Edge View Method.

7A-1. Fig. 264-1. $A(1\frac{1}{4}; 3\frac{3}{4}; 5)$ $B(2\frac{1}{4}; 3\frac{3}{4}; 6\frac{1}{4})$ $C(3\frac{1}{4}; 3\frac{3}{4}; 5\frac{1}{2})$ is the upper base of a right prism of $2\frac{3}{4}''$ altitude. $R(3\frac{3}{4}; 3\frac{1}{4}; 5\frac{3}{4})$ $S(3\frac{1}{2}; 1\frac{1}{2}; X)$ $T(3\frac{1}{4}; 2\frac{1}{2}; 4\frac{1}{2})$ is the right-hand base of a horizontal right prism and $TL(\frac{3}{4}; 2\frac{1}{2}; 5\frac{1}{2})$ is one of its lateral edges.   Draw the intersecting prisms as a unit.

7A-2. Fig. 264-2. $A(5; 2\frac{1}{2}; 4\frac{1}{2})$ $D(6\frac{1}{2}; 1; 4\frac{1}{2})$ is a diagonal of a frontal regular hexagon which is the front base of a right prism of 3″ altitude. $J(4; 3; 5\frac{3}{4})$ $K(4\frac{1}{2}; 1\frac{3}{4}; 4\frac{3}{4})$ $L(4; 1; 5\frac{1}{4})$ is the left-hand base of a horizontal prism having $KP(7\frac{3}{4}; 1\frac{3}{4}; 6\frac{1}{4})$ for one lateral edge. Draw the intersecting prisms as a unit.

7A-3. Fig. 264-3. $A(2; 3\frac{1}{2}; 6)$ $C(4; 3\frac{1}{2}; 5\frac{1}{2})$ is a diagonal of a horizontal square which is the upper base of a right prism of $2\frac{1}{2}''$ altitude. $J(4\frac{1}{2}; 3\frac{1}{2}; 6\frac{1}{2})$ $K(5; 2\frac{1}{4}; 5\frac{3}{4})$ $L(4\frac{1}{2}; 2\frac{3}{4}; 5)$ is one base of a frontal prism, one of whose lateral edges is $LM(\frac{1}{2}; 1\frac{1}{2}; 5)$. Draw the intersecting prisms as a unit.

7A-4. Fig. 264-4. $A(1\frac{3}{4}; 2\frac{1}{2}; 4\frac{1}{2})$ $C(4\frac{1}{4}; 1\frac{1}{2}; 4\frac{1}{2})$ is a diagonal of a frontal square which is the front base of a right prism of $2\frac{1}{2}''$ altitude. $R(5; 3\frac{1}{4}; 6\frac{1}{2})$ $S(5\frac{1}{2}; 1\frac{1}{2}; 5\frac{1}{2})$ $T(4\frac{1}{2}; 2\frac{1}{2}; 5)$ is one base of a prism having $SK(1\frac{1}{2}; 1; 5\frac{1}{2})$ for one lateral edge. Draw the intersecting prisms as a unit.

7A-5. Fig. 264-5. $A(246)$ $B(2\frac{1}{2}; 4; 7)$ $C(4; 4; 6\frac{1}{2})$ $D(345)$ is the upper base of a right prism of 3″ altitude. $J(4; 3\frac{3}{4}; 6)$ $K(4\frac{1}{2}; 3; 6\frac{3}{4})$ $L(5; 2\frac{1}{4}; 5)$ is one base and $KS(1\frac{1}{2}; 2\frac{1}{4}; 6\frac{3}{4})$ is a lateral edge of another prism. Draw the intersecting prisms as a unit.

7A-6. Fig. 264-6. $J(4; 3\frac{1}{2}; 6)$ $K(1; 1\frac{1}{2}; 6)$ is the axis of a right prism, and $A(3\frac{1}{2}; 4\frac{1}{4}; 6)$ $B(4\frac{1}{2}; 2\frac{3}{4}; 6)$ is a diagonal of one of its square bases. $E(1\frac{1}{4}; 3; 4\frac{3}{4})$ $F(3\frac{3}{4}; 3; 4\frac{3}{4})$ is a diagonal of a frontal square which is the front base of another prism of $2\frac{1}{2}''$ altitude. Draw the intersecting prisms as a unit.

Group 7B.   Intersection Problems for the Piercing Point Method.

7B-1. Fig. 265-1. $A(547)$ $B(4\frac{1}{4}; 1; 7)$ $C(237)$ is the base of a pyramid whose vertex is $V(3\frac{3}{4}; 2\frac{3}{4}; 4\frac{1}{2})$. $R(637)$ $S(5\frac{1}{2}; 2; 6)$ $T(5\frac{1}{2}; 1\frac{1}{2}; 6\frac{1}{2})$ is one base of a prism and $SJ(1\frac{1}{2}; 2\frac{3}{4}; 5)$ is one of its lateral edges. Draw the intersecting solids as a unit.

7B-2. Fig. 265-2. $A(437)$ $D(6; \frac{1}{2}; 4\frac{3}{4})$ is one of the lateral edges of an oblique prism and $AB(3\frac{1}{2}; 3; 6)$ $C(236)$ is one of its bases. $J(5; 2\frac{3}{4}; 7)$ $R(225)$ is a lateral edge of another prism having $JK(6; 2; 5\frac{1}{2})$ $L(5\frac{1}{2}; 1\frac{1}{4}; 6\frac{1}{4})$ for one base. Draw the intersecting prisms.

7B-3. Fig. 265-3. $A(317)$ $C(314)$ is a diagonal of a horizontal square which is the base of a right pyramid of $2\frac{1}{4}''$ altitude. $G(4\frac{1}{4}; 2\frac{1}{2}; 4\frac{1}{2})$ $E(4\frac{1}{4}; 2\frac{1}{2}; 7)$ is a diagonal of an ortho-frontal square which is the base of a right pyramid whose vertex is $J(2\frac{1}{4}; 1; 5\frac{3}{4})$. Draw the intersecting pyramids.

7B-4. Fig. 265-4. $V(3\frac{1}{2}; 2\frac{1}{2}; 4\frac{1}{2})$ is the vertex of a pyramid whose base is $A(2\frac{1}{2}; 4; 7)$ $B(5\frac{1}{4}; 2\frac{1}{2}; 7)$ $C(2\frac{1}{2}; 1; 7)$. $R(1\frac{3}{4}; 3\frac{1}{4}; 6\frac{1}{2})$ $S(2; 2\frac{3}{4}; 7)$ $T(1\frac{1}{2}; 2; 6)$ is the base of a prism and $TU(525)$ is one of its lateral edges. Draw the intersecting solids.

7B-5. Fig. 265-5. $A(314)$ $C(517)$ is a diagonal of a horizontal square which is the base of a right pyramid of $2\frac{1}{4}''$ altitude. $L(6; 2\frac{1}{2}; 5)$ $M(2; 2\frac{1}{2}; 6)$ is a lateral edge of a prism and $J(6\frac{1}{4}; 1\frac{1}{2}; 6)$ $K(5\frac{3}{4}; 2; 4)$ L is one of its bases. Draw the intersecting solids.

7B-6. Fig. 265-6. $A(2\frac{1}{2}; 1; 5\frac{1}{2})$ $D(5\frac{1}{2}; 1; 5\frac{1}{2})$ is a diagonal of a horizontal regular hexagon which is the base of a right pyramid of $2\frac{1}{2}''$ altitude. $G(5\frac{1}{2}; 1\frac{3}{4}; 6\frac{3}{4})$ $H(6\frac{1}{4}; 1\frac{1}{4}; 5\frac{1}{4})$ $J(5\frac{3}{4}; 2\frac{1}{2}; 6\frac{1}{4})$ is one base of a prism and $GK(2; 1\frac{3}{4}; 5)$ is one of its lateral edges. Draw the intersecting prism and pyramid.

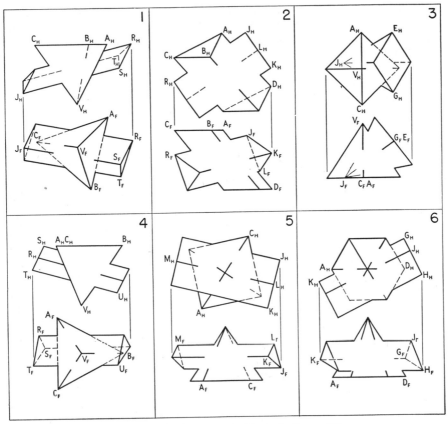

Fig. 265.—Intersection Problems in Group 7B.

7B-7. $A(2\frac{1}{2}; 1; 5\frac{1}{2})$ $D(5\frac{1}{2}; 1; 5\frac{1}{2})$ is a diagonal of a horizontal regular hexagon which is the base of a right pyramid of $2\frac{1}{2}''$ altitude. $V(2\frac{1}{2}; 2\frac{1}{4}; 6\frac{1}{4})$ is the vertex and $R(5\frac{3}{4}; 3; 6\frac{1}{2})$ $S(615)$ $T(5\frac{1}{4}; 2\frac{1}{4}; 4)$ is the base of another pyramid. Draw the intersecting pyramids.

7B-8. $A(237)$ $B(438)$ $C(3\frac{1}{4}; 3; 7)$ and $J(4\frac{1}{2}; 1; 4\frac{1}{2})$ $K(6\frac{1}{2}; 1; 5\frac{1}{2})$ $L(5\frac{3}{4}; 1; 4\frac{1}{2})$ are the bases of an oblique prism. $D(4\frac{3}{4}; 3\frac{1}{4}; 7\frac{3}{4})$ $E(5\frac{1}{2}; 3\frac{1}{4}; 7\frac{3}{4})$ $F(6; 3\frac{1}{4}; 6\frac{1}{2})$ and $G(2\frac{3}{4}; 1; 5\frac{1}{4})$ $H(3\frac{1}{2}; 1; 5\frac{1}{4})$ $I(414)$ are the bases of another oblique prism. Draw the intersecting prisms as a unit.

7B-9. $L(1; 1; 5\frac{1}{2})$ is the vertex of a right pyramid and $U(5; 2\frac{1}{4}; 4\frac{1}{4})$ $S(5; 2\frac{1}{4}; 6\frac{3}{4})$ is one diagonal of its square base. $V(3\frac{1}{2}; 3\frac{1}{2}; 5\frac{3}{4})$ is the vertex of another right pyramid and $A(1\frac{1}{2}; \frac{1}{4}; 4\frac{3}{4})$ is one corner of its horizontal square base. Draw the intersecting pyramids.

7B-10. $V(3; 2\frac{1}{2}; 5)$ is the vertex of a right pyramid and $C(5; 2\frac{1}{2}; 7)$ is one corner of its frontal base which is a regular pentagon. $J(5; 4\frac{1}{4}; 5\frac{3}{4})$ $M(\frac{1}{4}; 1\frac{1}{2}; 7)$ is a lateral edge of a prism which has $JK(5\frac{1}{2}; 3\frac{3}{4}; 6\frac{1}{4})$ $L(5\frac{1}{4}; 3\frac{1}{4}; 5\frac{1}{4})$ for one base. Draw the intersecting solids as a unit.

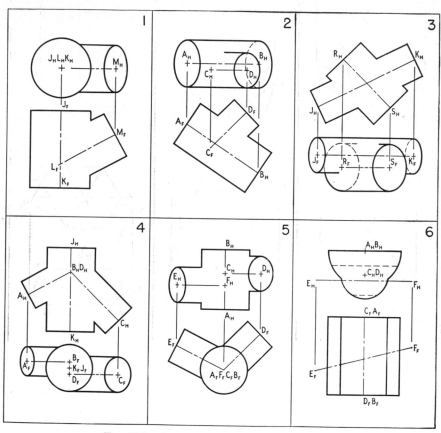

Fig. 266.—Intersection Problems in Group 7C.

Group 7C. Right Cylinder Intersection Problems for the Cutting Plane Method.

7C-1. Fig. 266-1. $J(246)$ $K(2; \frac{3}{4}; 6)$ is the axis of a 20″ diameter pipe and $L(2; 1\frac{3}{4}; 6)$ $M(4\frac{1}{4}; 3; 6)$ is the axis of a 16″ diameter pipe. Find their intersection. Scale: $1\frac{1}{2}″ = 1′\text{-}0″$.

7C-2. Fig. 266-2. A sheet metal pipe connection has the center lines $A(337)$

$B(617)$ and $C(4; 2; 6\frac{3}{4})$ $D(5\frac{1}{2}; 4; 6\frac{3}{4})$. Pipe AB is $16''$ in diameter and pipe CD is $12''$. Draw the intersecting pipes of the connection. Scale: $1\frac{1}{2}'' = 1'\text{-}0''$.

7C-3. Fig. 266-3. $J(2; 1\frac{1}{2}; 5)$ $K(6; 1\frac{1}{2}; 7)$ is the axis of a $12''$ diameter pipe and $R(317)$ $S(515)$ is the axis of a $16''$ diameter pipe. Draw the intersecting pipes. Scale: $1\frac{1}{2}'' = 1'\text{-}0''$.

7C-4. Fig. 266-4. A sheet metal pipe connection is made of three right circular pipes. $A(2\frac{1}{4}; 2\frac{1}{4}; 6)$ $B(4; 2\frac{1}{4}; 7)$ is the axis of a $10''$ diameter pipe; $C(6; 1\frac{3}{4}; 5)$ $D(4; 1\frac{3}{4}; 7)$ is the axis of a $12''$ diameter pipe; and $J(428)$ $K(4; 2; 4\frac{1}{2})$ is the axis of a $16''$ diameter pipe. Draw the connection. Scale: $1\frac{1}{2}'' = 1'\text{-}0''$.

7C-5. Fig. 266-5. A sheet metal pipe connection is made of three right circular pipes as follows: $C(417)$ $D(5\frac{1}{2}; 2\frac{1}{2}; 7)$ and $E(2; 2; 6\frac{1}{2})$ $F(4; 1; 6\frac{1}{2})$ are the axes of $12''$ diameter pipes cut to fit the $16''$ diameter pipe of which $A(4; 1; 5\frac{1}{2})$ $B(418)$ is the axis. Draw the connection. Scale: $1\frac{1}{2}'' = 1'\text{-}0''$.

7C-6. Fig. 266-6. $A(3\frac{1}{2}; 4\frac{1}{4}; 7)$ $B(3\frac{1}{2}; 1; 7)$ is the axis of a $3''$ diameter cylinder. $C(3\frac{1}{2}; 4\frac{1}{4}; 6)$ $D(3\frac{1}{2}; 1; 6)$ is the axis of a $2''$ diameter cylinder. The portions of these cylinders in front of a frontal plane through AB represents a piece of wood molding. Show a $1\frac{1}{4}''$ diameter hole with axis $E(1\frac{1}{2}; 2; 5\frac{3}{4})$ $F(5\frac{1}{2}; 3; 5\frac{3}{4})$ drilled through the molding.

Group 7D. Intersection of Cones with Cones, Prisms, Cylinders, and Pyramids: Axes Parallel or Coinciding.

7D-1. Fig. 267-1. $V(3; 3\frac{1}{2}; 6\frac{1}{2})$ is the vertex of a cone and $O(3; 1; 6\frac{1}{2})$ is the center of its $3''$ diameter horizontal base. $A(3\frac{1}{2}; 3\frac{1}{2}; 6)$ is the vertex of another cone and $Q(3\frac{1}{2}; 1; 6)$ is the center of its $2''$ horizontal base. Draw the intersecting cones.

7D-2. Fig. 267-2. $O(516)$ is the center of a $2\frac{1}{2}''$ diameter horizontal circle which is the base of a right cone of $3\frac{1}{2}''$ altitude. It is also the center of a horizontal square, one of whose $2''$ diagonals is frontal. The square is the lower base of a right prism of $2''$ altitude. Draw the intersecting solids and show the portion of each which is outside the other.

7D-3. Fig. 267-3. $Q(4; 1; 5\frac{1}{2})$ is the center of a $3\frac{1}{2}''$ diameter horizontal circle which is the base of a right cone of $2''$ altitude. $A(336)$ $B(5; 3; 6\frac{1}{4})$ $C(434)$ is the upper base of a right prism intersecting the cone. Draw the portion of the prism which is outside the cone.

7D-4. Fig. 267-4. $A(237)$ $B(547)$ $C(417)$ is the base of a pyramid and $J(3\frac{1}{2}; 2\frac{1}{4}; 4\frac{1}{2})$ is its vertex. $O(4; 2\frac{1}{2}; 7)$ is the center of a $3''$ diameter frontal circle which is the base of a cone with vertex $V(4; 2\frac{1}{2}; 4\frac{1}{2})$. Draw the intersecting cone and pyramid. Omit the portion of one which is inside the other.

7D-5. Fig. 267-5. $O(416)$ is the center of a $3\frac{1}{2}''$ diameter circle which is the base of a right cone of $2\frac{1}{4}''$ altitude. $A(3\frac{1}{2}; 3\frac{1}{4}; 5\frac{1}{2})$ is the center of the $1\frac{3}{4}''$ diameter base of a vertical right cylinder intersecting the cone. Find the intersection and draw the portion of each solid which is outside the other.

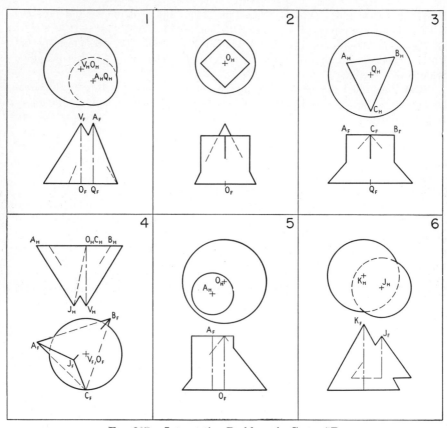

Fig. 267.—Intersection Problems in Group 7D.

7D-6. Fig. 267-6. $K(3; 3\frac{3}{4}; 6)$ is the vertex of a vertical right cone of $2\frac{3}{4}''$ altitude and having a base of $3''$ diameter. $J(3\frac{3}{4}; 3\frac{1}{4}; 5\frac{1}{2})$ is the vertex of another vertical cone, having a $2\frac{1}{2}''$ diameter horizontal base and an altitude of $1\frac{3}{4}''$. Draw the intersecting cones.

7D-7. $V(4; 3; 5\frac{1}{2})$ is the vertex of a right cone of $3''$ altitude having a $2\frac{1}{2}''$ diameter horizontal base, and $A(4\frac{1}{2}; 3; 6)$ is the vertex of another cone of the same altitude and with a $4''$ diameter horizontal base. Draw the intersecting cones as a unit.

7D-8. $A(1\frac{3}{4}; 2\frac{1}{2}; 6\frac{1}{4})$ is the vertex of a right circular cone whose elements make $60°$ with its horizontal base $2\frac{1}{2}''$ below A. $B(2\frac{1}{2}; 2\frac{1}{2}; 7)$ is the vertex of another right circular cone whose elements make $45°$ with its horizontal base $2\frac{1}{2}''$ below B. Find their intersection in the front and top views and in an auxiliary elevation made normal to AB. Omit the portion of the smaller cone inside the other. In this case it can be proved that the intersection appears as a circle in the top view.

7D-9. $A(336)$ is the vertex and $B(306)$ is the center of the 4″ diameter circular base of a cone. $C(436)$ is the vertex and $D(405)$ is the center of the $3\frac{1}{2}$″ diameter circular base of another cone. Find their intersection.

Group 7E.   Intersection of Right Cones and Inclined Prisms or Cylinders.

7E-1. Fig. 268-1. $A(3; 2\frac{1}{2}; 6)$ $B(5; \frac{3}{4}; 6)$ is the axis of a 10″ diameter pipe. $V(5; 2\frac{1}{2}; 6\frac{1}{4})$ is the vertex of a conical hood which has a 24″ diameter horizontal base 20″ below V. Draw the portion of the pipe which is outside the hood. Scale: $1\frac{1}{2}$″ = 1′-0″.

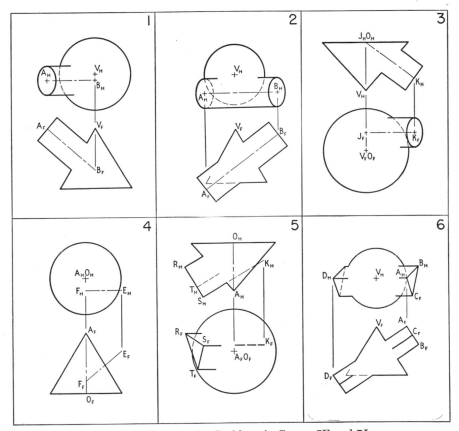

Fig. 268.—Intersection Problems in Groups 7E and 7J.

7E-2. Fig. 268-2. $V(3; 3; 6\frac{1}{2})$ is the vertex of a right cone whose $2\frac{1}{2}$″ diameter horizontal base is $2\frac{1}{4}$″ below the vertex. $A(1\frac{3}{4}; \frac{1}{2}; 5\frac{3}{4})$ $B(4\frac{3}{4}; 2\frac{3}{4}; 5\frac{3}{4})$ is the axis of a $1\frac{1}{4}$″ diameter cylinder intersecting the cone. Find the intersection and draw the objects as a unit.

7E-3. Fig. 268-3. $O(328)$ is the center of the $3\frac{1}{2}''$ diameter frontal base of a right cone whose vertex is $V(326)$. $J(3; 2\frac{3}{4}; 8)$ $K(5; 2\frac{3}{4}; 6\frac{1}{2})$ is the axis of a $1\frac{1}{4}''$ diameter cylinder intersecting the cone. Find the intersection and draw the portion of the cylinder which is outside the cone.

7E-4. Fig. 268-4. $E(4\frac{1}{2}; 2; 6)$ $F(3; \frac{3}{4}; 6)$ is the axis of a $1\frac{1}{2}''$ diameter hole drilled through the solid cone which has the $3''$ diameter horizontal circle with center $O(3; \frac{1}{4}; 6\frac{1}{2})$ for its base, and $A(3; 2\frac{3}{4}; 6\frac{1}{2})$ for its vertex. Draw the cone with the hole in it.

7E-5. Fig. 268-5. $A(4\frac{1}{2}; 1\frac{3}{4}; 5\frac{1}{4})$ is the vertex of a right cone and $O(4\frac{1}{2}; 1\frac{3}{4}; 7\frac{1}{4})$ is the center of its $3\frac{1}{2}''$ diameter base. $R(2\frac{1}{2}; 2\frac{1}{2}; 6\frac{1}{4})$ $S(3\frac{1}{4}; 2; 5)$ $T(31X)$ is the base of a right prism intersecting the cone. $SK(5\frac{3}{4}; 2; 6\frac{1}{2})$ is one lateral edge of the prism. Draw the portion of the prism outside the cone.

7E-6. Fig. 268-6. $V(3\frac{1}{2}; 3; 6)$ is the vertex of a right cone of $2''$ altitude. The base is a $2\frac{1}{2}''$ diameter horizontal circle. Find the intersection of the cone and the right prism which has $A(4\frac{3}{4}; 3; 6)$ $B(5\frac{1}{4}; 2\frac{1}{4}; 6\frac{1}{2})$ $C(5; X; 5\frac{1}{4})$ for one base and $AD(1\frac{3}{4}; 1; 6)$ for one lateral edge.

Group 7F.   Intersection of Oblique Cones by the Cutting Plane Method.

7F-1. Fig. 269-1. $O(228)$ is the center of a $2\frac{1}{2}''$ diameter frontal circle which is the base of an oblique cone whose vertex is $V(4; 3\frac{1}{2}; 6\frac{1}{2})$. $C(438)$ is the center of a $2''$ diameter frontal circle which is the base of a cone with vertex $A(1; 2\frac{1}{2}; 5)$. Draw the intersecting cones.

7F-2. Fig. 269-2. $J(435)$ is the vertex of a cone whose base is the $3''$ diameter horizontal circle with center $L(6\frac{1}{2}; 1; 5\frac{3}{4})$. $K(5\frac{1}{2}; 4; 5\frac{1}{2})$ is the vertex of another cone whose base is the $2\frac{1}{2}''$ diameter horizontal circle with center $M(516)$. Draw the intersecting cones.

7F-3. Fig. 269-3. $J(2\frac{1}{2}; 1; 5\frac{3}{4})$ is the center of a $3''$ diameter horizontal circle which is the base of a cone whose vertex is $S(5; 3\frac{1}{2}; 6)$. $K(4\frac{3}{4}; 1; 5\frac{1}{4})$ is the center of the $2\frac{1}{2}''$ diameter horizontal base of another cone with vertex $R(2; 3\frac{1}{2}; 6\frac{3}{4})$. Draw the intersecting cones.

7F-4. Fig. 269-4. $A(2; 4; 5\frac{1}{2})$ is the vertex of a cone and $C(5; 1; 6\frac{1}{4})$ is the center of its $2''$ diameter horizontal base. $D(2\frac{1}{4}; 1; 6)$ is the center of the $2\frac{1}{2}''$ diameter horizontal base of another cone whose vertex is $B(4; 3; 5\frac{3}{4})$. Draw the intersecting cones.

7F-5. Fig. 269-5. $V(2\frac{1}{4}; 3; 4\frac{1}{2})$ is the vertex and $O(5; 2\frac{1}{4}; 7)$ is the center of the $2\frac{1}{2}''$ diameter frontal base of a cone. $A(5\frac{3}{4}; 2\frac{1}{4}; 4\frac{1}{2})$ is the vertex of another cone and $Q(2\frac{1}{2}; 2\frac{1}{4}; 7)$ is the center of its $2''$ diameter frontal base. Draw the intersecting cones.

7F-6. Fig. 269-6. $J(245)$ is the vertex of an oblique cone and $K(4; 2\frac{1}{2}; 7)$ is the center of its $3''$ diameter frontal base. $L(5; 2\frac{1}{2}; 5)$ is the vertex and $M(237)$ is the center of the $2\frac{1}{2}''$ diameter frontal base of another oblique cone. Draw the intersecting cones.

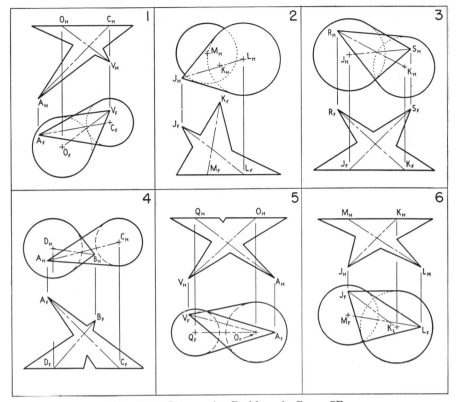

Fig. 269.—Intersection Problems in Group 7F.

Group 7G. Intersection of Right Cones: Planes of Bases at Right Angles to Each Other.

7G-1. Fig. 270-1. $V(3\frac{3}{4}; 3; 6\frac{1}{4})$ is the vertex of a right cone and $O(3\frac{3}{4}; 0; 6\frac{1}{4})$ is the center of its $3''$ diameter horizontal base. $Q(3\frac{1}{4}; 1\frac{1}{2}; 8)$ is the center of the $3''$ diameter frontal base of another cone whose vertex is $A(3\frac{1}{4}; 1\frac{1}{2}; 5)$. Draw the intersecting cones.

7G-2. Fig. 270-2. $L(4\frac{3}{4}; 1\frac{1}{2}; 6\frac{1}{4})$ is the vertex of a cone and $M(8; 1\frac{1}{2}; 6\frac{1}{4})$ is the center of its $2\frac{1}{2}''$ diameter profile base. $J(6\frac{1}{2}; 3\frac{1}{2}; 6\frac{1}{2})$ is the vertex of another cone and $K(6\frac{1}{2}; 0; 6\frac{1}{2})$ is the center of its $3''$ diameter horizontal base. Draw the intersecting cones.

7G-3. Fig. 270-3. $S(1\frac{1}{2}; 1\frac{1}{2}; 8)$ is the center of a $3''$ diameter frontal circle which is the base of a right cone with vertex $R(1\frac{1}{2}; 1\frac{1}{2}; 5)$. $J(2\frac{3}{4}; 2; 6\frac{1}{4})$ is the vertex of another right cone that has a $2\frac{1}{2}''$ diameter profile base with center $K(0; 2; 6\frac{1}{4})$. Draw the intersecting cones.

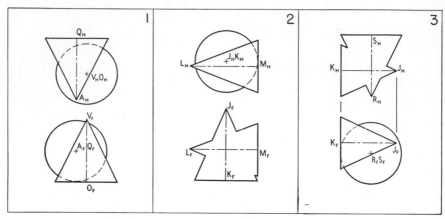

FIG. 270.—Intersection Problems in Group 7G.

7G-4. $C(4; 1\frac{1}{2}; 8)$ is the center of a $3''$ diameter frontal circle which is the base of a right cone with vertex $A(4; 1\frac{1}{2}; 5\frac{1}{4})$. Another right cone has the $3''$ diameter circle with center $D(3\frac{1}{4}; 0; 6)$ for its base and the vertex at $B(3\frac{1}{4}; 2\frac{1}{2}; 6)$. Draw the intersecting cones.

7G-5. $Q(5\frac{1}{2}; 0; 6\frac{1}{2})$ is the center of the $3''$ diameter horizontal base of a right cone of $3''$ altitude. $N(4\frac{1}{2}; 2; 8)$ is the center of the $3''$ diameter frontal base of a right cone whose vertex is $V(4\frac{1}{2}; 2; 5)$. Draw the intersecting cones.

7G-6. $C(2\frac{1}{2}; 2; 8)$ is the center of a $3''$ diameter frontal circle which is the base of a right cone with vertex $D(2\frac{1}{2}; 2; 5)$. $A(3\frac{1}{2}; 3; 6)$ is the vertex of another cone which has a $3''$ diameter horizontal base with the center at $B(3\frac{1}{2}; 1; 6)$. Draw the intersecting cones.

Group 7H.   Intersection of Oblique Cylinders.   Cutting Plane Method.

7H-1. Fig. 271-1. $A(3; 2\frac{1}{2}; 8)$ $B(616)$ is the axis of an oblique cylinder having $1\frac{1}{2}''$ diameter frontal bases. $C(638)$ $D(315)$ is the axis of another oblique cylinder which has $2''$ diameter frontal bases. Draw the intersecting cylinders.

7H-2. Fig. 271-2. $J(2\frac{1}{2}; \frac{1}{2}; 7)$ $K(5\frac{1}{2}; 3; 4\frac{1}{2})$ and $L(607)$ $M(2; 3; 4\frac{1}{2})$ are the axes of two oblique cylinders which have $2''$ diameter horizontal bases. Draw the intersecting cylinders.

7H-3. Fig. 271-3. $R(218)$ and $S(2; 3; 4\frac{1}{2})$ are the frontal ends of two $8''$ diameter horizontal pipes connected by an oblique cylinder having the axis RS. $T(2\frac{1}{2}; 3\frac{1}{2}; 4\frac{1}{2})$ is the frontal end of a $6''$ diameter horizontal pipe joined to the piece RS with an oblique cylinder having the axis $TU(608)$. Draw the intersecting cylinders of the pipe connection. Scale: $3'' = 1'\text{-}0''$.

7H-4. $A(2\frac{1}{2}; 0; 7)$ $B(6; 3; 4\frac{1}{2})$ is the axis of an oblique cylinder which has $2''$ diameter horizontal bases. $C(1\frac{3}{4}; 3; 4\frac{3}{4})$ $D(5\frac{1}{4}; 0; 7)$ is the axis of another oblique cylinder having $1\frac{1}{2}''$ diameter horizontal bases. Draw the intersecting cylinders.

7H-5. $G(2; 3; 4\frac{1}{2})$ $H(5\frac{1}{2}; 1; 7\frac{1}{2})$ is the axis of an oblique cylinder which has $2''$ diameter frontal bases; and $E(218)$ $F(5\frac{1}{2}; 3\frac{1}{2}; 4\frac{1}{2})$ is the axis of another oblique cylinder which has $1\frac{1}{2}''$ diameter frontal bases. Draw the intersecting cylinders.

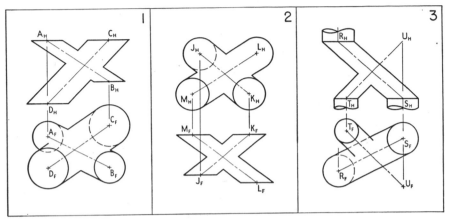

Fig. 271.—Intersection Problems in Group 7H.

Group 7I. Intersection Problems for the Cutting Sphere Method.

7I-1. Fig. 272-1. $V(524)$ is the vertex of a right cone and $O(527)$ is the center of its $3''$ diameter base. $A(324)$ O is the axis of a $1\frac{1}{2}''$ diameter cylinder intersecting the cone. Find the intersection and draw the portion of the cylinder outside the cone.

7I-2. Fig. 272-2. $S(5; 2; 7\frac{1}{2})$ is the vertex and $R(2\frac{1}{2}; 2; 5\frac{1}{2})$ is the center of the $3''$ diameter base of a right cone. $J(4; 2; 4\frac{1}{2})$ is the vertex and $K(428)$ is the center of the $4''$ diameter base of another right cone. Draw the intersecting cones.

7I-3. Fig. 272-3. An annular torus is generated by revolving the $1\frac{3}{4}''$ diameter horizontal circle with center $C(2\frac{3}{8}; 2\frac{1}{4}; 6\frac{1}{2})$ about the line $J(3\frac{3}{4}; 2\frac{1}{4}; 5)$ $K(3\frac{3}{4}; 2\frac{1}{4}; 8)$ as an axis. Find the intersection of the torus and the $1\frac{1}{2}''$ diameter right cylinder whose axis is $A(1\frac{1}{4}; 2\frac{1}{4}; 4\frac{1}{2})$ $B(6\frac{1}{4}; 2\frac{1}{4}; 7\frac{1}{2})$.

7I-4. Fig. 272-4. $A(1; 1; 6\frac{1}{2})$ $B(7; 3; 6\frac{1}{2})$ is the axis of a $24''$ diameter cylindrical pipe which is to be entered through a conical hopper having the center of its $48''$ diameter horizontal base at $C(4; 4; 6\frac{1}{2})$ and its vertex at $V(4; 1; 6\frac{1}{2})$. Find the intersection. Scale: $1'' = 1'-0''$.

7I-5. Fig. 272-5. The $2''$ diameter horizontal circle with center $A(3\frac{1}{2}; 3\frac{1}{2}; 6)$ is the upper end of the frustum of a right cone. The lower end is a $3''$ diameter circle with center $B(3\frac{1}{2}; 1; 6)$. $C(5\frac{3}{4}; 3\frac{3}{4}; 6)$ $D(3\frac{1}{2}; 1\frac{1}{2}; 6)$ is the axis of the frustum of another right cone. The base at D has a diameter of $2''$ and that at C has a diameter of $\frac{3}{4}''$. Draw the intersecting cones.

7I-6. Fig. 272-6. $J(3\frac{1}{2}; 2; 6\frac{1}{2})$ is the vertex of a right cone and $K(\frac{1}{2}; 2; 6\frac{1}{2})$ is the center of its $3''$ diameter base. $L(3; 2; 4\frac{1}{2})$ $M(\frac{1}{2}; 2; 7)$ is the axis of a $1\frac{1}{2}''$

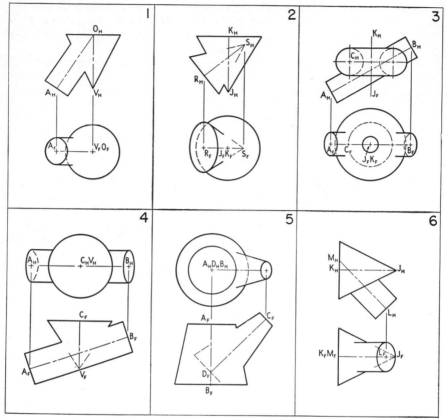

Fig. 272.—Intersection Problems in Group 7I.

diameter cylinder intersecting the cone. Draw the portion of the cylinder which is outside the cone.

7I-7. $A(3\frac{1}{2}; 2\frac{1}{2}; 4\frac{1}{2})$ is the vertex of a right cone and $Q(3\frac{1}{2}; 2\frac{1}{2}; 7\frac{1}{2})$ is the center of its $3''$ diameter base. Find the intersection of the cone and a right cylinder of $1\frac{1}{2}''$ diameter having $R(1\frac{1}{2}; 2\frac{1}{2}; 6\frac{1}{2})$ $S(5\frac{1}{2}; 2\frac{1}{2}; 6)$ as its axis.

7I-8. $L(216)$ is the vertex of a right cone and $M(5\frac{1}{2}; 2\frac{1}{4}; 6)$ is the center of its $2\frac{1}{2}''$ diameter base. $V(4; 3\frac{1}{2}; 6)$ is the vertex and $O(406)$ is the center of the $3\frac{1}{2}''$ diameter base of another right cone. Draw the intersecting cones.

Group 7J. Intersection Problems for the Cutting Cylinder Method.

7J-1. Fig. 268-1. $A(3; 2\frac{1}{2}; 6)$ $B(5; \frac{3}{4}; 6)$ is the axis of a $1\frac{1}{4}''$ diameter cylinder. $V(5; 2\frac{1}{2}; 6\frac{1}{4})$ is the vertex of a right cone whose $3''$ diameter horizontal base is $2\frac{1}{2}''$ below the vertex. Draw the intersecting cone and cylinder.

7J-2. Fig. 268-2. $V(3; 3; 6\frac{1}{2})$ is the vertex of a right cone of $2\frac{1}{4}''$ altitude. The base is $2\frac{1}{2}''$ in diameter, horizontal and below the vertex. $A(1\frac{3}{4}; \frac{1}{2}; 5\frac{3}{4})$ $B(4\frac{3}{4}; 2\frac{3}{4}; 5\frac{3}{4})$ is the axis of a $1\frac{1}{4}''$ diameter cylinder intersecting the cone. Find the intersection and draw the objects as a unit.

7J-3. Fig. 268-3. $O(328)$ is the center of the $3\frac{1}{2}''$ diameter frontal base of a right cone whose vertex is $V(326)$. $J(3; 2\frac{3}{4}; 8)$ $K(5; 2\frac{3}{4}; 6\frac{1}{2})$ is the axis of a $1\frac{1}{4}''$ diameter cylinder intersecting the cone. Find the intersection and draw the portion of the cylinder which is outside the cone.

7J-4. Fig. 268-4. $E(4\frac{1}{2}; 2; 6)$ $F(3; \frac{3}{4}; 6)$ is the axis of a $1\frac{1}{2}''$ diameter hole drilled through the solid cone which has the $3''$ diameter horizontal circle with center $O(3; \frac{1}{4}; 6\frac{1}{2})$ for its base, and $A(3; 2\frac{3}{4}; 6\frac{1}{2})$ for its vertex. Draw the cone with the hole in it.

7J-5. Fig. 268-5. $A(5\frac{1}{2}; 1\frac{3}{4}; 5\frac{1}{4})$ is the vertex of a right cone and $O(5\frac{1}{2}; 1\frac{3}{4}; 7\frac{1}{4})$ is the center of its $3\frac{1}{2}''$ diameter base. $R(3\frac{1}{2}; 2\frac{1}{2}; 6\frac{1}{4})$ $S(4\frac{1}{4}; 2; 5)$ $T(41X)$ is the base of a right prism intersecting the cone. $SK(6\frac{3}{4}; 2; 6\frac{1}{2})$ is one lateral edge of the prism. Draw the portion of the prism which is outside the cone.

7J-6. Fig. 268-6. $V(3\frac{1}{2}; 3; 6)$ is the vertex of a right cone of $2''$ altitude. The base is a $2\frac{1}{2}''$ diameter horizontal circle. Find the intersection of the cone and the right prism which has $A(4\frac{3}{4}; 3; 6)$ $B(5\frac{1}{4}; 2\frac{1}{4}; 6\frac{1}{2})$ $C(5; X; 5\frac{1}{4})$ for one base and $AD(1\frac{3}{4}; 1; 6)$ for one lateral edge.

7J-7. Fig. 273-1. In this layout, taken from a quick freezing unit, an $18''$ diameter pipe whose axis is $A(3; 1\frac{1}{2}; 5\frac{1}{2})$ $B(1\frac{1}{4}; \frac{1}{2}; 5\frac{1}{2})$ intersects a bent $20''$ diameter pipe. The bent portion is one-half of a torus generated by revolving the $20''$ diameter frontal circle with center B about $C(3; 2\frac{1}{2}; 5\frac{1}{2})$ $D(3; 0; 5\frac{1}{2})$ as an axis. Draw the intersecting pipes. Scale: $1'' = 1'-0''$.

7J-8. Fig. 273-2. A paraboloid is generated by revolving the parabola $B(\frac{1}{2}; 1; 6)$ $A(2; 3\frac{1}{4}; 6)$ $C(3\frac{1}{2}; 1; 6)$ about a vertical axis through A. $D(1; 1; 5\frac{3}{4})$ $E(4; 3; 5\frac{3}{4})$ is

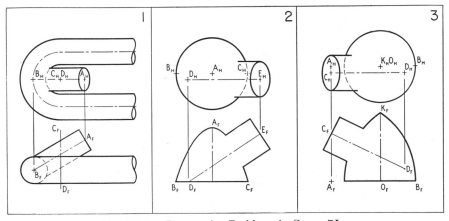

Fig. 27 3.—Intersection Problems in Group 7J.

the axis of a right cylinder of $1\frac{1}{2}''$ diameter. Find the intersection of the cylinder with the paraboloid and draw the portion of the cylinder from E to the intersection.

7J-9. Fig. 273-3. With $A(416)$ as a center and radius $AB(7\frac{1}{2}; 1; 6)$ draw a frontal circular arc intersecting a vertical line through $O(616)$ at K. Revolve arc KB about the axis KO to generate a surface of revolution and find its intersection with the $1\frac{1}{2}''$ diameter cylinder whose axis is $C(4; 3; 5\frac{3}{4})$ $D(7; 1\frac{1}{2}; 5\frac{3}{4})$.

Group 7K.   Intersection of Double Curved Surfaces.   Sphere Problems.

7K-1. Fig. 274-1. $A(4; 1\frac{1}{2}; 6)$ is the center of a $3''$ diameter sphere. Draw the portion of the sphere that is below the plane of the points $R(2; 3\frac{1}{2}; 6\frac{1}{2})$ $S(6\frac{1}{2}; 0; 7\frac{1}{2})$ $T(5; 3\frac{1}{2}; 5\frac{1}{2})$. Crosshatch the cut surface when visible.

7K-2. Fig. 274-2. $O(326)$ is the center of a $3''$ diameter sphere and $Q(2\frac{3}{4}; 1\frac{1}{2}; 5\frac{1}{4})$ is the center of a $2\frac{1}{2}''$ diameter sphere. Find their intersection and draw them as a unit.

7K-3. Fig. 274-3. $R(3; 1\frac{1}{2}; 4)$ $S(4; 3\frac{1}{4}; 4)$ $T(5; 1\frac{1}{4}; 4)$ is the front base of a horizontal right prism intersecting the $3''$ diameter sphere whose center is $D(426)$. Draw the portion of the prism which is outside the sphere.

7K-4. Fig. 274-4. $L(2\frac{1}{2}; 1; 5\frac{3}{8})$ $S(5\frac{1}{2}; 3\frac{1}{4}; 5\frac{3}{8})$ is the axis of a $1\frac{1}{2}''$ diameter hole drilled through the $2\frac{1}{2}''$ diameter sphere with center $P(4; 2\frac{1}{4}; 5\frac{3}{4})$. Draw the sphere with the hole in it.

7K-5. Fig. 274-5. $A(306)$ is the vertex of an inverted right cone of $3''$ altitude. The base is horizontal and of $3''$ diameter. Find the intersection of the cone and the $3''$ diameter sphere whose center is $B(4; 2; 5\frac{1}{4})$.

7K-6. Fig. 274-6. $C(5\frac{1}{2}; 1; 6)$ is the center of a $3\frac{1}{2}''$ diameter sphere. Find the intersection of the $1\frac{1}{4}''$ diameter cylinder whose axis is $J(3; 3; 6\frac{1}{2})$ $K(6; 1; 6\frac{1}{2})$ and the upper one-half of the sphere.

7K-7. Fig. 274-7. $J(2; 2\frac{1}{4}; 4)$ $K(6\frac{1}{2}; 2\frac{1}{2}; 7\frac{1}{2})$ is the axis of an oblique cylinder which has $1\frac{1}{2}''$ diameter frontal bases. Draw the portion of the cylinder which is outside the $3''$ diameter sphere whose center is $M(426)$.

7K-8. Fig. 274-8. $O(4\frac{1}{4}; 1\frac{1}{2}; 6)$ is the center of a $2\frac{1}{2}''$ diameter sphere which intersects a right cone. $V(3\frac{1}{2}; 3; 5\frac{1}{2})$ is the vertex of the cone and $M(3\frac{1}{2}; 0; 5\frac{1}{2})$ is the center of its $3''$ diameter base. Draw the intersecting solids.

7K-9. Fig. 274-9. $R(308)$ $S(708)$ $T(5; 0; 4\frac{1}{2})$ is the base of a pyramid whose vertex is $V(5; 3; 6\frac{1}{2})$. Find its intersection with the $2\frac{1}{2}''$ diameter sphere whose center is $K(5\frac{1}{2}; 1\frac{1}{2}; 6)$.

7K-10. $R(4\frac{1}{4}; 2\frac{1}{4}; 5\frac{1}{4})$ is the center of a $2\frac{1}{2}''$ diameter sphere and $S(5\frac{1}{2}; 2; 6)$ is the center of a $3\frac{1}{2}''$ diameter sphere. Find their intersection and draw the spheres as a unit.

Group 7L.   Intersection of Double Curved Surfaces.   Torus Problems.

7L-1. Fig. 275-1. A 90° elbow in a $24''$ diameter cast iron pipe is generated by revolving the $24''$ horizontal circle whose center is $C(516)$ about the axis $J(7\frac{1}{2}; 1; X)$ $K(7\frac{1}{2}; 1; X)$. $A(346)$ $B(5\frac{1}{2}; 2\frac{1}{2}; 6)$ is the axis of an $18''$ diameter pipe welded to the elbow. Find the intersection. Scale: $1'' = 1'\text{-}0''$.

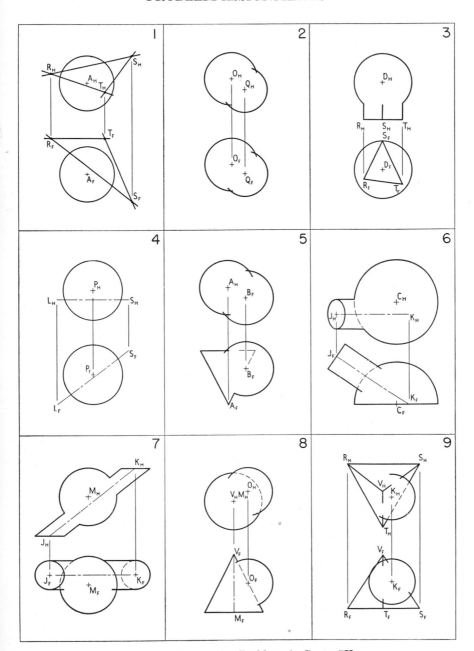

Fig. 274.—Intersection Problems in Group 7K.

7L-2. Fig. 275-2. An annular torus is generated by revolving the $1\frac{1}{4}''$ diameter frontal circle whose center is $B(2\frac{3}{8}; 2; 6)$ about the vertical line $L(3\frac{1}{2}; 3; 6)$ $M(3\frac{1}{2}; \frac{3}{4}; 6)$. Find its intersection with the vertical right cone having $C(4; 1; 5\frac{1}{2})$ for the center of its $3''$ diameter base, and an altitude of $2''$.

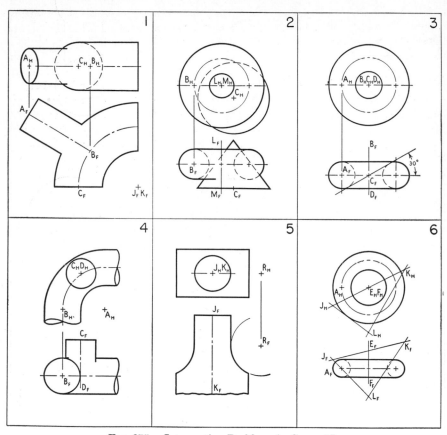

Fig. 275.—Intersection Problems in Group 7L.

7L-3. Fig. 275-3. $A(215)$ is the center of the $1\frac{1}{2}''$ diameter frontal generating circle for the annular torus whose axis is $B(3\frac{1}{2}; 2; 5)$ $D(3\frac{1}{2}; 0; 5)$. Show the section made by an ortho-frontal plane that passes through $C(3\frac{1}{2}; 1; 5)$ and is inclined downward to the left $30°$ to the horizontal.

7L-4. Fig. 275-4. $C(2; 3\frac{1}{4}; 6)$ $D(2; 1\frac{1}{4}; 6)$ is the axis of a $15''$ diameter cast iron pipe cut to fit the bend in a $90°$ elbow of an $18''$ diameter pipe. The elbow is one-fourth of a torus generated by revolving the $18''$ diameter frontal circle whose center is $B(1\frac{1}{4}; 1\frac{3}{4}; 4\frac{1}{2})$ about a vertical line through $A(3; X; 4\frac{1}{2})$. Find the intersection of the pipes. Scale: $1'' = 1'-0''$.

7L-5. Fig. 275-5. $J(4; 4\frac{1}{4}; 6)$ $K(416)$ is the axis of a $2'' \times 3''$ rectangular bar which has the $3''$ sides frontal. The upper end is to be turned to a diameter of $1\frac{1}{2}''$ for a distance of $1\frac{1}{4}''$. The end of the cut is in the form of a torus generated by a frontal circle with its center at $R(636)$. Show its intersection with the outside of the bar.

7L-6. Fig. 275-6. An annular torus is generated by revolving the $1''$ diameter frontal circle with center $A(2\frac{1}{2}; 1\frac{1}{2}; 6)$ about the vertical axis $E(4; 2\frac{1}{2}; 6)$ $F(4; \frac{1}{2}; 6)$. Draw the portion of the torus which lies below the plane of the points $J(225)$ $K(637)$ $L(4; 0; 3\frac{1}{2})$.

Group 7M.   Miscellaneous Intersection Problems.

7M-1. Fig. 276-1. $D(4; 2; 6\frac{1}{2})$ is the center of a horizontal ellipse whose axes are $4''$ and $2''$. The major axis is frontal. A spheroid is generated by revolving the ellipse about its minor axis. $A(1\frac{1}{2}; 2\frac{1}{2}; 6)$ $B(2\frac{1}{4}; 3\frac{1}{2}; 4\frac{1}{2})$ $C(215)$ is the front

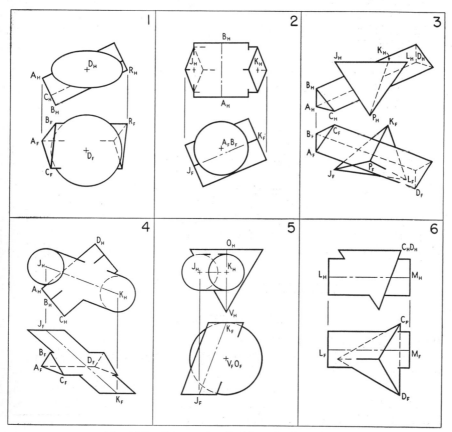

Fig. 276.—Intersection Problems in Group 7M.

base of a right prism having $BR(6\frac{1}{4}; 3\frac{1}{2}; 6\frac{1}{2})$ for a lateral edge. Draw the intersecting prism and spheroid.

7M-2. Fig. 276-2. $J(2\frac{1}{2}; 1\frac{1}{2}; 6\frac{1}{2})$ $K(6; 3; 6\frac{1}{2})$ is the axis of a right square base prism. One of the $2\frac{1}{2}''$ diagonals of each base is horizontal. Find the intersection of this prism with the $3''$ diameter right cylinder having the axis $A(4; 2\frac{1}{2}; 5)$ $B(4; 2\frac{1}{2}; 8)$.

7M-3. Fig. 276-3. $P(4; 1\frac{1}{2}; 4)$ is the vertex of a pyramid and $J(217)$ $K(5; 3\frac{1}{2}; 7)$ $L(6; \frac{1}{2}; 7)$ is its base. $A(1; 2; 4\frac{1}{2})$ $B(1; 3; 5\frac{1}{2})$ $C(2; 3\frac{1}{2}; 4\frac{1}{4})$ is one base of a prism and $AD(6\frac{1}{2}; 0; 7)$ is one of its lateral edges. Draw the intersecting prism and pyramid.

7M-4. Fig. 276-4. $J(2; 3\frac{1}{2}; 6\frac{1}{2})$ $K(605)$ is the axis of an oblique cylinder whose ends are $2''$ diameter horizontal circles. $A(1\frac{3}{4}; 1\frac{1}{2}; 5\frac{1}{4})$ $B(2\frac{1}{4}; 2\frac{1}{4}; X)$ $C(3; 1; 3\frac{3}{4})$ is the front base of a right prism and $AD(4\frac{3}{4}; 1\frac{1}{2}; 7\frac{3}{4})$ is one of its lateral edges. Draw the intersecting cylinder and prism.

7M-5. Fig. 276-5. $O(428)$ is the center of the $4''$ diameter frontal base of a right cone whose vertex is $V(4; 2; 4\frac{1}{2})$. $J(2\frac{1}{2}; 0; 6\frac{1}{4})$ $K(4; 4; 6\frac{1}{4})$ is the axis of an oblique cylinder which has $2''$ diameter horizontal bases. Draw the portion of the cylinder which is outside the cone.

7M-6. Fig. 276-6. $C(748)$ $D(708)$ is one side of a frontal equilateral triangle which is the rear face of a regular tetrahedron. Find its intersection with the $2''$ diameter cylinder having the axis $L(3; 2\frac{1}{2}; 6\frac{1}{2})$ $M(7\frac{1}{2}; 2\frac{1}{2}; 6\frac{1}{2})$.

7M-7. $A(125)$ $B(635)$ is the center line of a $\frac{3}{4}''$ diameter rod. $C(0; X; 5\frac{1}{2})$ and $D(6X7)$ are points in a vertical wall. A $1\frac{1}{2}''$ diameter sphere rolls along the rod and remains tangent to the wall. Find the horizontal distance from A to the center of the sphere where it will drop through. Also, find the distance to the highest point the sphere reaches. Hint: Use loci for the center of the sphere and find the path of its center.

7M-8. Find the intersection of the $2''$ diameter cylinder having the axis $A(3; 2\frac{3}{4}; 7)$ $B(7; 1\frac{1}{4}; 7)$ and the tetrahedron $J(3\frac{1}{2}; 4; 7\frac{1}{2})$ $K(737)$ $L(508)$ $M(525)$.

7M-9. $P(3; 1\frac{1}{4}; 5\frac{1}{4})$ $Q(6; 1\frac{1}{4}; 6\frac{3}{4})$ is the axis of a $2\frac{1}{2}''$ diameter cylinder. $R(5; 1\frac{1}{2}; 3\frac{3}{4})$ $S(5; 1\frac{1}{2}; 7)$ is the axis of a right square base prism. One $2''$ diagonal of each base is vertical. Draw the portion of the prism which is outside the cylinder.

PROBLEMS FOR CHAPTER VIII

WARPED SURFACES

Group 8A.   Hyperbolic Paraboloid.

8A-1. Fig. 277-1. $A(3; 3\frac{1}{2}; 4\frac{1}{2})$ $B(4; \frac{1}{2}; 6\frac{1}{2})$ and $C(5; \frac{1}{2}; 6\frac{1}{2})$ $D(7; 1\frac{1}{2}; 4\frac{1}{2})$ are the directrices of a hyperbolic paraboloid. Draw AC and BD and seven other equally spaced elements of one generation on both sides of the surface considered to be made of thin opaque material. Draw the hidden portions of the elements. Measure the strike and dip of the director plane.

8A-2. $R(4\frac{1}{2}; 3; 4)$ $S(4\frac{1}{2}; 1; 6\frac{1}{2})$ and $T(6; 3\frac{1}{2}; 4\frac{1}{2})$ $U(817)$ are the directrices of a hyperbolic paraboloid. Draw RU and ST and eight other equally spaced elements of one generation of the surface. Consider the elements to be drawn on both sides of a thin opaque surface and show the hidden portions. Draw a view showing an edge view of the plane director.

8A-3. Fig. 277-2. $J(135)$ $K(237)$ and $L(517)$ $M(1\frac{1}{2}; 1; 4\frac{1}{2})$ are the directrices of a hyperbolic paraboloid which is a surface of the wing wall of a dam. JM and KL are two elements of the surface. Draw these and six other equally spaced elements of the surface in the front, top, and right-side views. Show a section of the surface made by a profile plane through K.

8A-4. $A(135)$ $B(437)$ and $C(217)$ $D(415)$ are the directrices of a hyperbolic paraboloid which has a frontal plane director. Draw 13 equally spaced elements of one generation. Draw three principal views, and an auxiliary elevation 15° in front of the right.

8A-5. $J(515)$ $K(437)$ and $L(614)$ $M(837)$ are the directrices of a hyperbolic paraboloid. JM and LK are two elements of the surface. Draw JM and LK and seven other equally spaced elements on both sides of the thin opaque surface. Draw the hidden portions of the elements. Draw a view of the surface showing an edge view of the plane director.

8A-6. $A(\frac{1}{2}; 3\frac{1}{2}; 5)$ $B(3; 4; 4\frac{1}{2})$ and $C(126)$ $D(417)$ are the directrices of a hyperbolic paraboloid. Draw AD and BC and nine other equally spaced elements of one generation of the surface. Consider the elements to be drawn on both sides of a thin opaque surface and draw the hidden portions. Find the strike and dip of the plane director.

Group 8B. Cylindroid.

8B-1. Fig. 277-3. The upper one-half of the 4″ diameter circle with center $S(514)$ and the upper one-half of the vertical ellipse with center $R(2\frac{3}{4}; 1\frac{3}{4}; 6\frac{1}{4})$ are the directrices of a cylindroid. The major axis of the ellipse is horizontal and perpendicular to RS. The front view of the ellipse is a 2″ diameter circle. The plane director is the vertical plane containing RS. Draw 13 elements on the top side of the surface. Space the elements evenly around the semicircle at R in the front view.

8B-2. Fig. 277-4. $A(6; 3; 5\frac{3}{4})$ and $B(525)$ are the centers of the circular ends of a concrete connection between two ducts, built in the form of a cylindroid. The circle at A is horizontal and of 30″ diameter. The circle at B is of 21″ diameter and lies in the ortho-frontal plane through $BK(43X)$. Draw 16 equally spaced elements on the outside of the cylindroid having an ortho-frontal plane director. Scale: $1″ = 1′-0″$.

8B-3. $K(617)$ is the center of a 12′ diameter frontal circle and $J(415)$ is the center of a 12′ diameter vertical circle perpendicular to JK. The upper halves of the circles are the directrices of a cylindroid which forms the soffit of an archway. The plane director is horizontal. Draw 13 evenly spaced elements on the outside of the surface. Scale: $\frac{1}{4}″ = 1′-0″$.

8B-4. $A(437)$ is the center of a $2\frac{1}{2}''$ diameter profile circle and $B(616)$ is the center of a $2\frac{1}{2}''$ diameter horizontal circle. The front one-halves of these circles are the directrices of a cylindroid whose plane director is ortho-frontal and contains AB. Show 13 evenly spaced elements on the outside of the thin opaque surface.

8B-5. $A(2\frac{1}{2}; 2; 4\frac{1}{4})$ $B(4; 1\frac{3}{8}; 5\frac{3}{4})$ is the center line for a cylindroid connecting a $3''$ diameter frontal circle at A with a $2\frac{3}{16}''$ diameter circle at B lying in the vertical plane through B and C (5X4). Draw 24 elements equally spaced around the frontal circle, and consider them to be on the outside of thin opaque material.

Group 8C. Right Conoid.

8C-1. The circular arc $A(\frac{1}{2}; 2; 4)$ $B(3\frac{1}{2}; 2; 4)$ $C(234)$ is the front end of a reinforced concrete conoidal roof. $D(\frac{1}{2}; 2; 7)$ $E(3\frac{1}{2}; 2; 7)$ is the rear of the roof at the wall plate. Show elements $2'$ apart on the outside of the surface. Also show two frontal sections of the roof made by planes $8'$ and $16'$ respectively from the front. Scale: $\frac{1}{8}'' = 1'\text{-}0''$.

8C-2. Fig. 277-5. The rectangle $A(1; 3\frac{1}{2}; 5)$ $B(1; 3\frac{1}{2}; 7)$ $C(5; 2\frac{1}{2}; 7)$ $D(5; 2\frac{1}{2}; 5)$ and the $2''$ diameter horizontal circle whose center is $K(316)$ are the ends of a conoidal transition piece. Draw eight elements on the outside of each conoid. Space them evenly around the circle and show them in three principal views.

8C-3. $R(3\frac{1}{2}; 2\frac{1}{2}; 6)$ $S(506)$ and the $3\frac{1}{2}''$ diameter horizontal circle with center $M(206)$ are the directrices of a right conoid. Draw 24 elements on the outside of the surface, equally spaced around the circle. Draw sections of the conoid made by a horizontal plane $\frac{1}{2}''$ above M and by an ortho-frontal plane through $A(21X)S$.

8C-4. $J(6; 2\frac{1}{4}; 7\frac{1}{2})$ $K(6; 2\frac{1}{4}; 4\frac{1}{2})$ and the $3''$ diameter horizontal circle whose center is $C(606)$ are the directrices of a right conoid. Draw 24 elements on the outside of the surface. Space them evenly around the circle. Draw an auxiliary elevation $50°$ in front of the left. Show a horizontal section of the surface $1''$ above C.

8C-5. $J(334)$ $K(504)$ and the $3\frac{1}{2}''$ diameter horizontal circle whose center is $C(206)$ are the directrices of a right conoid. Show 24 elements on the outside of the surface evenly spaced around the circle. Also, show the intersection of the surface with an ortho-frontal plane through $A(1\frac{1}{2}; 1; X)$.

Group 8D. Oblique Conoid.

8D-1. The $2''$ diameter frontal circle with center $M(5; 2\frac{1}{2}; 5\frac{1}{2})$ and the rectangle $A(547)$ $B(747)$ $C(717)$ $D(517)$ are the ends of a conoidal transition piece. AB and the upper half of the circle are the directrices for the conoid, and CD and the lower half of the circle are directrices for the other. Show 12 elements on the outside of each conoid. Space them evenly around the circle.

8D-2. $A(4; 3\frac{1}{2}; 7)$ $B(5\frac{1}{2}; 2; 5\frac{1}{2})$ and the $3''$ diameter horizontal circle with center $O(3; 1; 5\frac{1}{2})$ are the directrices of an oblique conoid having an ortho-frontal plane director. Draw 24 elements on the outside of the surface. Space them evenly around the circle.

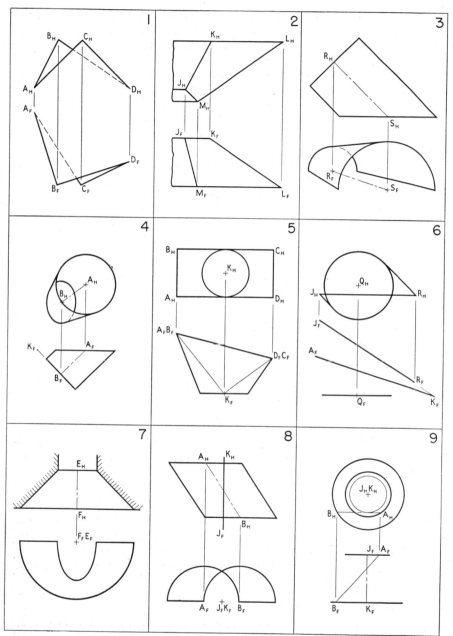

Fig. 277.—Warped Surfaces. Problems in Groups 8A through 8I.

8D-3. Fig. 277-6. $J(1; 4; 5\frac{1}{2})$ $R(6; 1; 5\frac{1}{2})$ and the $3\frac{1}{2}''$ diameter horizontal circle with center $Q(306)$ are the directrices for an oblique conoid. The plane director is vertical and inclined forward 45° to the right. Draw 24 elements, equally spaced around the circle, on the outside of the surface. Draw the section of the surface made by an ortho-frontal plane through $K(7\frac{1}{2}; 0; X)$ $A(12X)$.

8D-4. $A(614)$ $B(2\frac{1}{2}; 3; 4)$ and the $3\frac{1}{2}''$ diameter horizontal circle with center $C(216)$ are the directrices of an oblique conoid. The plane director is ortho-frontal and inclined 30° downward to the left. Draw 24 elements, evenly spaced around the circle, on the outside of the surface. Draw a section made by an ortho-frontal plane through $A(614)$ $P(1\frac{1}{2}; 2; X)$.

8D-5. $R(7\frac{1}{4}; 3\frac{1}{2}; 4)$ $S(2\frac{1}{2}; 3\frac{1}{2}; 4)$ and the $3''$ diameter horizontal circle with center $M(3; \frac{1}{2}; 6)$ are the directrices of an oblique conoid. The plane director is vertical and inclined forward 45° to the right. Draw 24 elements, evenly spaced around the circle, on the outside of the surface. Show a section made by a horizontal plane $1\frac{1}{2}''$ above M.

Group 8E.　Right Helicoid.

8E-1. $P(446)$ $Q(406)$ is the axis of a $\frac{1}{2}''$ diameter opaque cylinder. $C(4; 4; 6\frac{1}{4})$ $D(4; 4; 7\frac{3}{4})$ is one element of a left-hand helicoid of $2''$ lead wound on the cylinder. Show $16''$ equally spaced elements per turn on the upper side of the surface.

8E-2. $J(3; 1\frac{1}{4}; 3\frac{1}{2})$ $K(3; 1\frac{1}{4}; 7\frac{1}{2})$ is the axis of a $1''$ diameter shaft. $A(3; 2\frac{1}{2}; 4)$ $B(3; 1\frac{3}{4}; 4)$ is an element of a right helicoid of $2''$ lead welded to the shaft for a screw conveyor. Draw $1\frac{1}{2}$ turns of the helicoid, showing 16 elements per turn on the front side of the surface.

8E-3. $R(4; 3\frac{3}{4}; 6)$ $S(406)$ is the axis of a $3\frac{1}{2}''$ diameter steel spring made of $\frac{3}{4}''$ square material wound in the form of a right-hand helix of $1\frac{1}{2}''$ lead. The top and bottom are ground off horizontal through R and S. $A(4; 3\frac{3}{4}; 4\frac{1}{4})$ $B(4; 3\frac{3}{4}; 5)$ is an element of the lower helicoidal surface of the spring and $C(4; 3\frac{3}{4}; 7)$ $D(4; 3\frac{3}{4}; 7\frac{3}{4})$ is an element of the upper surface. Draw the spring, omitting the hidden lines.

8E-4. $A(446)$ $B(406)$ is the axis of a $1\frac{1}{2}''$ diameter shaft. $C(4\frac{3}{4}; \frac{1}{2}; 6)$ $D(5\frac{3}{4}; \frac{1}{2}; 6)$ is an element of the lower helicoidal surface of a screw conveyor made of material $\frac{1}{8}''$ thick welded to the shaft. The helical directrices have a lead of $3''$ and are right-hand. Draw one turn of the conveyor screw.

8E-5. $K(4; \frac{1}{2}; 4)$ is a point on the floor at the center of a semicircular concrete stairway whose outside radius is 14′. There are 25 risers of $6''$ height and the first one begins at $A(6; \frac{1}{2}; 4)$ $B(7\frac{1}{2}; \frac{1}{2}; 4)$. The stairway ascends counterclockwise. The thickness of concrete measured directly below the rear of each tread is $6''$. The lower surface is a right helicoid. Draw the stairway, omitting hidden lines. Scale: $\frac{1}{4}'' = 1'\text{-}0''$.

Group 8F.　Oblique Helicoid.

8F-1. The left-hand helix with a lead of $2''$ generated by point $A(5\frac{1}{2}; 3; 6)$, and its axis $J(4; 4\frac{1}{4}; 6)$ $K(416)$, are the directrices of an oblique helicoid. Beginning with element $R(446)$ A, draw 16 elements on the upper side of one turn of the helicoid.

8F-2. $C(424)$ $D(4; 2\frac{3}{4}; 4\frac{1}{2})$ is the foremost element of a right-hand oblique helicoid of 2″ lead. Draw $1\frac{1}{2}$ turns of the surface wound on the 1″ diameter cylinder having the axis $A(4; 1\frac{1}{2}; 3\frac{1}{2})$ $B(4; 1\frac{1}{2}; 8)$. Show 16 elements per turn on the front side of the surface.

8F-3. A left-hand oblique helicoid of 2″ lead is wound on the 1″ diameter cylinder which has the axis $M(4; 4\frac{3}{4}; 6\frac{1}{2})$ $N(4; \frac{1}{2}; 6\frac{1}{2})$. Beginning with the element $C(4; 4\frac{3}{8}; 8)$ $D(4; 3\frac{3}{4}; 7)$ draw $1\frac{1}{2}$ turns of the helicoid. Show 16 elements per turn on the lower side of the surface.

8F-4. $A(448)$ $B(408)$ is the axis of a 6″ diameter shaft. $K(7; 2\frac{1}{2}; 8)$ is a point on the crest of a 60° V-thread cut on the shaft. It is a right-hand single thread of 2″ lead and with a minor diameter of 4″. Draw the front view of one turn of the thread beginning directly behind AB, and one-half of the top view. Show 24 elements per turn on each of the oblique helicoids.

8F-5. $A(436)$ $B(406)$ is the axis of a 60° sharp V-type double right-hand screw thread cut on 4″ diameter material. The lead is 2″. The helix of one crest begins at $C(434)$. Show the threads between the horizontal planes through A and B. Draw on the helicoids the visible elements spaced 16 per turn. In the top view show a section taken midway between A and B.

Group 8G. Warped Cone.

8G-1. Draw 16 evenly spaced elements on the outside of the warped cone which has for its directrices the 3″ diameter frontal circle with center $B(5; 2\frac{1}{2}; 7)$, the 1″ diameter circle with center $A(3; 2\frac{1}{2}; 5)$ perpendicular to AB, and the line AB.

8G-2. The directrices for a warped cone are the left half of the $2\frac{1}{2}$″ diameter horizontal circle with center $C(216)$, the upper half of the $3\frac{1}{2}$″ diameter ortho-frontal circle with center $D(3\frac{1}{2}; 2; 6)$ perpendicular to CD, and the line CD. Draw 13 equally spaced elements on the outside of the surface.

8G-3. Fig. 277-7. The discharge end of a flume has its lower surface designed as a portion of a warped cone. The directrices are the 6′ radius frontal semicircle with center $F(445)$, the line $E(447)$ F, and the frontal semiellipse with center E. The axes of the ellipse are 4′ and 8′ respectively, and the major axis is vertical. Show 13 equally spaced elements on the inside of the surface. Scale: $\frac{1}{2}$″ = 1′-0″.

8G-4. $A(1\frac{1}{2}; 2\frac{1}{2}; 6\frac{1}{2})$ is the center of a 36″ diameter circle which lies in the ortho-frontal plane passing through A and $C(3; 1; 6\frac{1}{2})$. $B(1\frac{1}{2}; 1; 6\frac{1}{2})$ is the center of a 15″ diameter horizontal circle which is the upper end of a vertical pipe. Connect the two circles by means of a warped cone having 16 elements equally spaced around the larger circle. Draw the front, top, and right-side views of the warped cone considered to be opaque with elements on both sides. In the side view run the elements to an intersection with the center line. Scale: 1″ = 1′-0″.

8G-5. The directrices for a warped cone are the line $S(526)$ $R(5; 2; 7\frac{1}{2})$, the $1\frac{3}{4}$″ diameter circle, center S, in the vertical plane through $SK(7\frac{1}{4}; 2; 4\frac{1}{2})$, and the

$3''$ diameter frontal circle whose center is R. Draw 16 equally spaced elements on the outside of the surface.

Group 8H.   Cow's Horn.

8H-1. The frontal semicircles with $8'$ radii and with centers $A(417)$ and $B(514)$ are the ends of a masonry arch for a bridge. Design the soffit (under surface) of the arch as a cow's horn, showing 13 equally spaced elements on the upper side of the surface. The directrices are the semicircles and the line $J(4\frac{1}{2}; 1; 3\frac{1}{2})$ $K(4\frac{1}{2}; 1; 7\frac{1}{4})$. Show a section of the surface made by a frontal plane midway between A and B. Scale: $\frac{3}{16}'' = 1'\text{-}0''$.

8H-2. The $2\frac{1}{2}''$ diameter horizontal circle whose center is $C(3\frac{1}{2}; 3; 6)$, the $3''$ diameter circle whose center is $D(5; 1\frac{1}{2}; 6)$, and the line $E(4\frac{1}{4}; 3\frac{1}{2}; 6)$ $F(4\frac{1}{4}; 1; 6)$ are the directrices of a cow's horn. Draw 24 equally spaced elements on the outside of the surface.

8H-3. The frontal semicircles with centers at $E(217)$ and $F(415)$ each with a radius of $1\frac{1}{4}''$, and the line $R(314)$ $S(3; 1; 7\frac{1}{2})$, are the directrices of a cow's horn. Draw 13 equally spaced elements on the outside of the surface.

8H-4. Fig. 277-8. The directrices for the soffit of a masonry bridge, which is designed as a cow's horn, are $J(2\frac{3}{4}; 0; 4\frac{1}{4})$ $K(2\frac{3}{4}; 0; 7\frac{1}{4})$ and the two frontal semicircles of $12'$ radii and with centers at $A(207)$ and $B(3\frac{1}{2}; 0; 4\frac{3}{4})$. Draw 13 equally spaced elements on the outside of the surface in the front and top views. Draw a view parallel to BA and show the elements on the inside of the surface. Scale: $\frac{1}{8}'' = 1'\text{-}0''$.

Group 8I.   Hyperboloid of Revolution.

8I-1. $K(436)$ $L(406)$ is the axis of a skew gear. $A(2\frac{1}{2}; 0; 5)$ $B(4; 2\frac{1}{2}; 5)$ is the center line of one of its teeth at the pitch surface. Draw the outline curves for the pitch surface.

8I-2. Fig. 277-9. Draw 24 evenly spaced elements of the hyperboloid of revolution generated by revolving the line $A(4\frac{1}{2}; 3; 4\frac{3}{4})$ $B(2\frac{3}{4}; 1; 4\frac{3}{4})$ about the axis $J(4; 3; 5\frac{1}{2})$ $K(4; 1; 5\frac{1}{2})$. Consider the elements to be drawn on both sides of the thin opaque surface.

8I-3. Draw $J(236)$ $K(4\frac{1}{2}; 0; 4\frac{1}{2})$ and 23 other evenly spaced elements of the hyperboloid of revolution generated by revolving JK about the axis $L(436)$ $M(406)$. Draw the elements on both sides of the surface and show the hidden portions. Draw the section made by an ortho-frontal plane through $E(21X)$ $F(73X)$.

8I-4. $J(346)$ $K(306)$ is the axis of a $6''$ diameter turned column which has an enlarged portion to which the square end of a railing will fit perfectly at $A(1\frac{1}{2}; 2; 4\frac{1}{2})$ $B(3; 3\frac{1}{2}; 4\frac{1}{2})$ $C(4\frac{1}{2}; 2; 4\frac{1}{2})$ $D(3; \frac{1}{2}; 4\frac{1}{2})$. Draw the outline curves of the enlarged portion and identify them. Scale: $6'' = 1'\text{-}0''$.

8I-5. $A(4; 3\frac{1}{2}; 6)$ $B(406)$ is the axis of a hyperboloid of revolution. The horizontal circular ends at A and B are $2\frac{1}{2}''$ and $4''$ respectively, in diameter. The circle of the gorge has a diameter of $2''$. Draw 24 elements of one generation on both sides of the surface.

8I-6. The 3″ diameter frontal circles whose centers are $D(425)$ and $F(428)$ and the 2″ diameter frontal circle with center $E(4; 2; 6\frac{1}{2})$ are the directrices of a hyperboloid of revolution. Draw 16 elements of each of two generations of the surface. Draw the elements on both sides of the surface.

PROBLEMS FOR CHAPTER IX

GEOLOGY AND MINING PROBLEMS

Group 9A. Strike, Dip, and Thickness of a Vein. Shafts and Tunnels.

In every case the "top" of the paper is to be taken as north, and the strike is to be lettered in the top view as a bearing. The dip is to be measured and marked in an auxiliary elevation, and indicated in the top view by an arrow showing its direction and value. Required shafts, tunnels, and crosscuts are to be shown in the front and top views.

9A-1. Two apparent dips of a stratum of rock at $A(4X5)$ are 35° S 70° W and 40° S 55° E. Find the strike and true dip of the stratum.

9A-2. $B(4X3)$ is a point of outcrop in the upper bedding plane of a vein of copper ore. Two apparent dips at B are found to be 25° S 30° E and 19° N 60° W. Find the strike and true dip of the vein.

9A-3. At $C(4X4)$ two apparent dips of a seam of coal are 35° N 22° W and 46° N 38° E. Find the strike and true dip of the seam.

9A-4. $Q(127)$, $R(336)$, and $S(2; \frac{1}{2}; 5)$ are three points in the hanging wall of a vein of low grade ore. A point T 50′ directly below Q is in the foot wall. Find the strike, dip, and thickness of the vein. Find the shortest incline from $A(\frac{1}{2}; 2\frac{1}{2}; 5\frac{1}{2})$ to the vein. Also, find the shortest tunnel on a $12\frac{1}{2}\%$ upgrade from $C(3\frac{1}{2}; \frac{1}{2}; 7)$ to the vein. Show these workings in all views drawn. Scale: $1″ = 80$ ft.

9A-5. $R(537)$ is a point in the outcrop of the hanging wall of a vein of low grade copper ore. $Q(415)$ and $S(606)$ are points where drill holes reach the ore. The drill hole at Q reaches the foot wall 25′ directly below Q. Find the thickness of the vein, the bearing of its strike and the dip angle. Measure and show the following in all views drawn: the shortest incline from $A(726)$, the shortest connection on a 15% upgrade from $C(3\frac{1}{2}; 1\frac{1}{2}; 7\frac{1}{2})$, and a vertical shaft from $E(5\frac{1}{2}; 2\frac{1}{2}; 6)$. Scale: $1″ = 80$ ft.

9A-6. $R(526)$, $S(7; 3; 5\frac{1}{2})$, and $T(617)$ are points in the hanging wall of a vein of ore. Find the strike and dip of the vein. A vertical shaft at $A(5\frac{1}{2}; 3; 6\frac{1}{2})$ is in the ore for a distance of 40′. Find the depth of the shaft and the thickness of the vein. Find the length of the shortest level tunnel from $B(5; 2\frac{1}{2}; 7\frac{1}{2})$ to the ore. Scale: $1″ = 80$ ft. Draw the shaft and tunnel in front and top views.

9A-7. $A(\frac{1}{2}; 3; 6)$, $B(1\frac{1}{2}; 1; 7)$, and $C(226)$ are points in the hanging wall of a vein of iron ore. $D(2; \frac{3}{4}; 6)$ is a point in the foot wall, and $S(3\frac{1}{2}; 2; 6\frac{1}{2})$ is on the surface of the ground. Find strike, dip, and thickness of the vein. Draw and measure the shortest tunnel from S on a 10% upgrade to the vein. Scale: $1″ = 80$ ft.

9A-8. $A(\frac{1}{2}; X; 6)$ and $B(2X4)$ are points in the upper bedding plane of a vein of uranium ore where it outcrops in a vertical cliff. The vein appears to be 15' thick where it outcrops in the cliff. It strikes S 66° E and dips 50° southwesterly. Find the true thickness of the vein. Scale: $1'' = 40$ ft.

Group 9B.　Shortest Crosscut on a Given Grade.

The scale for each problem in this group is $1'' = 40$ ft.

9B-1. Fig. 278-1. $A(1; 4; 7\frac{1}{2})$ $B(328)$ and $C(\frac{1}{2}; 2; 7\frac{1}{2})$ $D(3\frac{1}{2}; 3\frac{1}{2}; 5)$ represent two workings in a mine. What extension is necessary to sink a vertical shaft EF from AB to CD? Show and measure EF. Show in the principal views and measure the following connections: the shortest level line LM, the shortest possible line PQ, the shortest line on a 25% downgrade RT, and the shortest line on a 25% upgrade US.

9B-2. Fig. 278-2. $A(115)$ $B(3; \frac{1}{2}; 6)$ and $C(1\frac{1}{2}; 2\frac{1}{2}; 6)$ $D(4; \frac{1}{2}; 4)$ represent two workings in a mine. Measure and show in all views drawn the shortest crosscut on a 20% upgrade from AB to CD.

9B-3. Fig. 278-3. $A(1; 3\frac{1}{2}; 5)$ $B(127)$ and $C(\frac{1}{2}; 4\frac{1}{4}; 6)$ $D(237)$ represent two workings in a mine. Measure and show in all views drawn the shortest connection on a 20% downgrade from CD to AB, a vertical shaft, and the shortest possible connection.

9B-4. Fig. 278-4. $A(126)$ $B(315)$ and $C(2; 2\frac{1}{2}; 5)$ $D(4; 1\frac{1}{2}; 6\frac{1}{2})$ represent two mine workings. Draw in all views needed and measure the shortest possible connection and the shortest connection on a 10% upgrade from AB to CD.

9B-5. Fig. 278-5. $A(\frac{1}{2}; 2; 5\frac{1}{2})$ $B(3; 3\frac{1}{2}; 7)$ and $C(127)$ $D(3\frac{1}{2}; 2; 6)$ represent two mine workings. Show in all views drawn and measure the shortest possible crosscut that will connect them, and the shortest crosscut on a 25% downgrade from AB to CD.

9B-6. Fig. 278-6. $C(425)$ $D(6\frac{1}{2}; 3; 7)$ represents a mine working and $E(745)$ $F(725)$ a mine shaft. Show in all views drawn and measure the shortest connection on a 20% downgrade from CD to EF, and the shortest level line from CD to EF. Give another name for this level line.

9B-7. $J(\frac{1}{2}; 3; 5)$ $K(3\frac{1}{2}; 1\frac{1}{2}; 3\frac{1}{2})$ and $L(\frac{1}{2}; 1; 4)$ $M(3\frac{1}{2}; 2; 6)$ represent two workings in a mine. Measure and show in all views drawn the shortest connection on a 30% upgrade from LM to JK.

9B-8. $C(5; 1\frac{1}{2}; 5)$ $D(826)$ and $E(5; \frac{1}{2}; 4\frac{1}{2})$ $F(7; 1\frac{1}{2}; 3\frac{1}{2})$ are the center lines of two workings in a mine. Draw and measure the length and bearing of the shortest crosscut on a $12\frac{1}{2}\%$ upgrade from EF to CD. Also find the distances from C and F to the crosscut in order to begin driving it from both ends.

Group 9C.　Intersections of Veins and Fault Planes.

9C-1. Fig. 278-7. $A(225)$ $B(3\frac{1}{2}; 2; 6)$ is the strike of a vein of copper ore that dips 50° northwesterly. $J(436)$ $K(6; 3; 5\frac{1}{2})$ is the strike of a fault plane that dips 60° northeasterly. Find the intersection of the vein and fault. If a drift is started

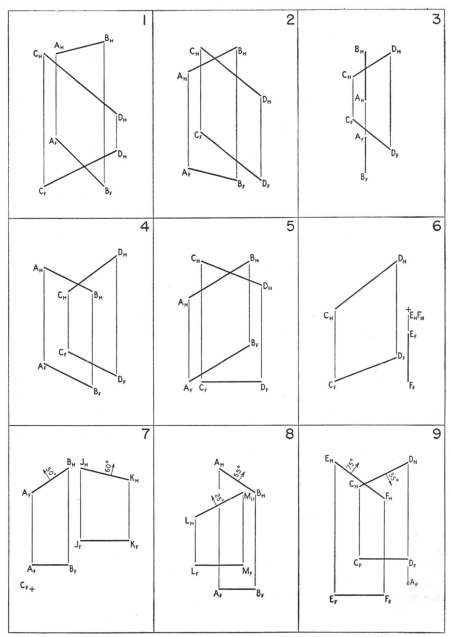

Fig. 278.—Mining Problems.   Groups 9B and 9C.

at $C(21X)$ in the vein, how far may it follow the vein before striking the fault. Scale: $1'' = 40$ ft.

9C-2. Fig. 278-8. $A(416)$ $B(5\frac{1}{2}; 1; 5)$ is the strike of a thin vein of gold ore which dips 55° northeasterly. $L(324)$ $M(525)$ is the strike of a fault plane which dips 25° northwesterly.   Find the line of intersection of the fault and the ore.

9C-3. Fig. 278-9. $C(5; 2\frac{1}{2}; 5\frac{1}{2})$ $D(7; 2\frac{1}{2}; 6\frac{1}{2})$ is the strike along the center line of a drift in a vein of silver ore which dips 55° southeasterly. $E(4; 1; 6\frac{1}{2})$ $F(615)$ is the strike of a fault plane which dips 75° northeasterly.   Find the line of intersection of the fault and vein.   Starting at $A(7; 1\frac{1}{2}; X)$ in the ore, how far could a level drift follow the ore before reaching the fault?   Scale: $1'' = 40$ ft.

9C-4. $B(236)$ is a point in a fault plane that strikes N 75° E and dips 60° southeasterly. $S(6; 2; 5\frac{1}{2})$ is a point in a vein of ore that strikes N 60° W and dips 50° northeasterly.   Find the intersection of the ore and the fault.

9C-5. $A(225)$ is a point in a thin vein of ore that strikes N 45° E and dips 40° southeasterly. $B(314)$ is in a thin vein that strikes N 75° E and dips 60° southeasterly. $C(4\frac{1}{2}; 2; 6)$ is in a third vein that strikes S 30° E and dips 50° southwesterly.   Find the three intersections and the point K in which the veins intersect.   Enriched ore may be found at the intersections.

Group 9D.   Location of Outcrop.   Profiles.

For these problems draw a $4\frac{1}{2}'' \times 4''$ rectangle with corners A and e located according to the given coordinates.   Place this rectangle over the required map and trace the contours and other necessary data.   Replace the sheet on the drawing board.

In Groups 9D, 9E, and 9F the coordinates for corners A and e have an "X" between the first and last numbers.   The "X" clearly separates the fractional coordinates without the use of semicolons.

The scale of $1'' = 80$ ft. was selected for these problems to enable students to use the architect's or mechanical engineer's scale.

9D-1. Trace the map of Fig. 279 at $A(2\frac{1}{2}X4)e(7X8)$. Q and R are points found on the outcrop of the hanging wall of a vein of ore.   A vertical shaft sunk at S reaches the ore at a depth of 80' and passes through at 95'.   Find the strike, dip, thickness, and the probable outcrop of the vein.

9D-2. Trace the map of Fig. 281 at $A(1\frac{1}{2}X3)e(6X7)$.   In one drawing show the profiles taken at the frontal planes through AE, Ff, Gg, Hh, and ae.

9D-3. Trace the map of Fig. 279 at $A(2\frac{1}{2}X3)e(7X7)$.   The outcrop of the upper bedding plane of a seam of coal is found at K.   The seam strikes S 15° W, dips 20° northwesterly, and has a thickness of 15'.   Find the probable outcrop of the seam, and the depth of a vertical shaft to the coal at F.   Also show a profile taken at a vertical plane normal to the seam at K.

9D-4. Trace the map of Fig. 279 at $A(2\frac{1}{2}X4)e(7X7)$. Q and S are points found on the outcrop of the hanging wall of a vein of low grade ore.   A vertical shaft sunk at R reaches the ore at a depth of 90' and passes through at 105'.   Find the

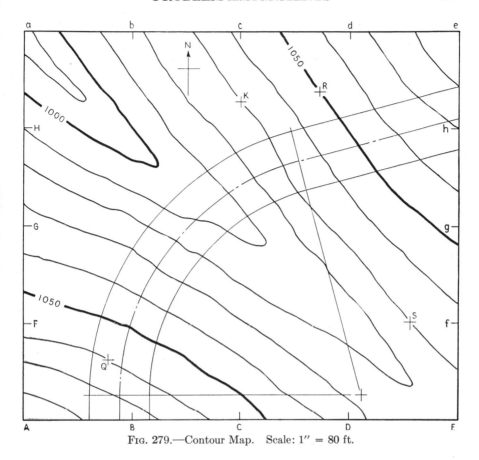

FIG. 279.—Contour Map. Scale: 1″ = 80 ft.

strike, dip, thickness, and probable outcrop of the vein. Also draw a profile taken through R and normal to the strike.

9D-5. Trace the map of Fig. 280 at $A(2\frac{1}{2}X3)e(7X7)$. The level line Bd at elevation 550 passes through a point M in the outcrop of the hanging wall of a vein of ore that dips 30° southeasterly and is 10′ thick. Find the probable outcrop of the vein. Also draw a profile through M taken normal to Bd.

9D-6. Trace the map of Fig. 280 at $A(2\frac{1}{2}X3)e(7X7)$. The point e at elevation 480 is on the hanging wall of a vein of low grade ore. The vein strikes S 75° W, dips 50° northwesterly, and is 45′ thick. Find the probable outcrop of the vein.

9D-7. Trace the map of Fig. 281 at $A(\frac{1}{2}X3)e(5X7)$. The points Q and S are found on the outcrop of the hanging wall of a vein of ore. A vertical shaft at R reaches the ore at a depth of 60′ and passes through at 77. Find and measure the strike, dip, and thickness of the vein. Find the probable outcrop. Interpolate contours where necessary. Show and measure a vertical shaft at g and the shortest tunnel on a 5% upgrade from A (Elev. 2020).

9D-8. Trace the map of Fig. 281 at $A(\frac{1}{2}\text{X}3)e(5\text{X}7)$. The outcrop of the hanging wall of a vein of copper ore is found at points Q and R. A vertical shaft at S reaches the ore at a depth of 120′ and passes through at 138. Find and measure the strike, dip and thickness of the vein. Find the probable outcrop of the vein. Also show and measure a vertical shaft and the shortest tunnel on a 5% upgrade from B to the vein.

9D-9. Trace the map of Fig. 281 at $A(3\text{X}3)e(7\frac{1}{2}\text{X}7)$. A point in the upper bedding plane of a tilted bed of fire clay is found at h. The bed is 10′ thick, strikes S 75° W, and dips 35° southeasterly. Find its probable outcrop. Find and measure a vertical shaft and the shortest tunnel on a 5% upgrade from C to the bed. Show a profile taken at a vertical plane along the tunnel.

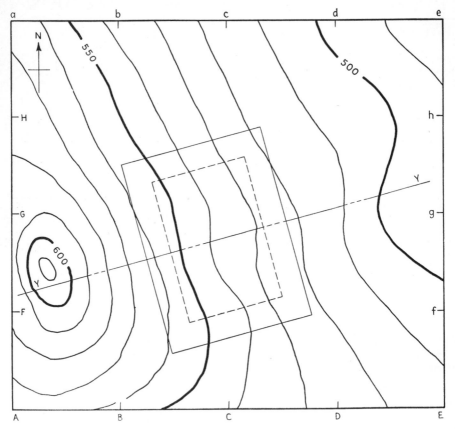

Fig. 280.—Contour Map.   Scale: 1″ = 80 ft.

9D-10. Trace the map of Fig. 281 at $A(3\text{X}3)e(7\frac{1}{2}\text{X}7)$. The points R and S are on the outcrop of the hanging wall of a vein of ore. A vertical shaft at Q reaches the ore at a depth of 100′ and passes through at 120. Find and measure the strike, dip, and thickness of the vein. Find the probable outcrop. Find and measure the shortest tunnel on a 5% upgrade from C to a point K in the footwall. Make a profile of the mountain taken along CK.

Group 9E. Cuts, Fills, and Mine Dumps.

9E-1. Trace the map of Fig. 279 at $A(2\frac{1}{2}\text{X}3)e(7\text{X}7)$. The center line for an earthen dam is Be. The top of the dam is 30′ wide and is at elevation 1050. Find the lines at the foot of the fill using a slope of 3 to 1 for both sides.

9E-2. Locate $V(3\frac{1}{2}; 2\frac{1}{2}; 4\frac{1}{2})$ and trace the map of Fig. 281 at $A(1\frac{1}{2}\text{X}3)e(6\text{X}7)$. The elevation of V is 2080. If loose material having an angle of repose of 35° is

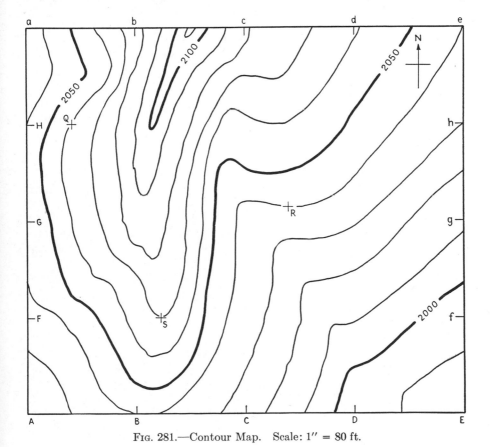

FIG. 281.—Contour Map. Scale: 1″ = 80 ft.

dumped at V, find the line of the toe of the dump. If the dump is made so that it has a level top 60′ in diameter, center V, find the outline of this dump.

9E-3. Trace the map of Fig. 280 at $A(1\frac{1}{2}X3)e(6X7)$. Let the elevation of the smaller rectangle be 590. From a mine to the west of the map, waste material having an angle of repose of 40° is dumped over this area so as finally to finish with this given level rectangle. Make a profile at Y–Y. Find the line of fill for the dump.

9E-4. Trace the map of Fig. 280 at $A(1\frac{1}{2}X3)e(6X7)$. Let the smaller rectangle with an elevation of 470 be the bottom of a reservoir. The material will stand on a slope of $\frac{1}{2}$ to 1 until the reservoir can be lined with concrete. Make a profile at Y–Y. Find the line of cut for the excavation.

9E-5. Trace the map of Fig. 280 at $A(1\frac{1}{2}X3)e(6X7)$. The larger rectangle represents a level area to be made at elevation 540. Draw a profile taken at Y–Y. Find the lines of cut and fill using slopes of 1 to 1 for cut and 2 to 1 for fill.

9E-6. Trace the map of Fig. 280 at $A(2X3)e(6\frac{1}{2}X7)$. The center of the map is the center of a 100′ by 150′ level rectangle whose elevation is 530. The long sides bear due North. Find the lines of cut and fill using slopes of 1 to 1 for cut and $2\frac{1}{2}$ to 1 for fill.

9E-7. Trace the map of Fig. 280 at $A(1\frac{1}{2}X3)e(6X7)$. A mining company owns the rectangular tract $AaeE$ and desires to determine how much material may be dumped within its boundaries by creating a level top at elevation 580′. Find the irregular outline of the top of the dump if the angle of repose for the material is 40°. Is it possible to reach the corners E and e by dumping at this level without covering adjacent land?

Group 9F.   Cuts and Fills for Level Roads and Roads on a Grade.

9F-1. Trace the map of Fig. 279 at $A(2X3)e(6\frac{1}{2}X7)$. Cd is the center line of a 50′ level road that has an elevation of 1040. Find the lines of cut and fill for the road using slopes of 1 to 1 for cut and 2 to 1 for fill. Draw a section taken midway between C and d. Find the length and grade of a suitable culvert under the fill.

9F-2. Trace the map of Fig. 279 at $A(2X3)e(6\frac{1}{2}X7)$. Bd is the center line of a 50′ level road that is at elevation 1035. Find the lines of cut and fill using slopes of 1 to 1 for cut and 2 to 1 for fill. Find the length and grade of a suitable culvert under the fill.

9F-3. Trace the map of Fig. 279 at $A(2X3)e(6\frac{1}{2}X7)$. A curved level roadbed at elevation 1040 is shown on the map. Find the lines of cut and fill using slopes of 1 to 1 for cut and 2 to 1 for fill.

9F-4. Trace the map of Fig. 280 at $A(2X3)e(6\frac{1}{2}X7)$. The center line of a 50′ level road at an elevation of 520′ is Cd. Show the lines of cut and fill using slopes of 1 to 1 for cut and 2 to 1 for fill. Also show a section taken midway between C and d.

9F-5. Trace the map of Fig. 280 at $A(1\frac{1}{2}X3)e(6X7)$. The center line for a 50′ level road is an arc having center A and radius AD. The elevation of the roadbed is 530. Find the lines of cut and fill using slopes of 1 to 1 for cut and 2 to 1 for fill. Interpolate for extra contours where necessary.

9F-6. Trace the map of Fig. 279 at $A(1X3)e(5\frac{1}{2}X7)$. The center line of a 50′ road is Bd. The elevation at B is 1050 and that at d is 1020. Show a profile of the ground and the road along Bd. Find the lines of cut and fill using a slope of 1 to 1 for cut and 2 to 1 for fill. If B is station 15, show a section of the fill at station $17 + 50$.

9F-7. Trace the map of Fig. 279 at $A(1X2)e(5\frac{1}{2}X6)$. Gg is the center line for a 50′ road that has an elevation of 1020 at G and 1040 at g. Show a profile of the ground taken along Gg. Find the lines of cut and fill for the road using slopes of 1 to 1 for cut and 2 to 1 for fill. Draw a section taken at Bb. Find the length and grade of a suitable culvert under the fill.

9F-8. Trace the map of Fig. 280 at $A(2\frac{1}{2}X3)e(7X7)$. Hf is the center line for a 50′ road that has elevations of 550 at H and 520 at f. Show a profile taken along Hf. Find the lines of cut and fill using slopes of 1 to 1 for cut and 2 to 1 for fill.

PROBLEMS FOR CHAPTER X

ENGINEERING PROBLEMS

Group 10A.   Rafters.

Actual sizes of dressed lumber or timbers are less than nominal sizes. For 1″ dimensions use $\frac{3}{4}''$, for 2″ use $1\frac{5}{8}''$, for 4″ use $3\frac{1}{2}''$, for 6″ use $5\frac{1}{2}''$, and for 8″ use $7\frac{1}{2}''$. For example, draw a 4″ × 6″ timber $3\frac{1}{2}'' \times 5\frac{1}{2}''$.

10A-1. $R(146)$ and $S(148)$ are on the center line of the upper surface of·the 2″ × 4″ ridge of a roof which has a rise of 8″ in a run of 12″. Draw the top, face, edge, and end views of a 2″ × 4″ common rafter for the roof. The roof has an overhang of 6″. The ends of the rafters are cut off vertically through $A(5XX)$. Notch rafters halfway through for wall plate. Measure angles for the cuts. Scale: 3″ = 1′-0″. Use stock sizes.

10A-2. Draw the top, face, edge, and end views of a 2″ × 4″ common rafter for a roof of $\frac{1}{3}$ pitch. The rafter is notched half way through for the wall plate, has an overhang of 6″, and its upper end terminates at $K(1XX)$. The outer edge of the top of the wall plate is at $J(52X)$. Measure angles for the cuts. Scale: 3″ = 1′-0″. Use stock sizes.

10A-3. Draw the top, face, edge, and end views of a 2″ × 6″ common rafter for a roof of $\frac{1}{2}$ pitch. The rafter has a vertical cut on the end 3″ above the wall plate at $A(51X)$. The top of the rafter is at $B(2XX)$. Measure angles for the cuts. Scale: $1\frac{1}{2}'' = 1'-0''$. Use stock sizes.

10A-4. $R(3X7)$ $S(747)$ is the center line of the upper surface of a 2″ × 4″ jack rafter for a roof of $\frac{1}{3}$ pitch. The rafter is notched halfway through for the wall plate and has an overhang of 6″. Draw top, face, edge, and end views of the rafter and measure the angles for the cuts. Scale: 3″ = 1′-0″. Use stock sizes.

10A-5. $J(147)$ $K(5X7)$ is the center line of the upper surface of a 2″ × 4″ jack rafter for a roof of $\frac{1}{4}$ pitch. The end of the rafter is cut off vertically 2″ above the wall plate. Draw top, face, edge, and end views of the rafter and measure the angles for the cuts. Scale: $3'' = 1'\text{-}0''$. Use stock sizes.

10A-6. $C(147)$ $D(5X7)$ is the center line of the upper surface of a $2'' \times 6''$ jack rafter for a roof of $\frac{1}{3}$ pitch. The lower end of the rafter has a vertical cut on the end $3''$ above the wall plate. Draw top, face, edge, and end views of the rafter and measure the angles for the cuts. Scale: $3'' = 1'\text{-}0''$. Use stock sizes.

10A-7. $J(\frac{1}{2}; X; 5)$ $K(3\frac{1}{2}; 1; 8)$ is the hip line of a roof which has a rise of $8''$ in a run of $12''$. K is $3''$ above the wall plate and the rafters are cut off flush with the walls. Draw the front, top, face, and edge views of a $2'' \times 6''$ hip rafter for the roof and measure the angles for the cuts. Scale: $3'' = 1'\text{-}0''$. Use stock sizes.

10A-8. $L(4\frac{1}{2}; 1; 8)$ $M(7\frac{1}{2}; X; 5)$ is the hip line for a roof of $\frac{1}{2}$ pitch. L is $3''$ above the wall plate and the rafters are cut off flush with the walls. Draw the front, top, face, and edge views of a $2'' \times 6''$ hip rafter for the roof and measure the angles for the cuts. Scale: $3'' = 1'\text{-}0''$. Use stock sizes.

10A-9. $A(4\frac{1}{2}; 1; 8)$ $B(7\frac{1}{2}; X; 5)$ is the hip line for a roof of $\frac{1}{3}$ pitch. A is $2''$ above the wall plate and the rafters are cut off flush with the walls. Draw the front, top, face, and edge views of a $2'' \times 4''$ hip rafter for the roof and measure the angles for the cuts. Scale: $3'' = 1'\text{-}0''$. Use stock sizes.

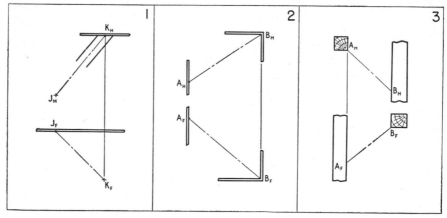

Fig. 282.—Timber Framing. Group 10B.

Group 10B. Timber Framing.

For this group use nominal size timbers (not dressed, dimensions not reduced).

10B-1. Fig. 282-1. $J(1; 3; 5\frac{1}{2})$ $K(318)$ is the center line of a $4'' \times 6''$ brace cut to fit a frontal wall at K and a horizontal ceiling at J. The $6''$ faces are vertical. Draw the front, top, face, and edge views of the brace and measure the angles for the cuts. Scale: $1\frac{1}{2}'' = 1'\text{-}0''$.

10B-2. Fig. 282-2. $A(1; 2\frac{1}{2}; 6)$ $B(408)$ is the center line of a $4'' \times 8''$ brace cut to fit a profile surface at A and the floor and two walls of a room at B. The $8''$

faces are ortho-frontal. Draw front, top, face, and edge views of the brace and measure the angles for the cuts. Scale: $1\frac{1}{2}'' = 1'-0''$.

10B-3. Fig. 282-3. $A(4\frac{1}{2}; 1; 7\frac{1}{2})$ $B(7; 3; 5\frac{1}{4})$ is the axis of a $6'' \times 6''$ timber cut to fit a $6'' \times 6''$ vertical column at A and a $6'' \times 8''$ horizontal-profile timber at B. The $8''$ faces of the timber are horizontal and B is on the lower left-hand edge. Two faces of the column are frontal and A is on the front right-hand edge. Two faces of the connecting piece are vertical. Draw front, top, face, and edge views of the brace and measure the angles for the cuts. Scale: $1\frac{1}{2}'' = 1'-0''$.

10B-4. $R(1; 2\frac{1}{2}; 5)$ $S(408)$ is the axis of a $6'' \times 8''$ timber brace cut to fit the corner of a room at the floor at S, and a $6'' \times 6''$ vertical column at R. R is on the right rear edge of the column which is the intersection of its frontal and profile faces. The $8''$ faces of the brace are vertical. Draw the front, top, face, and edge views and measure the angles for the cuts. Scale: $1\frac{1}{2}'' = 1'-0''$.

10B-5. $E(5; 0; 5\frac{1}{2})$ $F(7\frac{1}{2}; 3; 7\frac{1}{2})$ is the axis of a $4'' \times 6''$ brace cut to fit the floor of a room at A and a profile wall at F. The $6''$ sides are ortho-frontal. Draw the front, top, face, and edge views of the brace and measure the angles for the cuts. Scale: $1\frac{1}{2}'' = 1'-0''$.

Group 10C.   Grade Lines in a Plane.

10C-1. In the triangle $A(515)$ $B(4; 3\frac{1}{2}; 7)$ $C(726)$ draw the line AJ, $1\frac{3}{4}''$ long and on a 60% upgrade from A.

10C-2. In the triangle $C(337)$ $D(425)$ $E(116)$ draw the line CR intersecting DE at R and having a 70% grade.

10C-3. $A(537)$ is the vertex of an isosceles triangle whose sides AB and AC are each $2''$ long and have a grade of 25%. The strike of the triangle is S 65° W and it dips 35° southeasterly from A. Draw the triangle.

10C-4. $A(214)$ $B(318)$ $C(716)$ is the base of a pyramid whose vertex is $V(426)$. Draw all possible lines from V having a 60% grade and lying on the pyramid.

10C-5. $R(327)$ is a point on the ground which, within the area, is practically a plane which strikes S 63° E and dips 15° southwesterly. Lay out a straight path from R in a southeasterly direction, 150′ long and having a 10% downgrade. Scale: $1'' = 80$ ft.

Group 10D.   Location of a Road Having a Given Grade.

10D-1. Trace the map of Fig. 279 in a rectangle near the top of the sheet. Starting at elevation 1040 between G and F lay out a road on a uniform grade of 15% to a point on the 1080 contour near e. How long is the road?

10D-2. Trace the map of Fig. 279 in a rectangle near the top of the sheet. Starting on the 1000′ contour between a and b lay out a road on a 15% grade running to a point on the 1080 contour near e. How long is the road?

10D-3. Trace the map of Fig. 280 in a rectangle near the top of the sheet. Lay out a road on a uniform 15% grade starting from a point at elevation 490 between d and e and running to a point near the top of the hill. How long is the road?

10D-4. Trace the map of Fig. 281 in a rectangle near the top of the sheet. Lay out a road on a uniform 15% grade starting at elevation 2010 between C and D and running to the top of the hill. How long is the road?

Group 10E.   Guide Pulleys.

10E-1. $A(736)$ $B(726)$ and $C(1; 3\frac{1}{4}; 4\frac{1}{2})$ $D(1; 3\frac{1}{4}; 5\frac{1}{2})$ are the center lines of the shafts for pulleys which are respectively 16″ and 12″ in diameter. Locate the pulleys on the shafts so that by using a 10″ guide pulley the belt will run in either direction. The face of each pulley is 4″. Scale: $1\frac{1}{2}″ = 1$ ft. Show the guide pulley and belt in position.

10E-2. Statement the same as for Problem 10E-1 except that $A(1; 4; 5\frac{1}{2})$ $B(1; 3; 5\frac{1}{2})$ and $C(7; 2\frac{3}{4}; 4)$ $D(7; 2\frac{3}{4}; 5)$ are the center lines.

10E-3. Statement the same as for Problem 10E-1 except that $A(1; 3\frac{1}{2}; 5)$ $B(1; 3\frac{1}{2}; 6)$ and $C(7\frac{1}{4}; 3; 4\frac{3}{4})$ $D(7\frac{1}{4}; 2; 4\frac{3}{4})$ are the center lines.

10E-4. $C(745)$ $D(747)$ and $E(134)$ $F(114)$ are the center lines for two shafts. A pulley, 12″ diameter × 4″ face, is located at the midpoint of each shaft. Scale: $1\frac{1}{2}″ = 1$ ft. Show a 10″ guide pulley for each side of an open belt so arranged that the belt will run in either direction. Make the planes of the guide pulleys parallel.

Group 10F.   Resultants and Equilibrants for Concurrent Non-coplanar Forces.   Scale: 1″ = 400 lbs.

10F-1. Fig. 283-1. $K(536)$ $A(426)$, $KB(6; 2\frac{1}{2}; 7)$, and $KC(5\frac{1}{2}; 1\frac{1}{2}; 4\frac{1}{2})$ represent forces acting on point K. Find the equilibrant.

10F-2. Fig. 283-2. $A(4\frac{1}{2}; 3\frac{1}{2}; 7)L(636)$, $LB(7; 3\frac{1}{2}; 7)$, $C(7; 2; 4\frac{1}{2})$ L, and $LD(5; 1; 5\frac{1}{2})$ are forces acting on the point L. Find the resultant.

10F-3. Fig. 283-3.   Find the resultant of the forces $A(517)$ $M(626)$, $MC(4\frac{1}{2}; 3\frac{1}{2}; 5)$, and $B(7\frac{1}{2}; 2\frac{1}{2}; 5\frac{1}{2})$ M.

10F-4. Find the equilibrant of the forces $J(236)$ $A(1; 3\frac{1}{2}; 5)$, $JB(2\frac{1}{2}; 3\frac{1}{2}; 7)$, $JC(3; 2; 4\frac{1}{2})$, and $JD(\frac{1}{2}; 2; 7)$.

10F-5. Find the equilibrant of the forces $A(\frac{1}{2}; 3\frac{1}{2}; 7)$ $N(236)$, $B(4; 4; 6\frac{1}{2})$ N, and $C(215)$ N.

Group 10G.   Forces in Structures of Three Non-coplanar Members.   Scale: 1″ = 400 lbs.

$Q(6; 3\frac{1}{2}; 6)$. Find the forces in the legs $QB(4\frac{1}{2}; 2; 5\frac{1}{2})$, $QC(6\frac{1}{2}; 2; 7)$, and $QD(7\frac{1}{2}; 2; 5)$.

10G-2. Fig. 283-5. JA, JB, and JC are three members of a structure which supports a load of 1000 pounds at $J(625)$. $A(746)$, $B(826)$, and $C(845)$ are the points of attachment to the walls of a building. Find the magnitude of the force acting in each member.

10G-3. Fig. 283-6.   A 1000 pound chandelier is hung from the point $J(2; 2\frac{1}{2}; 6)$ by chains attached to the ceiling at $C(\frac{1}{2}; 4; 6\frac{1}{2})$, $D(2\frac{1}{2}; 4; 5)$, and $E(347)$. Find the forces in the chains.

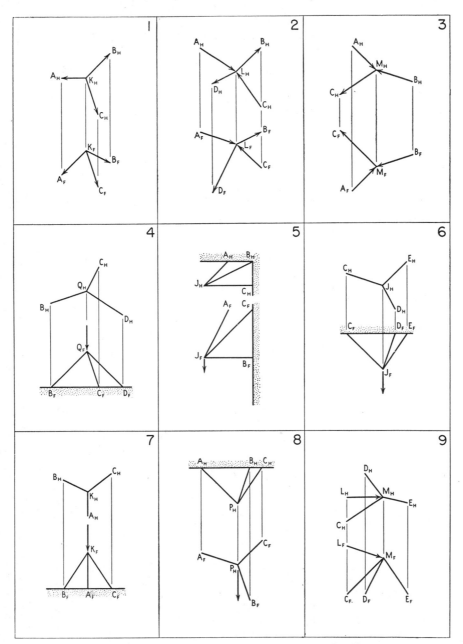

FIG. 283.—Force Diagrams. Groups 10F and 10G.

10G-4. Fig. 283-7. A vertical load of 800 pounds is supported by a tripod structure whose legs are $K(2; 3\frac{1}{2}; 6)$ $A(225)$, $KB(1; 2; 6\frac{1}{2})$, and $KC(3; 2; 3\frac{3}{4})$. Find the force in each leg.

10G-5. Fig. 283-8. A chain hoist attached at $P(6; 3; 5\frac{1}{2})$ lifts a load of 1000 pounds (including its own weight). The legs of the supporting structure are attached to a rear wall at $A(4\frac{1}{2}; 3\frac{1}{2}; 7)$, $B(6\frac{1}{2}; 1\frac{1}{2}; 7)$, and $C(747)$. Find the forces in PA, PB, and PC.

10G-6. Fig. 283-9. A force of 750 pounds acting in the direction $L(\frac{1}{2}; 4; 6)$ $M(2; 3\frac{1}{2}; 6)$ is resisted by a structure whose members are $MC(\frac{1}{2}; 2; 5)$, $MD(1\frac{1}{4}; 2; 7)$, and $ME(3; 2; 5\frac{3}{4})$. Find the magnitude of the force in each member.

10G-7. A force of 1000 pounds pulls in the direction of $J(2; 3\frac{1}{2}; 6)$ $K(3\frac{1}{2}; 4\frac{1}{2}; 5\frac{3}{4})$ on the structure whose members are $JA(\frac{1}{2}; 3\frac{1}{2}; 6)$, $JB(125)$, and $JC(1\frac{1}{2}; 2; 7)$. Find the force acting in each member.

Group 10H.   Miscellaneous Engineering Problems.

10H-1. Fig. 284-1. $J(746)$ $K(716)$ and $L(5\frac{1}{2}; 3\frac{1}{2}; 8)$ $M(5\frac{1}{2}; 1\frac{1}{2}; 4)$ are the center lines of two pipes to be connected by means of another pipe and two 45° fittings. Draw the connecting pipe extending downward from JK and find its length. Scale: $\frac{1}{4}'' = 1'\text{-}0''$.

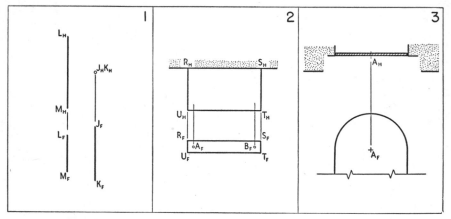

FIG. 284.—Miscellaneous Engineering Problems.   Group 10H.

10H-2. Fig. 284-2. $R(447)$ $S(747)$ $T(7; 3\frac{1}{2}; 5\frac{1}{4})$ $U(4; 3\frac{1}{2}; 5\frac{1}{4})$ is an awning fastened to a frontal wall at RS and supported by two braces of $1\frac{1}{2}''$ diameter pipe with 45° fittings. The braces are attached to the awning at $A(4\frac{1}{2}; 3\frac{3}{4}; X)$ and $B(6\frac{3}{4}; 3\frac{3}{4}; X)$. Find their length and the points where they are connected to the wall. Scale: $\frac{1}{8}'' = 1'\text{-}0''$. Neglect size of pipe and fittings.

10H-3. Fig. 284-3. $A(427)$ is the center of the semicircular top of a screen door recessed 8'' behind the outside frontal surface of a brick wall. The door is

3' wide. Find the minimum radius for a semicircular brick arch over the door that will allow the door to be opened 90°. Scale: $1'' = 1'\text{-}0''$.

10H-4. $R(125)$ $S(3\frac{1}{2}; \frac{3}{4}; 7\frac{1}{2})$ is the center line of a working in a mine. A passage is to be driven from $T(3\frac{1}{2}; 1\frac{3}{4}; 5)$ to RS which will have the same grade as RS. Find its length and bearing. Scale: $1'' = 80$ ft.

10H-5. A surveyor sets up his transit at $A(415)$ and looks upward N 62° E at a point $D(6XX)$ and reads the vertical angle (angle H) as 38°. He looks upward 19° in the direction N 56° W at point $C(1XX)$. Find the difference in elevation between D and C, the map distance between them, and the grade of a line CD. Scale: $1'' = 80$ ft.

10H-6. $K(336)$ $A(217)$, $KB(215)$, and $KC(426)$ are members of a steel support for a floodlight to be mounted on a roof. Find the length of each member and the angles between them. Scale: $\frac{1}{4}'' = 1'\text{-}0''$.

10H-7. $V(346)$ is the vertex and $C(316)$ is the center of the elliptical base of a right cone. The base has a 2' 5" horizontal-frontal minor axis and a 3' 0" major axis. The lower portion of the cone is a ventilating hood which is to be connected to an 18" diameter pipe, center line $A(5; 3\frac{1}{2}; 6)$ $B(7; 3\frac{1}{2}; 6)$, by a two-piece elbow made of two right circular cylinders. It joins the pipe at A and the elliptical cone in an 18" diameter circle. Draw the elbow. Scale: $1'' = 1'\text{-}0''$.

PROBLEMS FOR CHAPTER XI

THE MONGEAN METHOD

Group 11A. Traces of a Line.

The notation, $FH = 4$, means FH is located 4" above the origin of the coordinates.

11A-1. $FH = 4$. Find the frontal and horizontal traces of the lines $A(116)$ $B(435)$ and $C(3; 3; 6\frac{1}{4})$ $D(5; 2\frac{1}{4}; 5\frac{1}{4})$.

11A-2. $FH = 4$. Find the frontal and horizontal traces of the lines $E(070)$ $F(252)$, $J(3\frac{1}{2}; 6; 2\frac{1}{2})$ $K(5\frac{1}{2}; 5; 1)$, and $L(663)$ $M(861)$.

11A-3. $FH = 4$. Find the frontal and horizontal traces of all the edges of the tetrahedron $A(2\frac{1}{2}; 1; 7)$ $B(617)$ $C(3\frac{1}{2}; 1; 4\frac{1}{2})$ $V(436)$.

11A-4. $FH = 4$. $A(2; 3; 6\frac{1}{2})$ $B(337)$ $C(3; 3\frac{1}{2}; 6\frac{1}{2})$ and $D(4; 1\frac{1}{2}; 4\frac{1}{2})$ $E(5; 1\frac{1}{2}; 5)$ $F(5; 2; 4\frac{1}{2})$ are parallel sections of a prism. Find the intersection of the prism and the planes F and H, and show the prism terminating at these planes.

Group 11B. Points and Figures in a Plane.

11B-1. $FH = 4$. Draw the front and top views of the triangle $A(4X7)$ $B(5X5)$ $C(7X6)$ located in the plane S whose traces are $K(614)$ $L(144)$ and $LM(648)$.

11B-2. $FH = 4$. Draw the front and top views of the triangle $A(2; 5\frac{1}{2}; X)$ $B(4; 6\frac{1}{2}; X)$ $C(65X)$ located in the plane T whose traces are $J(064)$ $K(864)$ and $M(041)$ $N(841)$.

11B-3. $FH = 4$. Draw the front and top views of the triangle $C(31X)$ $D(43X)$ $E(72X)$ located in the plane W whose traces are $K(004)$ $L(444)$ and LM (746).

11B-4. $FH = 4$. The $2''$ diameter right cylinder whose axis is $A(2\frac{1}{2}; 8; 2)$ $B(2\frac{1}{2}; 4; 2)$ represents a smoke stack which passes through a roof plane S having as its traces $K(274)$ $L(744)$ and $LM(240)$. Find the front view of the required hole in the roof.

Group 11C.   Traces of a Plane.

11C-1. $FH = 4$. Find the traces of the plane T of the triangle $C(4; 7; 3\frac{1}{2})$ $D(761)$ $E(5; 5; 1\frac{1}{2})$. Check the direction of the traces by drawing frontal and horizontal lines of the triangle.

11C-2. $FH = 4$. Find the traces of the plane S containing the points $A(136)$, $B(325)$, and $C(6; 3\frac{1}{2}; 7)$.

11C-3. $FH = 4$. $D(2; 2\frac{1}{2}; 6)$, $E(4; 3\frac{1}{2}; 7)$, and $F(625)$ are points in the outcrop of a vein of ore. Find the traces of the plane W of the vein and its strike.

11C-4. $FH = 4$. Find the traces of the plane of each face of the tetrahedron given in Problem 11A-3.

PROBLEMS FOR CHAPTER XII

SHADES AND SHADOWS

The problems are stated in six groups, classified according to the preferred method of solution. In many cases, however, the instructor may wish to specify some other method.

Group 12A.   Shades and Shadows by the Piercing Point Method.

12A-1. $A(216)$ $B(256)$ $C(556)$ $D(516)$ is the front outline of the outside edges of an open frame made of two $6'' \times 6''$ posts and a $6'' \times 6''$ cap. Scale: $1'' = 1$ ft. Find its shadow on the level ground at A and on a frontal wall F $21''$ behind A.

12A-2. $C(346)$ is the center of the front face of a semicircular arch resting on two columns. The right sections of the arch and the columns are $6''$ squares. Scale: $1'' = 1$ ft. The radii for the arch are $12''$ and $18''$. Find the shadow on level ground $3'$ below C and on a frontal wall $21''$ behind C.

12A-3. $C(335)$ is the center of the front face of a semicircular arch resting on two square columns. The right sections of the arch and columns are $6''$ squares. Scale: $1'' = 1$ ft. The radii for the arch are $12''$ and $18''$. Find the shadow on level ground $3'$ below C and on a vertical wall through $J(0; X; 7\frac{1}{2})$ and $K(8X6)$.

12A-4. $A(358)$ is the center of a $6'' \times 6''$ beam where it joins a frontal wall and projects forward $24''$. Scale: $1'' = 1$ ft. Two faces of the beam are horizontal. $B(3; 4; 6\frac{1}{2})$ is the top point of a lighting fixture suspended from the beam by a small rod. The fixture is formed of a $12''$ square-base pyramid, $6''$ high, surmounting a 9″ square-base prism, 12″ high, having two faces frontal. Find the shadow of the beam, rod, and fixture on the wall.

12A-5. $A(237)$ and $B(537)$ are the upper front corners of a doorway in a frontal wall. The closed door sets back 24″. Scale: $\frac{1}{2}″ = 1$ ft. $C(3\frac{1}{2}; 4; 7)$ is the center of a horizontal semicircle, 5′ radius, which is the upper surface of a marquee 12″ thick over the doorway. Find the shade and shadow.

12A-6. $A(3; 4; 6\frac{1}{2})$ is the center of a sign made in the form of a profile disk 24″ in diameter by 3″ thick. Scale: $1″ = 1$ ft. The sign is supported by an L-shaped arm made of $3″ \times 3″$ rectangular bars whose center lines are $AB(3; 2; 6\frac{1}{2})$ and $BC(328)$, each having two faces profile. Find the shadow of the sign and arm on a frontal wall through C.

12A-7. Fig. 285-1. $A(1\frac{7}{8}; 1; 4\frac{1}{2})$ $B(5; 1; 4\frac{1}{2})$ is the front side of a $3\frac{1}{8}″ \times 2\frac{3}{8}″$ horizontal rectangle which is the lower base of a right prism $1\frac{1}{4}″$ tall. Discard from each upper corner a block 1″ wide, $\frac{3}{4}″$ deep, and $\frac{1}{2}″$ tall. Place upon the remaining central rectangle at the top, a block $1\frac{1}{8}″$ wide, $\frac{7}{8}″$ deep, and $1\frac{1}{4}″$ tall, forming a model of an office building. Draw the front and top views and cast the shadow on the building and on the ground at AB.

12A-8. Fig. 225-6. Locate corner O at $(1; 0; 3\frac{1}{2})$, double all dimensions, and draw the front and top views of the block. Find the shade and shadow.

Group 12B. Shades and Shadows by the Auxiliary View Method.

12B-1. $C(1\frac{1}{4}; 1\frac{1}{2}; 5\frac{1}{2})$ is the center of a $2\frac{1}{2}″$ sphere. On a horizontal table top $\frac{7}{8}″$ below C find the shadow of the portion of the sphere above the table. Use an auxiliary view, and find the shade-line.

12B-2. $A(258)$ is the center of a $6″ \times 6″$ beam where it joins a frontal wall and projects forward 24″. Scale: $1″ = 1$ ft. Two faces of the beam are horizontal. $C(2; 3; 6\frac{1}{2})$ is the center of an 18″ diameter sphere suspended by a small rod. Find the shade on the sphere, and the shadow of the sphere, rod, and beam on the wall.

12B-3. A vertical cylindrical post 18″ in diameter has for its top a hemisphere of the same size centered at $B(2; 3\frac{3}{4}; 6)$. B is 3′ 9″ above ground and 24″ in front of a frontal wall. Find the shade, and find the shadow on the ground and wall. Scale: $1″ = 1$ ft.

12B-4. $C(2\frac{1}{2}; 4\frac{1}{4}; 6)$ is the center of an 18″ sphere resting on the top of an 18″ square brick post having two frontal faces and a horizontal top. Scale: $1″ = 1$ ft. Find the shade, and find the shadow on a frontal wall 24″ behind C and on the ground 4′ 3″ below C. Use the short-cut construction.

Group 12C. Shades and Shadows by the Slicing Method.

12C-1. $A(2; 2\frac{1}{2}; 3)$ $C(3; 2\frac{1}{2}; 4)$ is a diagonal of a horizontal square that is the top of a chimney. $E(1\frac{1}{2}; 0; 6)$ $H(606)$ is a diagonal of a horizontal hexagon that represents the eaves of the pyramidal roof of a tower, the vertex being at $V(3\frac{3}{4}; 1\frac{1}{4}; 6)$. Find the shadow of the chimney on the roof.

12C-2. $A(2; 2; 5\frac{1}{2})$ is the center of a frontal arc of $\frac{3}{4}''$ radius drawn to the right of A. A scotia, Fig. 202, is generated by revolving the arc about $B(4; 3; 5\frac{1}{2})$ $C(4; 1; 5\frac{1}{2})$ as an axis. The upper and lower diameters are $3\frac{1}{2}''$ and $4''$ respectively. Find the shade and shadow on the scotia by the slicing method.

12C-3. $A(4; 2\frac{1}{2}; 7)$ $B(407)$ is the axis of the cylindrical part of an observatory model $4''$ in diameter. A is the center of the spherical dome of $2''$ radius, and is at the top of a $4\frac{1}{8}''$ diameter ring $\frac{1}{4}''$ high. A circular balcony $4\frac{1}{2}''$ in diameter and $\frac{1}{8}''$ thick is $1''$ below A. Find the visible shade and shadow on the structure.

12C-4. $A(3; 1\frac{1}{4}; 6\frac{1}{4})$ is the center of a frontal circular arc of $1\frac{1}{4}''$ radius to the left of A. $B(2; 3; 6\frac{1}{4})$ is the center of an arc tangent to the first arc and to the right of B. Revolve these arcs about $C(4; 0; 6\frac{1}{4})$ $D(4; 3\frac{3}{4}; 6\frac{1}{4})$ as an axis to generate a flower bowl the base of which is a horizontal plane through C, and the top of which is $3\frac{1}{2}''$ in diameter. By the slicing method find the shade and shadow.

12C-5. $A(0; 2\frac{1}{2}; 7)$ $B(6; 2\frac{1}{2}; 8)$ $C(705)$ $D(104)$ is a portion of a roof. $E(335)$ is the center of a $12''$ metal sphere supported on the roof by a $1''$ round vertical rod, and used as a radio aerial. Scale: $1\frac{1}{2}'' = 1$ ft. Find twelve points on the shade line, and find the shadow on the roof.

12C-6. Fig. 285-2. $C(3; 2; 5\frac{1}{2})$ is the center of the top of an $18''$ diameter ventilating pipe and the center of the base of a $30''$ diameter conical hood whose vertex is $V(3; 3\frac{1}{4}; 5\frac{1}{2})$. Scale: $1'' = 1'$-$0''$. Find the intersection of the pipe and the roof $Q(104)$ $R(1; 1\frac{1}{2}; 8)$ $S(7; 1\frac{1}{2}; 8)$ $T(704)$. Find the shade and shadow.

12C-7. Fig. 225-1. Locate corner G at (103), double all dimensions, and draw the front and top views of the block. Find the shade and shadow.

12C-8. Fig. 225-2. Locate corner M at $(1; 0; 3\frac{1}{2})$, double all dimensions, and draw the front and top views of the block. Find the shade and shadow.

12C-9. Fig. 225-3. Locate corner N at $(1; 0; 3\frac{1}{2})$, double all dimensions, and draw the front and top views of the block. Find the shade and shadow.

12C-10. Fig. 225-4. Locate corner I at (103), double all dimensions, and draw the front and top views of the block. Find the shade and shadow.

12C-11. Fig. 225-5. Locate corner K at (103), double all dimensions, and draw the front and top views of the block. Find the shade and shadow.

Group 12D. Shades and Shadows by the Method of Tangent Surfaces.

Cone problems are included in this group as preparation for the method of tangent surfaces.

12D-1. $A(335)$ is the vertex and $D(305)$ is the center of the $3''$ circular base of a right cone. Discard the portion above the horizontal plane through $C(315)$. The upper base of the frustum is the base of a $45°$ cone. Discard the portion above the horizontal plane at $B(3; 1\frac{1}{2}; 5)$. The top of this frustum is the base of a cone having a $35° 16'$ base angle. Find the shade on the object and the shadow on a table top at D.

12D-2. $A(2; 4\frac{1}{2}; 6)$ and $B(236)$ are the centers of horizontal circles $1\frac{1}{2}''$ and $2''$ in diameter respectively. The frustum of the cone between the circles represents an open top lamp shade. On the drawing the base of the stand is a right cone having $C(216)$ as its vertex and a $1''$ circle with center $D(206)$ as its base, and the rod BC is $\frac{1}{8}''$ in diameter. Find the shadow on the floor at the level of D and on the frontal wall at 8. Also, find the shade lines. Use conventional light.

12D-3. The outline formed by the rectangle $A(3; 3\frac{1}{2}; 6)$ $B(4; 3\frac{1}{2}; 6)$ $C(4; 1\frac{1}{2}; 6)$ $D(3; 1\frac{1}{2}; 6)$ and the semicircle to the right of BC is revolved about AD as an axis to generate a disk. By means of tangent cones find the shade-line. Also, find the shadow of the front half of the disk on the plane of $ABCD$.

12D-4. $E(4; 2\frac{1}{2}; 6\frac{1}{2})$ is the center of a $3\frac{1}{2}''$ spherical knob joined to the top of a $1\frac{1}{2}''$ diameter vertical cylindrical rod. Find the shade-line of the knob by using tangent cones, and find the shade and shadow on the rod.

Group 12E. Shades and Shadows by the Method of Sections.

12E-1. $C(436)$ is the center of a $4''$ diameter hemispherical recess in a frontal wall. Find the shadow within the recess.

12E-2. $A(425)$ is the center of the $3''$ diameter base and $V(4; 2; 7\frac{1}{2})$ is the vertex of a cone cut into a frontal wall whose surface contains the base. Find the shade inside the cone.

12E-3. $A(236)$ $B(636)$ is the center line of a semicylindrical groove of $1\frac{1}{2}''$ radius in a frontal wall. The ends of the groove are quarters of a spherical surface of the same radius. Find the shade in the groove.

12E-4. $D(1; 2; 5\frac{1}{2})$ is the center of a frontal arc of $\frac{3}{4}''$ radius drawn to the right of D. A scotia, Fig. 202, is generated by revolving the arc about axis $E(3; 3; 5\frac{1}{2})$ $F(3; 1; 5\frac{1}{2})$. The upper and lower diameters are $3\frac{1}{2}''$ and $4''$ respectively. Find the shade and shadow on the scotia by using horizontal sections.

12E-5. $C(245)$ is the center of the $1\frac{1}{4}''$ circular base and $D(2; 1\frac{1}{4}; 5)$ is the vertex of a right cone which respresents an opaque drinking glass that has a $1\frac{1}{2}''$ circular bottom at D joined to the conical part by a $\frac{1}{4}''$ diameter stem. Find its shadow on the table top at D, and on a frontal plane $1\frac{1}{2}''$ behind CD. Find the shade-lines outside and the shadow inside the glass.

12E-6. $A(428)$ is the center of the front half of a $4''$ sphere attached to a frontal wall at A. $B(2; 4\frac{1}{4}; 5\frac{1}{2})$ is the center of a $2\frac{1}{2}''$ frontal circular disk. Find the shadow of the disk on the hemisphere by the method of sections. Also, find the shade-line, and find the shadow on the wall.

12E-7. Fig. 285-3. $V(307)$ is the vertex and $A(327)$ is the center of the $2''$ diameter base of a right cone. $AB(3; 2\frac{1}{4}; 7)$ is the axis of a $2\frac{1}{2}''$ diameter disc. The front halves of the cone and disc are attached to a frontal wall at BV to form a bracket below a niche, center line $BC(347)$, in the wall. The head of the niche is one-quarter of a sphere, center C, radius $1''$. Find the shade and shadow.

Group 12F. Shades and Shadows by the Envelope Method.

12F-1. $A(2; 3\frac{1}{2}; 4\frac{3}{4})$ $B(2; 0; 4\frac{3}{4})$ is the center line of a vase. Divide AB into seven equal parts by horizontal cutting planes. The radii of the sections beginning at A and ending at B are as follows: $\frac{3}{4}''$, $\frac{5}{8}''$, $\frac{7}{8}''$, $1''$, $1''$, $\frac{15}{16}''$, $\frac{3}{4}''$, and $\frac{1}{2}''$. Find the shadow on a horizontal plane at B and the shade-line on the vase.

12F-2. $C(2\frac{1}{2}; 3; 4\frac{1}{2})$ $D(2\frac{1}{2}; 0; 4\frac{1}{2})$ is the axis of a surface of revolution. Divide CD into six equal parts to locate right sections. The radii of the sections beginning at C and ending at D are as follows: $\frac{1}{2}''$, $\frac{3}{4}''$, $\frac{7}{8}''$, $1''$, $\frac{13}{16}''$, $\frac{11}{16}''$, and $\frac{3}{4}''$. Find the shadow on a horizontal plane at D, and find the shade-line on the object.

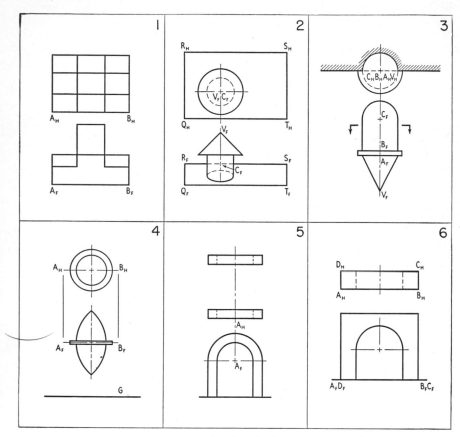

Fig. 285.—Problems for Shades, Shadows and Perspectives.

12F-3. $E(2\frac{1}{2}; 3; 4\frac{1}{2})$ $F(2\frac{1}{2}; 0; 4\frac{1}{2})$ is the center line of a vase. Divide EF into six equal parts to locate right sections. The radii of the sections beginning at E and ending at F are as follows: $\frac{3}{4}''$, $\frac{1}{2}''$, $\frac{3}{4}''$, $1''$, $\frac{7}{8}''$, $\frac{3}{4}''$, and $\frac{1}{2}''$. Find the shadow on a horizontal plane at E, and find the shade-line on the vase.

12F-4. $A(3; 3; 4\frac{1}{2})$ $B(3; 0; 4\frac{1}{2})$ is the axis of a prolate spheroid generated by revolving an ellipse, whose axes are $2''$ and $3''$, about its major axis. Find the shadow in a horizontal plane at B, and find the shade-line on the spheroid.

12F-5. Fig. 285-4. $A(1\frac{3}{4}; 2\frac{1}{4}; 4\frac{3}{4})$ and $B(4; 2\frac{1}{4}; 4\frac{3}{4})$ are the centers for two intersecting frontal arcs, each having a $1\frac{3}{4}''$ radius. In the front view these arcs form the outline of a surface of revolution having a vertical axis. On the center line AB add a horizontal cylindrical ring $\frac{1}{8}''$ thick, $1\frac{3}{4}''$ outside diameter, around the original surface. Find the shadow on the ground $2\frac{1}{4}''$ below AB. Find the shade lines and the shadow on the object.

PROBLEMS FOR CHAPTER XIII

PERSPECTIVE

These problems are intended for the standard $8\frac{1}{2}'' \times 11''$ sheets. Unless otherwise specified the short dimension is horizontal. If the long dimension is to be horizontal, locate the origin $\frac{1}{4}''$ each way from a corner of the sheet, the title strip being to the right. In most cases data are given for a perspective layout. $F = 4$ or $FH = 4$ means the picture plane is $4''$ back of the origin, $H = 3$ means the horizon is $3''$ above the origin, $L = 0$, $R = 8$ means the left and right vanishing points are located on FH at 0 and 8 respectively. $CV = 3$ is the location of the center of vision on FH.

Group 13A. Angular Perspective.

13A-1. $A(315)$ is the lower front corner of a house whose floor plan is a rectangle $16' \times 20'$, the ends and sides making respectively, angles, of $60°$ to the left and $30°$ to the right with the picture plane through A. Scale: $\frac{1}{8}'' = 1$ ft. The height of the side walls is $10'$. The gable roof, which has no overhang, has a rise of $8'$ and a span of $16'$. The point of sight S is $40'$ in front of and $6'$ above A. By the visual ray method draw the perspective of the house.

13A-2. $F = 5$, $CV = 2$, $H = 3$. $A(2X5)$ is at the nearest corner of a house whose floor plan is a rectangle $16' \times 20'$, the ends and the sides making respectively $60°$ to the left and $30°$ to the right with F. Scale: $\frac{1}{8}'' = 1$ ft. The height of the side walls is $10'$. The gable roof which has no overhang has a rise of $8'$ and a span of $16'$. The point of sight S is $28'$ in front of A and $6'$ above the ground. By the orthographic plan and vanishing point method draw a perspective of the house. Find the vanishing points for the gable lines.

13A-3. Same as Problem 13A-2, except that the roof has an overhang of $24''$.

13A-4. $FH = 4$, $L = 0$, $R = 8$, $CV = 3\frac{1}{2}$. The floor plan of a house is $20' \times 32'$ with the long dimension to the right. Scale: $\frac{1}{8}'' = 1$ ft. The height of the eaves, which do not overhang, is $9'$ and the gable roof has a rise of 10 in a run of 12. Located centrally on the $32'$ front face there is a gable roof dormer $16'$ wide whose roof begins at the main eave line and has the same pitch. Place the nearest edge of the house in the picture plane at CV. Take the height of S as $5'$, and draw the perspective after finding six vanishing points.

13A-5. $FH = 4$, $L = 0$, $R = 8$, $CV = 4\frac{1}{2}$. The floor plan of a house is $A(0; X; 6\frac{1}{4})$ $B(0; X; 8)$ $C(2\frac{1}{4}; X; 8)$ $D(2\frac{1}{4}; X; 6\frac{1}{2})$ $E(1\frac{7}{8}; X; 6\frac{1}{2})$ $F(1\frac{7}{8}; X; 6\frac{1}{4})$. Scale: $\frac{1}{16}'' = 1$ ft. For the perspective use $\frac{1}{8}'' = 1$ ft. Place the intersection of walls AF and CD in the picture plane at CV. Height of eaves is $10'$. Height of S is $5'$. The gable roofs over AF and CD have a rise of 10 in a run of 12, and no overhang. Draw the perspective after finding six vanishing points.

13A-6. $FH = 7$, $L = 0$, $R = 8$, $CV = 3$, $G = 4$, $G' = 1$. A $4' \times 4'$ landing platform is reached by two steps at the front face (the right-front face in the perspective). A second $4' \times 4'$ platform is reached by two steps which ascend from the right side of the first. The step dimensions are $4' \times 12'' \times 8''$ high. Scale: $\frac{1}{2}'' = 1$ ft. In each case there are three risers and two treads. Draw the steps and platforms as a solid concrete unit. $A'(31X)$ is the front corner of the perspective plan and $A(34X)$ is the same point in the perspective.

13A-7. Long edges of sheet horizontal. $FH = 7\frac{1}{2}$; $L = 0$; $R = 10\frac{1}{2}$; $CV = 7$. Beginning $480'$ below CV lay off two city blocks, each $240'$ square, one to the right and two to the left with an $80'$ street between. Scale: $1'' = 80$ ft. On each corner of both blocks there is an L-shaped apartment building resulting from the removal of a prism with a $50'$ square base from a $90'$ cube. The prism is removed from the corner which is toward the center of the block. Draw an airplane perspective of the project.

13A-8. Fig. 285-1. Long edges of sheet horizontal. $FH = 5$, $L = 0$, $R = 8$, $CV = 4$, $G = 3$, $G' = \frac{1}{2}$. Place corner B $\frac{1}{2}''$ to the right of CV, and draw a perspective of the building described in Problem 12A-7.

13A-9. Fig. 225-1. Long edges of sheet horizontal. $FH = 6$, $L = 0$, $R = 8$, $CV = 5$, G and $G' = 3$. Double all dimensions of the block, place corner O in front of CV, and draw a perspective.

13A-10. Fig. 225-2. Long edges of sheet horizontal. $FH = 7\frac{1}{4}$, $L = 0$, $R = 8$, $CV = 5$, $G = 3\frac{3}{4}$, $G' = 0$. Double all dimensions of the block, place corner K in front of CV, and draw a perspective.

13A-11. Fig. 225-3. Long edges of sheet horizontal. $FH = 7$, $L = 0$, $R = 8$, $CV = 4\frac{1}{2}$, $G = 4\frac{1}{2}$, $G' = 2\frac{1}{2}$. Complete the rectangle of the base in the isometric, place the nearest corner in front of CV, and draw a perspective.

13A-12. Fig. 225-4. Long edges of sheet horizontal. $FH = 7$, $L = 0$, $R = 10\frac{1}{2}$, $CV = 6$, $G = 3\frac{1}{2}$, $G' = \frac{1}{2}$. Double all dimensions of the block, place corner L in front of CV, and draw a perspective.

13A-13. Fig. 225-5. Long edges of sheet horizontal. $FH = 6$, $L = 0$, $R = 8$, $CV = 5$, G and $G' = 2\frac{1}{2}$. Double all dimensions of the block. Complete the rectangle of the base in the isometric, place the nearest corner in front of CV, and draw a perspective.

13A-14. Fig. 225-6. Long edges of the sheet horizontal. $FH = 6$, $L = 0$, $R = 8$, $CV = 5$, G and $G' = 3\frac{1}{2}$. Double all dimensions of the block. Complete the rectangle of the base in the isometric, place the nearest corner in front of CV, and draw a perspective.

Group 13B.   Parallel Perspective.

13B-1. $FH = 5$, $CVP = 3$. Draw a parallel perspective of a room 14' wide, 16' deep, and 10' high with walls and floor 6" thick. Scale: $\frac{1}{4}'' = 1$ ft. The point of sight is $5\frac{1}{2}'$ above the floor, at the center of width of the room, and 20' in front of the picture plane F. The room is entirely beyond F. There is a $3' \times 6'$ window in the center of each side wall and a $3' \times 7'$ door in the center of the rear wall. The floor is laid off in 2' squares.

13B-2. $FH = 7$, $CVP = 8$. $A(2\frac{1}{2}; 4; X)$ is the center of the front face of a hollow cylinder having a 2" outside and a 1" inside diameter and a length of 1". $B(5\frac{1}{2}; 4; X)$ is the center of the front face of a hollow cylinder having a $1\frac{1}{4}''$ outside and a $\frac{5}{8}''$ inside diameter and a length of 1". The cylinders are joined by an arm of rectangular cross-section $\frac{1}{2}''$ thick, centrally located, to form a crank. A and B are in the picture plane F; and S is 8" in front of F. Draw a one-point perspective of the crank.

13B-3. $FH = 6$, $CVP = 8$. $A(2\frac{1}{2}; 3; X)$ is the center of the front face of a hollow right cylinder having a 2" outside and a 1" inside diameter and a length of 1". $B(5\frac{1}{2}; 3; X)$ and $C(2\frac{1}{2}; 6; X)$ are the centers of the front faces of hollow right cylinders, each having a $1\frac{1}{4}''$ outside and a $\frac{5}{8}''$ inside diameter and a length of 1". Each small cylinder is joined to the large cylinder by an arm of rectangular cross-section $\frac{1}{2}''$ thick, centrally located. A, B, and C are in the picture plane F, and S is 8" in front of F. Draw a one-point perspective of the object.

13B-4. Long edges of sheet horizontal. $FH = 6$, $CVP = 6$. $A(1; 4\frac{1}{2}; X)$ $C(2\frac{1}{2}; 3; X)$ is a diagonal of a frontal square which is the front face of a cube. Show eleven more cubes directly behind this one. Use the vanishing point of a system of diagonals for constructing the additional cubes. $J(7\frac{1}{2}; 4\frac{1}{2}; X)$ $L(83X)$ is a diagonal of the front face of a duplicate series of cubes to be shown in the perspective.

13B-5. $FH = 7$, $CVP = 8$. $A(13X)$ is the foot of a telephone pole 18' high. A horizontal-frontal cross-arm 6' long is 2' below the top. Scale: $\frac{1}{16}'' = 1$ ft. Make a perspective of a straight row of fifteen poles spaced 50' apart on level ground. The point of sight is 125' in front of the picture plane. Use the vanishing point of a system of diagonals sloping downward and backward.

13B-6. Fig. 285-5. $FH = 4$, $CVP = 10\frac{1}{2}$, $G = 2\frac{1}{2}$, $M_R = 0$. $A(7; 4\frac{1}{2}; X)$ is the center for semicircles having radii of 4' and 6' forming the front face of an arch resting on 2' square piers, 8' tall. Scale: $\frac{1}{4}'' = 1'-0''$. The front face of the second arch is 12' back of A. Draw a parallel perspective of the arches.

Group 13C.   Circles in Perspective.

13C-1. Long edges of sheet horizontal. $FH = 5$; $L = 0$; $R = 10$; $CV = 6\frac{1}{2}$. A 4" cube has a 3" circular hole perpendicular to its left face, and 3" square holes perpendicular to its right and top faces, all centrally located and passing entirely through the cube. Place the nearest edge in F at CV, and the base $2\frac{1}{2}''$ below H. By using a circumscribing octagon for the circles, draw the perspective.

13C-2. $FH = 4$; $L = 0$; $R = 8$; $CV = 5$. A Spanish type stone building $20' \times 12' \times 13'$ high has two open doorways with semicircular heads in the $20'$ front face which is to the left. The doorways, which are each $6'$ wide and $6'$ high to the springing line of the arch, are symmetrically located $2'$ apart. The walls are $2'$ thick. Scale; $\frac{1}{4}'' = 1$ ft. Place the nearest edge in the picture plane at CV. Height of S is $5'$. Draw the perspective.

13C-3. $FH = 4$, $L = 0$, $R = 8$, $CV = 5$. A wall of a building extends to the left of $D(68X)$ $E(60X)$, which is in the picture plane, and the wall has three arched windows on a vertical center line $5'$-$6''$ to the left of DE. Each window is $7'$ wide and extends $4'$ below the center of its semicircular arch. One center is in H and the others are $12'$ above and $12'$ below respectively. The wall is $18''$ thick. Scale: $\frac{1}{4}'' = 1$ ft. Draw a perspective of the three openings.

13C-4. Long edges of sheet horizontal. $FH = 5$, $L = 0$, $R = 10$, $CV = 5$. Draw the perspective of a well curbing that shows as a vertical cylinder of $6'$ outside and $4'$ inside diameters extending $2'$-$6''$ above the ground which is $7'$-$6''$ below H. Scale $\frac{1}{2}'' = 1$ ft. The front element of the outside surface extended passes through CV. The point of sight is $10'$ in front of F. Use circumscribing octagons.

13C-5. Fig. 285-6. $F = 5$, $H = 3\frac{1}{4}$, $G = 2$, point of sight $S(5; 3\frac{1}{4}; 1)$. $A(2\frac{1}{2}; X; 5)$ $B(5X7)$ is the location of the front side of a horizontal rectangle whose adjacent sides are $6'$ long. Scale: $\frac{1}{8}'' = 1'$-$0''$. The rectangle encloses the base of an arched gateway $22'$ tall. The radius of the arch is $8'$ and its center is $10'$ above the ground. Draw a perspective of the gateway.

Group 13D. Shadows in Perspective.

13D-1. $FH = 4$, $L = 0$, $R = 8$, $CV = 3\frac{1}{2}$. A $2' \times 2' \times 8'$ column stands on a foundation consisting of a $4' \times 4' \times 1'$ block resting on a $6' \times 6' \times 1'$ footing, all centrally located. Scale: $\frac{1}{2}'' = 1$ ft. The point of sight is $3'$ above the lower surface of the footing. By the perspective plan method draw an angular perspective, the nearest edge of the footing being in the picture plane on a vertical line through CV. Draw the shade and shadow for light passing downward to the right at $45°$ and parallel to the picture plane.

13D-2. Long edges of sheet horizontal. Data the same as in Problem 13D-1 for the perspective. Assume the vanishing point of the light rays at $Z(10; 1; X)$, and find the shade and the complete shadow on base, footing, and level ground.

13D-3. $FH = 4$, $L = 0$, $R = 8$, $CV = 3\frac{1}{2}$. The roof of a tower is in the form of a right pyramid $28'$ square and $12'$ high. The tower is $12'$ square and $24'$ high to the eaves. Scale: $\frac{1}{8}'' = 1$ ft. Place the nearest corner of the roof in the picture plane on a vertical line through CV, and take the height of S as $10'$. Locate the vanishing point of the light rays at $Z(72X)$. Draw the perspective and find shade and shadow.

13D-4. Long edges of sheet horizontal. $FH = 6$; $L = 0$; $R = 10$; $CV = 3$; G and $G' = 3$. Scale: $\frac{3}{4}'' = 1$ ft. A table $3'$-$3''$ high has a top $4' \times 6' \times 3''$ thick attached to a frame $3'$-$6'' \times 5'$-$6'' \times 8''$ high having a $6'' \times 6''$ leg at each corner. Place the nearest corner of the top in F on a vertical line through CV. Assume $Z(72X)$ as the vanishing point of sunlight. Find the shadows on the table and floor.

13D-5. Starting with the perspective of Problem 13A-8, locate the vanishing point of the light rays at $Z(10\frac{1}{2}; 2\frac{3}{4}; X)$. Find the shade and shadow.

13D-6. Starting with the perspective of Problem 13A-9, locate the vanishing point of the light rays at $Z(10\frac{1}{2}; 2\frac{1}{2}; X)$. Find the shade and shadow.

13D-7. Starting with the perspective of Problem 13A-10, locate the vanishing point of the light rays at $Z(10\frac{1}{2}; 3\frac{3}{4}; X)$. Find the shade and shadow.

13D-8. Starting with the perspective of Problem 13A-11, locate the vanishing point of the light rays at $Z(10\frac{1}{2}; 3; X)$. Find the shade and shadow.

13D-9. Starting with the perspective of Problem 13A-13, locate the vanishing point of the light rays at $Z(10\frac{1}{2}; 3\frac{1}{4}; X)$. Find the shade and shadow.

13D-10. Starting with the perspective of Problem 13A-14, locate the vanishing point of the light rays at $Z(10\frac{1}{2}; 3; X)$. Find the shade and shadow.

13D-11. Starting with the perspective of Problem 13C-5, use $J(545)$ $K(6\frac{1}{2}; 3; 7)$ as the direction of light. Find the shade and shadow.

INDEX